The
East Mi
Bus Han

British Bus Publishing

Body codes used in the Bus Handbook series:

Type:
A	Articulated vehicle
B	Bus, either single-deck or double-deck
BC	Suburban/Interurban service vehicle with high-back seats
C	Coach
M	Van derived minibus with design capacity of sixteen seats or less
N	Low-floor bus (*Niederflur*), either single-deck or double-deck
NC	Low-floor (*Niederflur*) vehicle with high back seating
O	Open-top bus (CO = convertible - PO = partial open-top)

Seating capacity is then shown. For double-decks the upper deck quantity is followed by the lower deck.

Door position:-
C	Centre entrance/exit
D	Dual doorway.
F	Front entrance/exit
R	Rear entrance/exit (no distinction between doored and open)
T	Three or more access points

Equipment:-
L	Lift for wheelchair	TV	Training Vehicle.
M	Mail compartment	RV	Used as tow bus or Engineers vehicle.
T	Toilet	w	Vehicle is withdrawn from service.

e.g. - B32/28F is a double-deck bus with thirty-two seats upstairs, twenty-eight down and a front entrance/exit.
       N43D is a low-floor bus with two doorways.

Re-registrations:-
Where a vehicle has gained new index marks the details are listed at the end of each fleet showing the current mark, followed in sequence by those previously carried starting with the original mark.

Other books in the series:
The Scottish Bus Handbook
The Ireland & Islands Bus Handbook
The North East Bus Handbook
The Yorkshire Bus Handbook
The Lancashire, Cumbria and Manchester Bus Handbook
The Merseyside and Cheshire Bus Handbook
The North and West Midlands Bus Handbook
The South Midlands Bus Handbook
The North and West Wales Bus Handbook
The South Wales Bus Handbook
The Chilterns and West Anglia Bus Handbook
The East Anglia Bus Handbook
The South East Bus Handbook
The South West Bus Handbook
The South Central Bus Handbook

Annual books are produced for the major groups:
The Stagecoach Bus Handbook
The FirstBus Bus Handbook
The Arriva Bus Handbook

Editions for earlier years of these and the East Midlands Bus Handbook are available. Please contact the publisher.

Associated series:
The Hong Kong Bus Handbook
The Leyland Lynx Handbook
The Model Bus Handbook
The Postbus Handbook
The Toy & Model Bus Handbook - Volume 1 - Early Diecasts
The Fire Brigade Handbook (fleet list of each local authority fire brigade)
The Fire Brigade Handbook - Special Appliances Volume 1
The Fire Brigade Handbook - Special Appliances Volume 2
The Police Range Rover Handbook

Contents

The East Midlands Bus Handbook

This Third edition of the East Midlands Bus Handbook is part of the Bus Handbook series that details the fleets of stage carriage and express coach operators. The operators included in this edition cover those who provide stage and express services in the counties of Derbyshire, Leicestershire, Lincolnshire and Nottinghamshire. Also included are a number of those operators who provide significant coaching activities.

Quality photographs for inclusion in the series are welcome, for which a fee is payable. The publishers unfortunately cannot accept responsibility for any loss and request you show your name on each picture or slide. Details of changes to fleet information are also welcome.

To keep the fleet information up to date we recommend the Ian Allan publication, Buses, published monthly, or for more detailed information, the PSV Circle monthly news sheets.

Principal Editor: Steve Sanderson

Acknowledgments:
We are grateful to Richard Belton, David Donati, Barry Hayes, Paul Hill, Mark Jameson, Tony Wilson, the PSV Circle and the management and officials of operating companies for their kind assistance and co-operation in the compilation of this book.

The cover pictures and frontispiece are by Tony Wilson

ISBN 1 897990 66 9
Published by British Bus Publishing Ltd
The Vyne, 16 St Margaret's Drive, Wellington, Telford, TF1 3PH
Fax and orderline (+44) (0) 1952 255 669

E-mail   A2GWP@AOL.COM
internet:- http://www.britishbuspublishing.co.uk
© British Bus Publishing, September 1999

A & S

A A, A A & N A Sarang, 34 Hartington Road, Leicester, LE2 0GL

Registration	Chassis	Body	Seating	Year	Notes
B12ABU	Mercedes-Benz L307D	Reeve Burgess	M12	1985	Kingsway, Blyth 1994
329FBH	Mercedes-Benz 709D	Coachcraft	BC24F	1987	
329FTU	Mercedes-Benz 811D	Coachcraft	BC26F	1989	
A14ABU	Mercedes-Benz 609D	?	BC24F	1988	McFall & McFadden, Clydebank, 1994
A16ABU	Mercedes-Benz 609D	Coachcraft	BC26F	1989	
A19ABU	Mercedes-Benz 508D	Coachcraft	M16	1990	
A20ABU	Mercedes-Benz 811D	Dormobile Routemaker	B33F	1990	Barnes, Bedlington, 1994
A17ABU	Mercedes-Benz 609D	Whittaker Europa	BC23F	1991	
M18ABU	Mercedes-Benz 709D	Alexander Sprint	B29F	1995	
M354TMJ	Mercedes-Benz 609D	Autobus Classique	C23F	1995	Popat, Leicester, 1996
P169EUT	Peugeot Boxer	Peugeot	M16	1997	?????, 1998
P15ABU	Mercedes-Benz Vario O814	Leicester Carriage Builders	BC33F	1997	

Previous Registrations:

329FBH	D329WVL	A16ABU	G384MAG	A20ABU	G492TYS
329FTU	F319TJV	A17ABU	H996TAK	B12ABU	C660MCN
A14ABU	F820XEG	A19ABU	G89NRH		

Livery: White and green

Depot: Vulcan Road, Charnwood Ind Est, Leicester

Abu & Sons (A&S) operate a number of tendered services in the Leicester area with a small fleet of minibuses. Thurmaston is the location of this view of A20ABU which has a registration that reflects the owner's name. It is a Mercedes-Benz 811D fitted with a body from the now defunct Dormobile factory. The vehicle is seen on service 106 which runs between Thurmaston and Loughborough through Syston and Sileby.

ALBERT WILDE COACHES

P J Wilde & D A Ward, 121 Parkside, Heage, Derbyshire, DE56 2AF

ENF514Y	Ford R1114	Duple Dominant IV	C44FT	1983	Stone, Rochdale, 1988
ABW178X	Bova EL26/581	Bova Europa	C53F	1982	Heyfordian, Upper Heyford, 1996
A206LPP	Bova EL26/581	Bova Europa	C53F	1983	Graham, Gilsland, 1995
A737HFP	Bova EL26/581	Bova Europa	C53F	1984	Channel, Rochford, 1992
JIW3697	Bova FHD 12.280	Bova Futura	C49F	1988	Tally Ho!, Kingsbridge, 1998

Previous Registrations:

ABW178X	GGJ341X, YAY137	JIW3697	A663EMY

Named vehicles: ENF514Y *Windmill Cruiser*

Livery: White and red

Albert Wilde Coaches are a long established coach operator in the Derbyshire village of Heage. Until recently the company operated the village service to Ripley and Belper. The fleet is now largely of Bova manufacture. This depot view is of Europa A206LPP. *Steve Sanderson*

ANDREW'S

Andrews of Tideswell Ltd, Anchor Garage, Tideswell, Buxton, Derbyshire, SK17 8RB

PUA917	Leyland Atlantean AN68/2R	Alexander AL	B48/34F	1977	Stagecoach Busways, 1997
TIW2654	Leyland Atlantean AN68A/2R	Alexander AL	B49/37F	1978	Stagecoach Busways, 1996
LAZ6923	Ford R1014	Plaxton Supreme IV	C35F	1979	Davies, Alpraham, 1996
RIW8127	Ford R1114	Plaxton Supreme IV	C53F	1980	Gray, Hoyland Common, 1995
476BTO	Volvo B10M-61	Plaxton Paramount 3200	C53F	1983	Richmond, Barley, 1995
GIL7549	Kässbohrer Setra S228DT	Kässbohrer Imperial	C54/20CT	1984	Airey, Arkholme, 1998
IIL8593	Kässbohrer Setra S228DT	Kässbohrer Imperial	C54/20CT	1984	Eurobus, Perivale, 1998
NIB6064	Volvo B10M-61	Van Hool Alizée	C49FT	1984	Crossland, Sheffield, 1995
345BLA	Volvo B10M-61	Plaxton Paramount 3500	C49FT	1984	
PJI5529	Volvo B10M-61	Van Hool Alizée H	C53F	1986	Shearings, 1993
PJI3746	Volvo B10M-61	Van Hool Alizée H	C53F	1986	Shearings, 1993
RBA480	Scania K113CRB	Plaxton Paramount 3500 III	C49FT	1989	
BAZ8577	Volvo B10M-60	Van Hool Alizée H	C49FT	1990	Shearings, 1995
BAZ8578	Volvo B10M-60	Van Hool Alizée H	C49FT	1990	Shearings, 1995
EUA366	Volvo B10M-60	Van Hool Alizée H	C48FT	1993	Wallace Arnold, 1998
R86BUB	Mercedes-Benz Sprinter 412D	Crest	M16	1997	
R109BUB	Mercedes-Benz Vario 614D	Crest	BC24F	1997	
R469BUA	Mercedes-Benz Vario 614D	Crest	BC24F	1997	

Previous Registrations:

345BLA	B853KRY	NIB6064	A795TGG
476BTO	RMU964Y	PJI3746	C338DND, XTW359, C440GVM
BAZ8577	G877VNA	PJI5529	C337DND, 205CCH, C441GVM
BAZ8578	G878VNA	PUA917	MVK564R
EUA366	K803HUM, 7243WA	RBA480	G33HKY
GIL7549	A412GPY, 1817TW, A892KAJ	TIW2654	SCN274S
IIL8593	A413GPY, 1270KW, A953NJK	RIW8127	CDN649V
LAZ6923	GUS819T		

Livery: Cream and red

Named vehicles: 345BLA, *Peakland Queen XII*; PJI5529, *Peakland Queen XVII*; RBA480, *Peakland Queen XVI*; PJI3746, *Peakland Queen XVIII*; BAZ8577, *Peakland Queen XX*; BAZ8578, *Peakland Queen XXI*; 476BTO, *Peakland Queen XXIII*; PIW8618, *Peakland Queen XIX*; EUA366 *Peakland Queen XXXII*.

EUA366 is a registration number which has been carried by a number of vehicles in the Andrew's of Tideswell fleet. The current recipient is a Van Hool-bodied Volvo B10M which joined the fleet after five years service with Wallace Arnold. It is seen in the coach park at Skegness.
Steve Sanderson

ANSTEY BUSLINE

Anstey Busline Ltd, 38 Netherfield Road, off Link Road, Anstey, Leicestershire, LE7 7ES

1	XRR298S	Leyland Fleetline FE30AGR	Northern Counties	B40/30F	1978	R Garratt, Syston, 1998
2	GTO299V	Leyland Fleetline FE30AGR	Northern Counties	B43/30F	1980	Midland Fox (Derby), 1998
3	GTO49V	Leyland Fleetline FE30AGR	Northern Counties	B43/29F	1980	Midland Fox, 1998
4	GTO305V	Leyland Fleetline FE30AGR	Northern Counties	B43/30F	1980	Midland Fox (Derby), 1998
5	LJI8156	DAF MB200DKFL600	Van Hool Alizée	C53F	1984	Arriva Fox County, 1998
6	E219GNV	Volvo B10M-61	Jonckheere Jubilee P599	C51FT	1987	First Leicester, 1999

Previous Registrations:

E219GNV	E219GNV, 542GRT	LJI8156	B310CRP

Named vehicles: 4 *Princess Kayleigh*; 5 *Abbie*

Livery: Blue and cream

Depot: c/o Arriva Fox County, Melton Road, Thurmaston.

Ralph Garratt has managed a number of ventures around Leicester. His latest is Anstey Busline which is based at the Arriva Fox County depot at Thurmaston. The livery of this fleet is dark blue, cream and light blue. A number of school services are operated for Wreake Valley College from where 2, GTO299V, is seen departing. *Steve Sanderson*

APPLEBYS

R W Appleby Ltd; Fleetjet Ltd; Halcyon Leisure Ltd,
Conisholme, Louth, Lincolnshire, LN11 7LT

Appleby - Halcyon - North Bank

869NHT	Bristol Lodekka FS6G	Eastern Coach Works	O33/27R	1961	Jones, Weston super Mare, 1988
WJY760	Leyland Atlantean PDR1/1	Metro Cammell	O43/34F	1962	Citybus, Plymouth, 1991
JTD387P	Daimler Fleetline CRL6-33	Northern Counties	O49/31D	1975	NPT, Bilsthorpe, 1993
KMW176P	Daimler Fleetline CRG6LX	Eastern Coach Works	O43/31F	1976	Emblems Jazz Band, Knottingley, 1992
KON326P	Leyland Fleetline FE30ALR	MCW	O43/33F	1976	SS Suncruisers, Scarborough, 1994
OFB968R	Bristol LH6L	Eastern Coach Works	B43F	1977	Jaronda, Cawood, 1997
NPJ475R	Leyland National 11351/1R (Volvo)		B49F	1976	Go-Ahead (OK), 1999
PKG741R	Leyland National 11351/1R (Volvo)		B49F	1977	Stagecoach Red & White, 1999
NOE604R	Leyland National 11351A/1R (DAF)		B49F	1977	Stagecoach Midland Red, 1999
VAT176S	Bedford YLQ	Plaxton Supreme III	C45F	1977	Boddy, Bridlington, 1983
CFM347S	Leyland National 11351A/1R (Gardner)		B49F	1978	ITG, Anston, 1999
CFM355S	Leyland National 11351A/1R (Gardner)		B49F	1978	ITG, Anston, 1999
YRH808S	Bedford YMT	Plaxton Supreme III	C53F	1978	Boddy, Bridlington, 1983
SWS769S	Bristol LH6L	Eastern Coach Works	B45F	1978	NE Bus (Teeside), 1997
XPG171T	Leyland Atlantean AN68A/1R	Park Royal	B43/30F	1978	North Western (Liverline), 1997
WAE193T	Bristol LH6L	Eastern Coach Works	B43F	1979	Enterprise & Silver Dawn, 1997
KMA405T	Leyland National 11351A/1R (Gardner)		B49F	1979	Newcastle Airport, 1999
YBO67T	Leyland Leopard PSU4E/2R	East Lancashire	B45F	1979	Go-Ahead (OK), 1997
YBO68T	Leyland Leopard PSU4E/2R	East Lancashire	B45F	1979	Go-Ahead (OK), 1997
MGR915T	Leyland Leopard PSU3E/4R	Duple Dominant	B55F	1979	NE Bus (United), 1996
GSU835T	Leyland Leopard PSU3E/5R	Alexander AYS	B53F	1979	KCB Network, 1996
GSU844T	Leyland Leopard PSU3E/5R	Alexander AYS	B53F	1979	KCB Network, 1996
GSU858T	Leyland Leopard PSU3E/5R	Alexander AYS	B53F	1979	KCB Network, 1996
GSU860T	Leyland Leopard PSU3E/5R	Alexander AYS	B53F	1979	KCB Network, 1996
ANJ304T	Leyland Leopard PSU3E/4RT	Plaxton Supreme IV Express	C49F	1979	Timeline, 1994
ANJ313T	Leyland Leopard PSU3E/4RT	Plaxton Supreme IV Express	C49F	1979	Timeline, 1994
FFE477T	Bedford YMT	Plaxton Supreme IV	C45F	1979	
FRH615T	Bedford YMT	Plaxton Supreme IV	C53F	1979	Boddy, Bridlington, 1983
BNC952T	Leyland Atlantean AN68A/1R	Park Royal	B43/32F	1979	Eagre, Morton, 1997

D22SAO is a Reeve Burgess-bodied Renault-Dodge S56 that was once part of the Cumberland fleet and used on services at Whitehaven. It is now one of a small number of minibuses used by Applebys on tendered services. Applebys vehicles can be seen in many locations both north and south of the Humber.
Steve Sanderson

Reg	Chassis	Body	Seating	Year	History
WDA948T	Leyland Fleetline FE30AGR	MCW	B43/33F	1979	Amberley Travel, Pudsey, 1993
BYW406V	Leyland National 10351A/2R (Volvo)		B44F	1979	PSV Products, Warrington, 1999
YNL228V	Leyland Atlantean AN68A/2R	MCW	B49/37F	1979	Go-Ahead (OK), 1997
FTO544V	Leyland Leopard PSU3E/4R	Plaxton Supreme IV Express	C53F	1979	Trent (Barton), 1996
JYG431V	Bristol VRT/SL3/6LX	Eastern Coach Works	B43/31F	1979	Enterprise & Silver Dawn, 1997
YAE518V	Bristol LH6L	Eastern Coach Works	B43F	1979	Stephenson, Rochford, 1997
MGE8V	Bedford YMT	Plaxton Supreme IV	C53F	1980	Haldane, Glasgow, 1982
MRH398V	Bedford YMT	Plaxton Supreme IV	C53F	1980	Boddy, Bridlington, 1983
MVL750V	Bedford YLQ	Plaxton Supreme IV Express	C41F	1980	
JGV317V	Bedford YMT	Duple Dominant	B55F	1980	Rider York, 1993
GTO701V	Leyland National 2 NL116L11/1R		B50F	1980	City of Nottingham, 1998
GTO703V	Leyland National 2 NL116L11/1R		B50F	1980	City of Nottingham, 1998
GTO704V	Leyland National 2 NL116L11/1R		B50F	1980	City of Nottingham, 1998
DOC19V	Leyland National 2 NL116L11/1R		B50F	1980	Arriva Teeside, 1999
MNW131V	Leyland National 2 NL116L11/1R		B52F	1980	Arriva Teeside, 1999
MVO411W	Leyland Atlantean AN68C/1R	Northern Counties	B47/33D	1980	City of Nottingham, 1999
MVO415W	Leyland Atlantean AN68C/1R	Northern Counties	B47/33D	1980	City of Nottingham, 1999
AUP365W	Leyland Atlantean AN68B/1R	Roe	B43/30F	1980	Go-Coastline, 1999
AUP381W	Leyland Atlantean AN68B/1R	Roe	B43/30F	1980	Go-Coastline, 1999
AUP383W	Leyland Atlantean AN68B/1R	Roe	B43/30F	1980	Go-Coastline, 1999
FBV485W	Leyland Atlantean AN68B/1R	Eastern Coach Works	B43/31F	1980	Carlton Cs, Carlton-le-Moorland, 1999
ORJ366W	Leyland Atlantean AN68A/1R	Northern Counties	O43/32F	1981	GMN, 1996
PBC458W	Volvo B10M-61	Plaxton Supreme IV	C53F	1981	Ebdon, Sidcup, 1996
UVL89W	Bedford YNT	Plaxton Supreme IV Express	C53F	1981	
UVL653W	Bedford YNT	Plaxton Supreme IV Express	C53F	1981	
ORA451W	Leyland Atlantean AN68A/1R	East Lancashire	B47/31D	1981	City of Nottingham, 1997
ORA455W	Leyland Atlantean AN68A/1R	East Lancashire	B47/31D	1981	City of Nottingham, 1997
VUA473X	Bristol VRT/SL3/6LX	Eastern Coach Works	B43/31F	1981	Enterprise & Silver Dawn, 1997
RNU431X	Leyland Atlantean AN68C/1R	Northern Counties	B47/33D	1981	City of Nottingham, 1999
RNU436X	Leyland Atlantean AN68C/1R	Northern Counties	B47/33D	1981	City of Nottingham, 1999
LBO79X	Leyland Leopard PSU3F/2R	East Lancashire	B51F	1981	Go-Ahead (OK), 1998
LBO81X	Leyland Leopard PSU4F/2R	East Lancashire	B45F	1981	Go-Ahead (OK), 1997
LBO82X	Leyland Leopard PSU4F/2R	East Lancashire	B45F	1981	Go-Ahead (OK), 1997
LBO83X	Leyland Leopard PSU4F/2R	East Lancashire	B45F	1981	Go-Ahead (OK), 1997
LJI8027	Volvo B10M-61	Duple Dominant III	C57F	1981	The Isleworth, 1995
DSV721	Volvo B10M-61	Duple Dominant IV	C57F	1982	Lothian Transit, Newtongrange, 1993
795BFU	Volvo B10M-61	Duple Goldliner IV	C57F	1982	McDade, Uddingston, 1995
BJV787	Volvo B10M-61	Plaxton Supreme V	C53F	1982	Stagecoach Midland Red, 1996
KRO718	Volvo B10M-61	Duple Dominant IV	C53F	1982	Sykes, Appleton Roebuck, 1996
TDC856X	Leyland Tiger TRCTL11/2R	Duple Dominant	B55F	1982	NE Bus (United), 1998
SND422X	Leyland Atlantean AN68A/1R	Northern Counties	B43/32F	1981	Evans, Prenton, 1997
SND488X	Leyland Atlantean AN68A/1R	Northern Counties	B43/32F	1982	Bluebird, Middleton, 1997
SNU457X	Leyland Atlantean AN68A/1R	East Lancashire	B47/31D	1982	City of Nottingham, 1997
SNU458X	Leyland Atlantean AN68A/1R	East Lancashire	B47/31D	1982	City of Nottingham, 1997
SNU460X	Leyland Atlantean AN68A/1R	East Lancashire	B47/31D	1982	City of Nottingham, 1997
SNU465X	Leyland Atlantean AN68A/1R	East Lancashire	B47/31D	1982	City of Nottingham, 1997
YSU324	Volvo B10M-61	Duple Dominant IV	C53F	1982	Tillingbourne, Cranleigh, 1998
ATO58Y	Leyland Tiger TRCTL11/3R	Duple Dominant IV	C49F	1982	City of Nottingham, 1999
EAT170Y	Leyland Leopard PSU3F/5R	Plaxton Supreme IV	C53F	1982	Boddy, Bridlington, 1983
105NHY	Bedford YNT	Plaxton Supreme V	C53F	1982	
UKY608Y	Bedford YMT	Duple Dominant	B55F	1983	Coach Services, Thetford, 1998
FJV931	Volvo B10M-61	Duple Dominant IV	C53F	1983	Gregory, Blaencwm, 1995
RBO504Y	Leyland Olympian ONLXB/1R	East Lancashire	B43/31F	1983	Cardiff Bus, 1998
RBO505Y	Leyland Olympian ONLXB/1R	East Lancashire	B43/31F	1983	Cardiff Bus, 1998
UVE288	DAF MB200DKFL600	Plaxton Paramount 3200	C51F	1983	Cooper, Killamarsh, 1999
FAZ4478	Leyland Tiger TRCTL11/2RH	Plaxton Paramount 3200 E	C49F	1983	ITG, Anston, 1999
ANA613Y	Leyland Atlantean AN68D/1R	Northern Counties	B43/32F	1983	Stagecoach Manchester, 1997
A661HNB	Leyland Atlantean AN68D/1R	Northern Counties	B43/32F	1983	Stagecoach Manchester, 1997
A664HNB	Leyland Atlantean AN68D/1R	Northern Counties	B43/32F	1983	Stagecoach Manchester, 1997
A665HNB	Leyland Atlantean AN68D/1R	Northern Counties	B43/32F	1983	Stagecoach Manchester, 1997
A674HNB	Leyland Atlantean AN68D/1R	Northern Counties	B43/32F	1983	Stagecoach Manchester, 1997
A687HNB	Leyland Atlantean AN68D/1R	Northern Counties	B43/32F	1983	Stagecoach Manchester, 1997
A714LNC	Leyland Atlantean AN68D/1R	Northern Counties	B43/32F	1984	Stagecoach Manchester, 1997

Opposite, top: **An annual influx of new coaches has been a feature of the Applebys fleet for many years. In recent years Irizar Century bodies, built in Spain, have been specified on Swedish built Scania chassis. N356REE is a tri-axle version of this type.** *David Heath*
Opposite, bottom: **Applebys of Conisholme, near Louth is a long established and well-known Lincolnshire coaching and bus company. While it serves much of the northern Wolds, an arms-length operation was established some years ago in Scarborough. The Leyland Leopard has been one of the main vehicle types used and is illustrated here by MGR915T operating a town service in that seaside location in June 1998. Bearing a Duple Dominant 55-seater body the bus was originally operated by United.** *Tony Wilson*

	9190NK	Volvo B10M-61	Plaxton Paramount 3200	C53F	1984	
	Q723GHG	Leyland Tiger TRCTL11/2R(Rear eng) ECW		B51F	1985	Go-Ahead (OK), 1999
	841TPU	Volvo B10M-61	Plaxton Paramount 3200 II	C53F	1985	
	NEE496	Volvo B10M-61	Plaxton Paramount 3200 II	C53F	1985	
	957XYB	Volvo B10M-61	Plaxton Paramount 3200 II	C53F	1986	
	6257RO	Volvo B10M-61	Plaxton Paramount 3200 II	C53F	1986	
	WSV317	Volvo B10M-61	Plaxton Paramount 3200 II	C53F	1986	
	D22SAO	Renault-Dodge S56	Reeve Burgess	B23F	1986	AJC Coaches, Leeds, 1994
	D32SAO	Renault-Dodge S56	Reeve Burgess	B25F	1986	Preston Bus, 1994
	D768YCW	Renault-Dodge S46	Northern Counties	B22F	1987	Preston Bus, 1994
	D769YCW	Renault-Dodge S46	Northern Counties	B24F	1987	Preston Bus, 1994
	YJV178	Volvo B10M-61	Plaxton Paramount 3200 III	C55F	1987	
	XAT586	Volvo B10M-61	Plaxton Paramount 3200 III	C53F	1987	
	E459WJK	Renault-Dodge S56	Alexander AM	B25F	1987	Brighton, 1995
	RVL445	Volvo B10M-61	Plaxton Paramount 3200 III	C53F	1987	
	5517RH	Volvo B10M-61	Plaxton Paramount 3200 III	C53F	1988	
	E824MDD	Iveco Daily 49.10	Robin Hood City Nippy	B21F	1988	Royal Orthopaedic Hospital, 1994
	E48MCK	Renault-Dodge S56	Northern Counties	B25F	1988	Preston Bus, 1996
	E75LFR	Renault-Dodge S56	Northern Counties	B25F	1988	Preston Bus, 1996
	E985GFW	Volkswagen Caravelle	Volkswagen	M8	1988	
	UTL798	Scania K112CRB	Van Hool Alizée H	C53F	1988	
	F970GJK	Iveco Daily 49.10	Robin Hood City Nippy	B21F	1989	Translink, Folkestone, 1994
	XWC339	Bedford YNV	Duple 320	C57F	1988	Enterprise & Silver Dawn, 1997
	252GXM	Scania K93CRB	Duple 320	C55F	1989	Hardings, Huyton, 1998
	XLK673	Scania K93CRB	Duple 320	C55F	1989	J&L International, St Leonards, 1998
	5447FH	Scania K93CRB	Duple 320	C55F	1989	J&L International, St Leonards, 1998
	251CNX	Scania K93CRB	Van Hool Alizée H	C53F	1989	
	XJV146	Scania K93CRB	Plaxton Paramount 3200 III	C53F	1989	
	YNA887	Scania K93CRB	Berkhof Excellence 1000L	C53F	1990	
	ORJ442	Scania K93CRB	Berkhof Excellence 1000L	C53F	1990	
	990ULG	Toyota Coaster HB31R	Caetano Optimo	C18F	1989	Davidson, Edinburgh, 1994
	HVL611	Scania K93CRB	Van Hool Alizée H	C53F	1990	
	UJV489	Scania K93CRB	Van Hool Alizée H	C53F	1990	
H	G495VFU	Mazda E2200	Coachwork Walker	M8	1990	
H	ASV895	Scania K113TRB	Berkhof Excellence 2000HD	C57/17CT	1990	
H	J23HRH	Scania K113CRB	Berkhof Excellence 2000HL	C49FT	1992	
H	WEE584	Scania K113CRB	Berkhof Excellence 2000HL	C49FT	1992	
	388XYC	Scania K113CRB	Berkhof Excellence 1000	C53F	1992	
	361EKH	Scania K113CRB	Berkhof Excellence 1000	C49FT	1993	
	520FUM	Scania K113CRB	Berkhof Excellence 1000	C49FT	1993	
H	485DKH	Scania K113CRB	Berkhof Excellence 2000HL	C49FT	1993	
	VFW721	Scania K113TRB	Irizar Century 12.37	C49FT	1995	
	LJV273	Scania K113TRB	Irizar Century 12.37	C49FT	1995	
H	WAC828	Scania K113TRB	Irizar Century 12.37	C49FT	1995	
	M594GFE	Volkswagen Caravelle	Volkswagen	M8	1995	
	N875AKY	Mercedes-Benz 811D	Mellor	B33F	1995	
	N489DJH	LDV 400	LDV	M16	1995	van, 1999
	N757GWR	Mercedes-Benz 208D	Mercedes-Benz	Mxx	1996	van, 1998
	N539OFE	Scania K113CRB	Irizar Century 12.35	C49FT	1996	
	N135OFW	Scania K113CRB	Irizar Century 12.35	C49FT	1996	
	N734RBE	Scania K113TRB	Irizar Century 12.37	C49FT	1996	
	N356REE	Scania K113TRB	Irizar Century 12.37	C49FT	1996	
H	P415UKH	Scania K113TRB	Berkhof Excellence 2000HD	C57/16CT	1997	
	P75UJV	Scania K113TRB	Irizar Century 12.37	C49FT	1997	
	P388WVL	Scania K113TRB	Irizar Century 12.37	C49FT	1997	
H	R278RRH	Scania K113TRB	Irizar Century 12.37	C49FT	1998	
	R253EJV	Scania K113TRB	Irizar Century 12.37	C49FT	1998	
	R862MFE	Scania K124IB4	Irizar Century 12.35	C49FT	1998	
	R863MFE	Scania K113TRB	Irizar Century 12.37	C49FT	1998	
	R417LFW	Scania K124IB4	Irizar Century 12.35	C49FT	1998	
	S158WOL	Iveco Daily 49.10	Jubilee	BC16F	1998	
	S193MRH	Mercedes-Benz Vario O814	Plaxton Beaver 2	B33F	1998	
	S741RNE	Mercedes-Benz Vario O814	Plaxton Beaver 2	B33F	1998	
	S310BLG	Mercedes-Benz Vario O814	Plaxton Beaver 2	B33F	1999	
H	T654LAT	Scania K124IB4	Irizar Century 12.35	C49FT	1999	
	T486JVV	Scania K124IB6	Irizar Century 12.37	C49FT	1999	
	T814RTL	Scania K124IB4	Irizar Century 12.35	C49FT	1999	
	T849JFU	Scania K124IB4	Irizar Century 12.35	C49FT	1999	
		Scania L94UB	Wright Axcess Floline	N43F	On order	
		Mercedes-Benz Vario O814	Plaxton Beaver 2	B33F	On order	

The Applebys double deck fleet has expanded in the past three years with the acquisition of the Lincoln operations of Enterprise & Silver Dawn and a major tendering success in the Hull area. RBO505Y is an East Lancashire-bodied Olympian obtained from the Cardiff fleet. It is seen in Unity Square, Lincoln, in between trips to Waddington on the former Enterprise service. *Steve Sanderson*

Previous Registrations:

105NHY	DFW782X	ATO58Y	WAU795Y, 75RTO	UJV489	G649WFE
251CNX	F327OVL	ASV895	G545PRH	UTL798	E562FFW
252GXM	F363CHE	BJV787	YKV811X, 3669DG, ARW163X	UVE288	ANA442Y
361EKH	K669SFE	DSV721	FGD826X	VFW721	M433GFE
388XYC	J677LVL	E75LFR	E77LFR	WAC828	M985LAG
485DKH	K560RRH	FAZ4478	A102EPA	WEE584	J884MFE
520FUM	K671SFE	FJV931	ENF553Y	WJY760	From new
5447FH	F365CHE, XGV226, F286OUD	HVL611	G592WFW	WSV317	From new
5517RH	E899HFW	KRO718	OHE273X	XAT586	D413SFW
6257RO	C320NFW	LJI8027	BKF348X	XJV146	F141DCT
795BFU	FGD825X	LJV273	M135NBE	YJV178	D240WTL
841TPU	From new	NEE496	B273ETL	YNA887	G630VVL
869NHT	A646WFE	OHE271X	OHE271X, MIL1853	XLK673	F364CHE, TJT788, F285OUD
9190NK	From new	ORJ442	G288VTL	XWC399	E433PFU
957XYB	From new	PBC458W	PBC458W, UVE288	YSU324	OHE271X
990ULG	G864VAY	RVL445	From new		

Livery: Ivory, green and red (Appleby); pink, green & yellow (Halcyon); blue, cream and red (North Bank)

Depots: Bardney; Bessingby Industrial Estate, Bridlington; Brighowgate, Grimsby; Julian Street, Grimsby; Horncastle; Wincolmlee, Hull; Newark Road, Lincoln; North Somercotes; Scarborough.

ARRIVA FOX COUNTY

ARRIVA serving the Fox County; ARRIVA serving Derby

Arriva Fox County Ltd, POBox 613, Melton Road, Thurmaston, Leicester, LE4 8ZN

2	FAZ2784	Leyland Tiger TRCTL11/3RH	Plaxton Paramount 3200 IIE	C53F	1986	Crosville Cymru, 1996
4	FIL3452	Leyland Tiger TRCTL11/3RH	Plaxton Paramount 3200 II	C50FT	1985	
9	A125EPA	Leyland Tiger TRCTL11/2R	Plaxton Paramount 3200 E	C53F	1983	London Country NE, 1989
19	109CRC	Leyland Tiger TRCTL11/3R	Plaxton Paramount 3200	C48FT	1983	London & Country, 1990
20	LJI5632	Leyland Tiger TRCTL11/3R	Plaxton Paramount 3200	C48FT	1983	London & Country, 1990
21	111XKT	Leyland Tiger TRCTL11/3R	Plaxton Paramount 3200	C46FT	1983	London & Country, 1990
22	JDE972X	Leyland Tiger TRCTL11/3R	Plaxton Supreme VI Exp	C53F	1982	Hills, Nuneaton, 1991
87	LJI8157	DAF MB200DKFL600	Van Hool Alizée	C49FT	1984	Orsborn, Wollaston, 1989
153	662NKR	DAF MB200DKFL615	Plaxton Supreme VI	C57F	1982	Bland, Stamford, 1990
192	C632PAU	DAF MB200DKFL600	Plaxton Paramount 3500	C49F	1985	
209	T	DAF DE33WSSB3000	Van Hool Alizée 2	C46FT	1999	
210	T119AUA	DAF DE33WSSB3000	Van Hool Alizée 2	C46FT	1999	
211	N211TBC	Volvo B10M-62	Plaxton Expressliner 2	C49FT	1996	
212	N212TBC	Volvo B10M-62	Plaxton Expressliner 2	C49FT	1996	
213	FIL3451	Volvo B10M-60	Van Hool Alizée	C50F	1989	Tellings-Golden Miller, Byfleet, 1992
214	XPA110	Volvo B10M-60	Van Hool Alizée	C52F	1989	Tellings-Golden Miller, Byfleet, 1992
233	GIL6253	Volvo B10M-61	Plaxton Paramount 3200 III	C50F	1987	The Shires, 1997
234	HIL7594	Volvo B10M-61	Plaxton Paramount 3500 III	C53F	1988	The Shires, 1997
235	GIL6949	Volvo B10M-61	Plaxton Paramount 3200 III	C50F	1987	The Shires, 1997
236	F406DUG	Volvo B10M-60	Plaxton Paramount 3200 III	C50F	1989	Wallace Arnold, 1992
237	F407DUG	Volvo B10M-60	Plaxton Paramount 3200 III	C50F	1989	Wallace Arnold, 1992
246	J246MFP	Volvo B10M-60	Plaxton Expressliner	C46FT	1992	Express Travel, Liverpool, 1995
247	J247MFP	Volvo B10M-60	Plaxton Expressliner	C46FT	1992	Express Travel, Liverpool, 1995
785	BVP785V	Leyland Leopard PSU3E/4R	Plaxton Supreme IV	C53F	1980	Midland Red, 1981

2047-2053 Dennis Dart SLF Plaxton Pointer MPD N33F 1999

2047	T47WUT	2049	T49WUT	2051	T51WUT	2052	T52WUT	2053	T53WUT
2048	T48WUT	2050	T50WUT						

2141	SIB6707	Leyland NL106AL11/1R(6HLXB)	East Lancs Greenway(1992)	B41F	1981	Arriva North East, 1999
2142	JIL2193	Leyland 11351/1R	East Lancs Greenway(1994)	B49F	1974	Southern Counties (C&NS), 1998
2143	JIL2197	Leyland 1151/1R	East Lancs Greenway(1994)	B49F	1973	Southern Counties (C&NS), 1998
2144	JIL2196	Leyland 11351/1R	East Lancs Greenway(1994)	B49F	1975	Southern Counties (C&NS), 1998
2145	JIL2198	Leyland 11351A/1R	East Lancs Greenway(1994)	B49F	1976	Southern Counties (C&NS), 1998
2146	JIL2199	Leyland 11351A/1R	East Lancs Greenway(1994)	B49F	1976	Southern Counties (C&NS), 1998
2147	JIL2190	Leyland 11351/1R	East Lancs Greenway(1994)	B49F	1976	Southern Counties (C&NS), 1998
2148	JIL5367	Leyland 11351A/1R(Volvo)	East Lancs Greenway(1994)	B49F	1977	Southern Counties (C&NS), 1998
2149	SJI5569	Leyland 11351A/1R(Volvo)	East Lancs Greenway(1994)	B49F	1977	Southern Counties (C&NS), 1998
2150	SIB1278	Leyland 10351B/1R	East Lancs Greenway(1994)	B41F	1979	Southern Counties (C&NS), 1998
2151	SJI5570	Leyland 11351/1R(Volvo)	East Lancs Greenway(1994)	B49F	1976	Southern Counties (C&NS), 1998
2152	MSU433	Leyland National 2 NL116L11/1R		B49F	1980	Stevensons, 1997
2154	EON831V	Leyland National 2 NL116L11/1R		B49F	1980	London & Country, 1997
2156	JIL2156	Leyland National 11351/1R	East Lancs Greenway (1994)	B49F	1974	National Welsh, 1989
2157	JIL2157	Leyland National 1151/1R/0402	East Lancs Greenway (1994)	B49F	1973	Kinch, Barrow-on-Soar, 1989
2158	JIL2158	Leyland National 11351A/1R	East Lancs Greenway (1994)	B49F	1977	Midland Red, 1981
2159	JIL2159	Leyland National 11351A/1R	East Lancs Greenway (1994)	B49F	1977	Midland Red, 1981
2160	JIL2160	Leyland National 11351/1R	East Lancs Greenway (1994)	B49F	1975	London & Country, 1994
2161	JIL2161	Leyland National 11351/1R	East Lancs Greenway (1994)	B49F	1974	Kinch, Barrow-on-Soar, 1989
2162	JIL2162	Leyland National 1151/1R/0102	East Lancs Greenway (1994)	B49F	1974	Kinch, Barrow-on-Soar, 1989
2163	JIL2163	Leyland National 11351/1R	East Lancs Greenway (1994)	B49F	1974	National Welsh, 1989
2164	JIL2164	Leyland National 11351A/1R	East Lancs Greenway (1994)	B49F	1978	London & Country, 1994
2165	JIL2165	Leyland National 11351A/1R	East Lancs Greenway (1994)	B49F	1976	London & Country, 1994

2166-2179 Scania L113CRL East Lancashire European B51F 1996

2166	N166PUT	2169	N169PUT	2172	N172PUT	2175	N175PUT	2178	N178PUT
2167	N167PUT	2170	N170PUT	2173	N173PUT	2176	N176PUT	2179	N179PUT
2168	N168PUT	2171	N171PUT	2174	N174PUT	2177	N177PUT		

As part of a British Bus project, a large number of Leyland Nationals were re-built at the Blackburn factory of East Lancashire Coachbuilders. Fox County's 2145, JIL2198 was new to Ribble as SCK703P but re-built for London and Country. It made the transition to the east midlands in 1998 when a number of this type were reallocated within the Arriva group. *Tony Wilson*

2201-2206

		Dennis Dart SLF		Plaxton Pointer		N39F	1997		
2201	P201HRY	2203	P203HRY	2204	P204HRY	2205	P205HRY	2206	P206HRY
2202	P202HRY								

2207	S207DTO	Dennis Dart SLF	Plaxton Pointer 2	N39F	1998	
2208	S208DTO	Dennis Dart SLF	Plaxton Pointer 2	N39F	1998	
2534	PWE534R	Leyland Fleetline FE30AGR	Alexander AL	B45/29D	1977	South Yorkshire's Transport, 1990
2547	GTO307V	Leyland Fleetline FE30AGR	Northern Counties	B43/30F	1980	

4001	L94HRF	DAF DB250RS200505	Optare Spectra	B48/29F	1993	Midland (Stevensons), 1998
4002	L95HRF	DAF DB250RS200505	Optare Spectra	B48/29F	1993	Midland (Stevensons), 1998

4134-4145

		Scania N113DRB		Northern Counties		B47/33F	1990-91 Arriva North West (L), 1999		
4134	G34HKY	4136	G36HKY	4138	G38HKY	4142	G714LKW	4144	H804RWJ
4135	G35HKY	4137	G37HKY	4141	G711LKW	4143	H803RWJ	4145	H805RWJ

4151	E701XKR	Scania N112DRB	Alexander RH	B47/31F	1988	Kentish Bus, 1996
4152	E702XKR	Scania N112DRB	Alexander RH	B47/31F	1988	Kentish Bus, 1996

4153-4158

		Scania N113DRB		Alexander RH		B47/33F	1989	BTS, Borehamwood, 1993	
4153	F153DET	4155	F155DET	4156	F156DET	4157	F157DET	4158	F158DET
4154	F154DET								

4159-4178

		Scania N113DRB		East Lancashire		B47/33F	1994-95		
4159	M159GRY	4163	M163GRY	4167	M167GRY	4171	M171GRY	4175	M175GRY
4160	M160GRY	4164	M164GRY	4168	M168GRY	4172	M172GRY	4176	M176GRY
4161	M161GRY	4165	M165GRY	4169	M169GRY	4173	M173GRY	4177	M177GRY
4162	M162GRY	4166	M166GRY	4170	M170GRY	4174	M174GRY	4178	M178GRY

Now with Arriva Fox County 4182, N162VVO was new for the Derby operations in 1995. It is a Volvo Olympian which carries an East Lancashire E-type body. Transfers of vehicles between the Derby and Fox County operations are commonplace now that there is a single management structure. Consequently, this view was taken in the centre of Leicester. *Steve Sanderson*

4180-4184		Scania N113DRB		East Lancashire		B45/33F		1995	
4180	N160VVO	**4181**	N161VVO	**4182**	N162VVO	**4183**	N163VVO	**4184**	N164VVO

4320-4334		Volvo Citybus B10M-50		East Lancashire		B45/35F		1990-91 London South, 1998	
4320	H650GPF	**4323**	H654GPF	**4326**	H663GPF	**4329**	H671GPF	**4332**	H680GPF
4321	H652GPF	**4324**	H655GPF	**4327**	H664GPF	**4330**	H672GPF	**4333**	H682GPF
4322	H653GPF	**4325**	H659GPF	**4328**	H669GPF	**4331**	H674GPF	**4334**	H684GPF

4336	YAU126Y	Volvo Citybus B10M-50	Marshall	B45/33F	1983	
4337	YAU127Y	Volvo Citybus B10M-50	Marshall	B45/33F	1983	
4476	TPD127X	Leyland Olympian ONTL11/1R	Roe	B43/29F	1982	Southern Coutnies (CNS), 1998
4477	TPD128X	Leyland Olympian ONTL11/1R	Roe	B43/29F	1982	Southern Counties (CNS), 1998
4478	D80UTF	Leyland Olympian ONLXCT/1RH	Eastern Coach Works	C39/27F	1986	Reading, 1994
4480	C42HHJ	Leyland Olympian ONLXCT/1RH	Eastern Coach Works	B47/31F	1985	Colchester, 1994
4481	D44RWC	Leyland Olympian ONLXCT/1RH	Eastern Coach Works	B47/31F	1986	Colchester, 1994

Opposite, top: **Dennis and Plaxton have combined to produce a midibus which is fully accessible. The Dennis Dart was originally conceived as a small bus and with the MPD (Midi Pointer Dart) the model albeit in low floor form has reverted to the dimensions of the earlier Darts. Number 2048, T48WUT is allocated to the Derby fleet and operates on the park & ride service to/from Pride Park, home of Derby County Football Club.** *Tony Wilson*
Opposite, bottom: **The Optare Spectra, in comparison to some double-deck breeds, is a hard beast to find. Other than in some southern enclaves, this standard floor vehicle type has found few places to operate. Two of this design did operate with Stevensons of Spath for some years in Staffordshire. However, re-organization since the takeover by Arriva has led to these two being transferred within the empire to the Fox County operation, and has since been constantly employed on route X61 between Leicester and Market Harborough. It is in the latter town's bus station that 4001, L94HRF was found in September 1998.** *Tony Wilson*

4486	ACM706X	Leyland Olympian ONT11/1R	Eastern Coach Works	B46/31F	1981	Merseybus, 1993
4487	ACM707X	Leyland Olympian ONT11/1R	Eastern Coach Works	B46/31F	1981	Merseybus, 1993
4489	ACM711X	Leyland Olympian ONT11/1R	Eastern Coach Works	B46/31F	1981	Merseybus, 1993
4491	MTU117Y	Leyland Olympian ONLXB/1R	Eastern Coach Works	B45/32F	1983	Crosville Cymru, 1989
4492	MTU118Y	Leyland Olympian ONLXB/1R	Eastern Coach Works	B45/32F	1983	Crosville Cymru, 1989
4493	MTU119Y	Leyland Olympian ONLXB/1R	Eastern Coach Works	B45/32F	1983	Crosville Cymru, 1989
4494	MTU121Y	Leyland Olympian ONLXB/1R	Eastern Coach Works	B45/32F	1983	Crosville Cymru, 1989

4501-4514   Leyland Olympian ONLXB/1R   Eastern Coach Works   B45/32F   1983-84

4501	A501EJF	4504	A504EJF	4508	A508EJF	4510	A510EJF	4512	B512LFP
4502	A502EJF	4505	A505EJF	4509	A509EJF	4511	A511EJF	4514	B514LFP
4503	A503EJF	4507	A507EJF						

4516	A132SMA	Leyland Olympian ONLXB/1R	Eastern Coach Works	B45/32F	1983	Crosville Cymru, 1989
4517	A133SMA	Leyland Olympian ONLXB/1R	Eastern Coach Works	B45/32F	1983	Crosville Cymru, 1989
4518	A134SMA	Leyland Olympian ONLXB/1R	Eastern Coach Works	B45/32F	1983	Crosville Cymru, 1989
4519	A135SMA	Leyland Olympian ONLXB/1R	Eastern Coach Works	B45/32F	1983	Crosville Cymru, 1989

4527	B187BLG	Leyland Olympian ONLXB/1RZ	Eastern Coach Works	B45/32F	1984	Crosville Cymru, 1990
4528	B190BLG	Leyland Olympian ONLXB/1RZ	Eastern Coach Works	B45/32F	1984	Crosville Cymru, 1990

4601-4613   Volvo Olympian YN2RV18Z4   Northern Counties Palatine   B47/29F   1996

4601	P601CAY	4604	P604CAY	4607	P607CAY	4610	P610CAY	4612	P612CAY
4602	P602CAY	4605	P605CAY	4608	P608CAY	4611	P611CAY	4613	P613CAY
4603	P603CAY	4606	P606CAY	4609	P609CAY				

4614-4643   Volvo Olympian   Northern Counties Palatine   B47/29F   1998

4614	R614MNU	4620	R620MNU	4626	R626MNU	4632	R632MNU	4638	R638MNU
4615	R615MNU	4621	R621MNU	4627	R627MNU	4633	R633MNU	4639	R639MNU
4616	R616MNU	4622	R622MNU	4628	R628MNU	4634	R634MNU	4640	R640MNU
4617	R617MNU	4623	R623MNU	4629	R629MNU	4635	R635MNU	4641	R641MNU
4618	R618MNU	4624	R624MNU	4630	R630MNU	4636	R636MNU	4642	R642MNU
4619	R619MNU	4625	R625MNU	4631	R631MNU	4637	R637MNU	4643	R643MNU

4644-4653   Volvo Olympian   Northern Counties Palatine   B47/29F   1998

4644	S644KJU	4646	S646KJU	4648	S648KJU	4650	S650KJU	4652	S652KJU
4645	S645KJU	4647	S647KJU	4649	S649KJU	4651	S651KJU	4653	S653KJU

4654	F114TML	Volvo Citybus B10M-50	Alexander RV	B47/29D	1989	Arriva London, 1999
4655	F111TML	Volvo Citybus B10M-50	Alexander RV	B47/29D	1989	Arriva London, 1999

D021-D026   Scania K92CRB   Alexander PS   B51F   1988

D021	E21ECH	D023	E23ECH	D024	E24ECH	D025	E25ECH	D026	E26ECH

D027	F27JRC	Scania K93CRB	Alexander PS	B51F	1989
D028	F28JRC	Scania K93CRB	Alexander PS	B51F	1989

D029-D033   Scania L113CRL   East Lancashire European   N51F   1996

D029	N429XRC	D030	N430XRC	D031	N431XRC	D032	N432XRC	D033	N433XRC

D034-D038   Dennis Dart 9.8SDL3040   East Lancashire EL2000   B40F   1994

D034	L34PNN	D035	L35PNN	D036	L36PNN	D037	L37PNN	D038	L38PNN

D045	R45VJF	Dennis Dart SLF	Alexander ALX200	N40F	1997
D046	R46VJF	Dennis Dart SLF	Alexander ALX200	N40F	1997

Under common management with Fox County, a number of vehicles in the Derby City subsidiary of Arriva began to have suffix letters affixed, on paper, to their fleet numbers during 1997. The former city-run company has changed livery chameleon-like a number of times in recent years, ranging from green and cream, through hues of blue and yellow with red, to the present stone and turquoise of Arriva. DO32, N432XRC an Alexander-bodied Scania, pauses in Derby bus station beneath threatening skies. *Tony Wilson*

D048	GTO48V	Leyland Fleetline FE30AGR		Northern Counties		B43/29F	1980			

D072-D081

Mercedes-Benz 709D — Alexander Sprint — B27F — 1996

D072	N472XRC	**D074**	N474XRC	**D076**	N476XRC	**D078**	N478XRC	**D080**	N480XRC	
D073	N473XRC	**D075**	N475XRC	**D077**	N477XRC	**D079**	N479XRC	**D081**	N481XRC	

D082-D092

Mercedes-Benz 709D — Plaxton Beaver — B27F — 1996

D082	P482CAL	**D084**	P484CAL	**D086**	P486CAL	**D088**	P488CAL	**D091**	P491CAL	
D083	P483CAL	**D085**	P485CAL	**D087**	P487CAL	**D090**	P490CAL	**D092**	P492CAL	

D112	SRC112X	Ailsa B55-10		Northern Counties	B38/35F	1982
D113	SRC113X	Ailsa B55-10		Northern Counties	B38/35F	1982
D114	SRC114X	Ailsa B55-10		Northern Counties	B38/35F	1982
D115	SRC115X	Ailsa B55-10		Northern Counties	B38/35F	1982
D118	TCH118X	Ailsa B55-10		Northern Counties	B38/35F	1982
D119	TCH119X	Ailsa B55-10		Northern Counties	B38/35F	1982
D120	TCH120X	Ailsa B55-10		Northern Counties	B38/35F	1982
D121	TCH121X	Ailsa B55-10		Northern Counties	B38/35F	1982
D128	YAU128Y	Volvo Citybus B10M-50		Marshall	B43/33F	1983

D129-D133

Volvo Citybus B10M-50 — East Lancashire — B45/31F — 1984

D129	A129DTO	**D130**	A130DTO	**D131**	A131DTO	**D132**	A132DTO	**D133**	A133DTO	

D134-D143

Volvo Citybus B10M-50 — Marshall — B45/33F — 1984

D134	B134GAU	**D136**	B136GAU	**D138**	B138GAU	**D140**	B140GAU	**D142**	B142GAU	
D135	B135GAU	**D137**	B137GAU	**D139**	B139GAU	**D141**	B141GAU	**D143**	B143GAU	

D144-D153

Volvo Citybus B10M-50 — Northern Counties — B42/33F — 1986/88

D144	C144NRR	D146	C146NRR	D148	C148NRR	D150	E150BTO	D152	E152BTO
D145	C145NRR	D147	C147NRR	D149	E149BTO	D151	E151BTO	D153	E153BTO

D165-D169

Volvo Olympian YN2RV18Z4 — Northern Counties Palatine I — B47/30F — 1996

D165	N165XVO	D166	N166XVO	D167	P167BTV	D168	P168BTV	D169	P169BTV

D301-D315

Leyland Fleetline FE30AGR — Northern Counties — B43/30F — 1978-81

D301	GTO301V	D305	GTO305V	D310	MTV310W	D312	MTV312W	D314	MTV314W
D302	GTO302V	D306	GTO306V	D311	MTV311W	D313	MTV313W	D315	MTV315W
D304	GTO304V	D309	MTV309W						

M101-M126

Mercedes-Benz Vario O810 — Alexander ALX100 — B29F — 1997

M101	P101HCH	M106	P106HCH	M112	P112HCH	M117	P117HCH	M122	P122HCH
M102	P102HCH	M107	P107HCH	M113	P113HCH	M118	P118HCH	M123	P123HCH
M103	P103HCH	M108	P108HCH	M114	P114HCH	M119	P119HCH	M124	P124HCH
M104	P104HCH	M109	P109HCH	M115	P115HCH	M120	P120HCH	M125	P125HCH
M105	P105HCH	M110	P110HCH	M116	P116HCH	M121	P121HCH	M126	P126HCH

M127-M170

Mercedes-Benz Vario O814 — Plaxton Beaver 2 — B27F — 1998

M127	R127LNR	M136	R136LNR	M145	R145LNR	M154	R154UAL	M163	R163UAL
M128	R128LNR	M137	R137LNR	M146	R146LNR	M155	R155UAL	M164	R164UAL
M129	R129LNR	M138	R138LNR	M147	R147UAL	M156	R156UAL	M165	R165UAL
M130	R130LNR	M139	R139LNR	M148	R148UAL	M157	R157UAL	M166	R166UAL
M131	R131LNR	M140	R140LNR	M149	R149UAL	M158	R158UAL	M167	R167UAL
M132	R132LNR	M141	R141LNR	M150	R150UAL	M159	R159UAL	M168	R168UAL
M133	R133LNR	M142	R142LNR	M151	R151UAL	M160	R160UAL	M169	R169UAL
M134	R134LNR	M143	R143LNR	D52	R152UAL	D61	R161UAL	M170	R170UUT
M135	R135LNR	M144	R144LNR	M153	R153UAL	M162	R162UAL		

M171	R765DUB	Mercedes-Benz Vario O810	Plaxton Beaver 2	B27F	1997	Arriva Yorkshire, 1999
M227	F27XVP	Iveco Daily 49.10	Carlyle Dailybus 2	B25F	1988	
M282	E62UKL	Mercedes-Benz 609D	Reeve Burgess Beaver	B20F	1988	Maidstone & District, 1997
M289	F379UCP	Mercedes-Benz 609D	Reeve Burgess Beaver	B20F	1988	Edinburgh Transport, 1994
M291	D906MVU	Mercedes-Benz 609D	Mercedes	B27F	1987	
M296	D226SKD	Mercedes-Benz L608D	Alexander	B20F	1986	North Western 1992
M301	F301RUT	Mercedes-Benz 709D	Robin Hood	B26F	1989	
M302	F302RUT	Mercedes-Benz 709D	Robin Hood	B26F	1989	

M303-M322

Mercedes-Benz 709D — Alexander Sprint — B25F — 1994

M303	L303AUT	M307	L307AUT	M311	L311AUT	M315	L315AUT	M319	L319AUT
M304	L304AUT	M308	L308AUT	M312	L312AUT	M316	L316AUT	M320	L320AUT
M305	L305AUT	M309	L309AUT	M313	L313AUT	M317	L317AUT	M321	L321AUT
M306	L306AUT	M310	L310AUT	M314	L314AUT	M318	L318AUT	M322	L322AUT

M323	L323AUT	Mercedes-Benz 709D	Leicester Carriage Builders	B25F	1994	
M324	L324AUT	Mercedes-Benz 709D	Leicester Carriage Builders	B25F	1994	
M325	L325AUT	Mercedes-Benz 709D	Leicester Carriage Builders	B25F	1994	
M326	N331OFP	Mercedes-Benz 709D	Leicester Carriage Builders	B25F	1995	Leicester Carriage demonstrator, 1996
M329	L227HRF	Mercedes-Benz 709D	Dormobile Routemaker	B29F	1993	Stevensons, 1994
M330	L228HRF	Mercedes-Benz 709D	Dormobile Routemaker	B29F	1993	Stevensons, 1994
M331	L231HRF	Mercedes-Benz 709D	Dormobile Routemaker	B27F	1993	Stevensons, 1994
M332	G64SNN	Mercedes-Benz 709D	Carlyle	BC29F	1990	Midland Red North, 1995
M333	L233HRF	Mercedes-Benz 709D	Dormobile Routemaker	B27F	1993	Stevensons, 1994
M335	G65SNN	Mercedes-Benz 709D	Carlyle	B29F	1990	Stevensons, 1994

The Mercedes-Benz Vario with Plaxton Beaver 2 bodywork has been introduced in large numbers into the Arriva Group operations. The Fox County subsidiary, much of which is centered upon Leicestershire, operates most town services in Melton Mowbray. June 1998 found M139, R139LNR heading towards the centre of the town. *Tony Wilson*

M336	J151WEH	Mercedes-Benz 709D	Dormobile Routemaker	B29F	1992	Stevensons, 1994
M337	K148BRF	Mercedes-Benz 709D	Dormobile Routemaker	B27F	1992	Stevensons, 1994
M338	K158BRF	Mercedes-Benz 709D	Dormobile Routemaker	B27F	1993	Stevensons, 1994
M339	G301RJA	Mercedes-Benz 709D	Reeve Burgess Beaver	B25F	1990	Stevensons, 1994
M341	K131XRE	Mercedes-Benz 709D	Dormobile Routemaker	B29F	1992	Stevensons, 1994
M342	G142GOL	Mercedes-Benz 709D	Carlyle	B29F	1990	Stevensons, 1994
M343	G143GOL	Mercedes-Benz 709D	Carlyle	B29F	1990	Stevensons, 1994

M344-M358 Mercedes-Benz 709D   Alexander Sprint   B27F   1995

M344	N344OBC	**M347**	N347OBC	**M350**	N350OBC	**M353**	N353OBC	**M356**	N356OBC
M345	N345OBC	**M348**	N348OBC	**M351**	N351OBC	**M354**	N354OBC	**M357**	N357OBC
M346	N346OBC	**M349**	N349OBC	**M352**	N352OBC	**M355**	N355OBC	**M358**	N358OBC

M359	P111MML	Mercedes-Benz 709D	Reeve Burgess Beaver	B27F	1996	
M360	P222MML	Mercedes-Benz 709D	Reeve Burgess Beaver	B27F	1996	
M361	G104TND	Mercedes-Benz 811D	Carlyle	B33F	1989	Arriva North West, 1999
M362	G124TJA	Mercedes-Benz 811D	Carlyle	B33F	1990	Arriva North West, 1999
M363	M456JPA	Mercedes-Benz 709D	Alexander Sprint	B23F	1994	Arriva Southern Counties, 1999
M364	M455JPA	Mercedes-Benz 709D	Alexander Sprint	B23F	1994	Arriva Southern Counties, 1999
M365	M465LPG	Mercedes-Benz 709D	Alexander Sprint	B23F	1995	Arriva Southern Counties, 1999
M366	M236KNR	Mercedes-Benz 709D	Alexander Sprint	B23F	1995	Arriva Southern Counties, 1999
M367	G125TJA	Mercedes-Benz 811D	Carlyle	B33F	1990	Arriva North West, 1999
M368	G106TND	Mercedes-Benz 811D	Carlyle	B33F	1989	Arriva North West, 1999
M369	L641DNA	Mercedes-Benz 709D	Plaxton Beaver	B27F	1993	Arriva North West, 1999
M370	L643DNA	Mercedes-Benz 709D	Plaxton Beaver	B27F	1994	Arriva North West, 1999
M371	M67WKA	Mercedes-Benz 709D	Alexander Sprint	B25F	1994	Arriva North West, 1999
M372	M166WTJ	Mercedes-Benz 709D	Alexander Sprint	B25F	1994	Arriva North West, 1999
M390	K390NGG	Mercedes-Benz 811D	Dormobile Routemaker	BC33F	1992	Irving & McIntyre, Greenock, 1995
M391	J401FNS	Mercedes-Benz 709D	Dormobile Routemaker	B29F	1991	Irving & McIntyre, Greenock, 1995
M402	F272OPX	Mercedes-Benz 811D	Robin Hood	B22F	1988	

T50	L149NHP	Carbodies Taxi	Carbodies FX4	M5	1994	
T51	M651ERW	Carbodies Taxi	Carbodies FX4	M5	1994	
T57	M331MRW	Carbodies Taxi	Carbodies Fairway Driver	M5	1994	
T58	M332MRW	Carbodies Taxi	Carbodies Fairway Driver	M5	1994	

T59-T67

		Carbodies Taxi		Carbodies FX	M5	1997

T59	P36LOE	**T61**	P28LOE	**T65**	P94MOX	**T66**	P95MOX	**T67**	P96MOX
T60	P37LOE							

T68	R278VOK	Reliant Metrocab	Metrocab	M5	1997
T69	R279VOK	Reliant Metrocab	Metrocab	M5	1997
T70	R288VOK	Reliant Metrocab	Metrocab	M5	1997
T71	R289VOK	Reliant Metrocab	Metrocab	M5	1997

Ancilliary vehicles:

317	TVC402W	Leyland Leopard PSU5C/4R	Plaxton Supreme IV	TV	1981	Hills, Nuneaton, 1991
612	796UHT	Leyland Leopard PSU5D/5R	Plaxton Supreme IV	TV	1981	Fen Travel, Syston, 1992
9045	D59TLV	Freight Rover Sherpa	Carlyle	B2F	1987	North Western, 1991
9047	RBC500W	Bedford YMT	Plaxton Supreme IV	C53F	1981	
D350	JDJ350N	Bedford YRT	Plaxton Panorama Elite III	TV	1975	Grayway, Wigan, 1996
D395	SVL830R	Bristol LH6L	Eastern Coach Works	TV	1977	RoadCar, 1994
M75	C475TAY	Ford Transit 190	Robin Hood	B16F	1985	

Previous Registrations:

109CRC	A103HNC	JIL2164	XNG760S
111XKT	A102HNC	JIL2165	JOX516P
662NKR	OWA23X	JIL2190	JOX499P
796UHT	NMV612W	JIL2193	RKE520M
FAZ2784	B282KPF	JIL2196	KDW332P
FIL3451	F803TMD	JIL2197	BCD808L
FIL3452	B104LJU	JIL2198	SCK703P
GIL6253	D209LWX	JIL2199	UHG736R
GIL6949	D210LWX	JIL5367	NOE598R
HIL7594	E662UNE	LJI5631	B568NJF
JIL2156	GHB677N	LJI5632	A104HNC, XPA110, A927KFP
JIL2157	NPD142L	LJI8157	B310LUT
JIL2158	PUK649R	MSU433	STW18W
JIL2159	PUK643R	SIB1278	BPL481T
JIL2160	JOX482P	SJI5569	NPJ471R
JIL2161	HWC87N	SJI5570	JOX491P
JIL2162	SEO208M	TVC402W	PWK5W, DJI8467
JIL2163	GHB790N	XPA110	F804TMD

Named vehicles: D034 *John Barton*; D035 *Peter Varley*

Allocations and liveries

Coalville (Ashby Road)

Mercedes-Benz	D52	D61	M155	M302	M303	M304	M305	M306
	M311	M312	M335	M338	M339	M342	M343	M348
	M349							
Iveco	M227							
National	2144	2145	2146	2147	2148	2149	2150	2154
	2164	2165						
Dart	2205	2206						
Olympian	4501	4502	4503	4505	4512	4516	4517	4527
	4614	4615	4620	4621	4622	4623		

Derby (London Road) - *(The D-prefix is not carried on the vehicles)*

Mercedes-Benz	D72	D73	D74	D75	D76	D77	D78	D79
	D80	D81	D82	D83	D84	D85	D86	D87
	D88	D89	D90	D91	D92			
Dart	2047	2048	D34	D35	D36	D37	D38	D45
	D46							
Scania K	D21	D23	D24	D25	D26	D27	D28	
Scania L	D29	D30	D31	D32	D33			
Ailsa	D112	D113	D114	D115	D118	D119	D120	D121
Fleetline	D301	D304	D306	D310	D311	D312	D315	
Volvo Citybus	4320	4321	4322	4323	4324	4325	4326	4327
	4328	4329	4330	4331	4332	4333	4334	D128
	D129	D130	D131	D132	D133	D134	D135	D136
	D137	D138	D139	D140	D141	D142	D143	D144
	D145	D146	D147	D148	D149	D150	D151	D152
	D153							
Olympian	4625	4626	4627	4629	4630	4631	4639	4640
	4641	4642	4643	D165	D166	D167	D168	D169

Derby Taxis

Derby 75	T50/1/7-61/5-71

Hinckley (Jacknell Road, Dodwells Bridge)

Mercedes-Benz	M128	M129	M130	M131	M132	M133	M134	M291
	M296	M301	M310	M326	M329	M344	M390	M391
	M402							
Tiger	9	19	22					
DAF	153							
National	2151	2156	2157	2158				
Fleetline	2534							
Olympian	4476	4508	4514					

Arriva Fox County have the contract for the provision of vehicles on a major Leicester Park & Ride scheme. Arriva 2203, P203HRY is one of the Dennis Dart SLF buses allocated to this operation. A dedicated livery of silver and blue is carried by this vehicle which also carries the Quicksilver Shuttle branding.
Steve Sanderson

Southgates (Peacock Lane, Leicester)

Mercedes-Benz	M101	M102	M103	M104	M105	M106	M147	M148
	M149	M150	M151	M154	M157	M158	M159	M171
	M289	M330	M331	M332	M333	M350	M351	M357
	M358							
National	2152	2159	2160	2161	2162	2163		
Scania L	2166	2167	2168	2169	2170	2171	2172	2173
	2174	2175						
Scania N	4169	4170	4171	4172	4173	4174	4175	4176
	4177	4178	4180	4181	4182	4183	4184	
Olympian	4477	4534	4644	4645	4646	4647	4648	4649
	4650	4651	4652	4653				

Stamford

Mercedes-Benz	M356			
Tiger	2	20	21	
Fleetline	2547	D048	D302	D314
Volvo Citybus	4336	4337		

Thurmaston (Melton Road, Thurmaston, Leicester)

Mercedes-Benz	M107	M108	M109	M110	M112	M113	M114	M115
	M116	M117	M118	M119	M120	M121	M122	M127
	M135	M136	M137	M138	M139	M140	M141	M142
	M143	M144	M145	M146	M156	M162	M163	M164
	M165	M166	M167	M168	M169	M170	M307	M316
	M317	M318	M319	M320	M321	M322	M323	M324
	M325	M352	M353	M354	M355	M361	M362	M367
	M368	M369	M370	M371	M372			
Dart	2201	2202	2203	2204	2207	2208		
Tiger	4							
DAF Coach	87	192	209	210				
Volvo Coach	211	212	213	214	233	234	235	236
	237	247						
National	2141							
Scania L	2176	2177	2178	2179				
Olympian	4489	4504	4507	4509	4511	4518	4519	4616
	4617	4618	4619	4624	4632	4633	4634	4636
	4637	4638						

Wigston (Station Street, South Wigston)

Mercedes	M123	M124	M125	M126	M153	M160	M282	M313
	M314	M315	M336	M337	M341	M345	M346	M347
	M359	M360	M363	M364	M365	M366		
National	2142	2143						
DAF/Spectra	4001	4002						
Scania N	4134	4135	4136	4137	4138	4141	4142	4143
	4144	4145	4151	4152	4153	4154	4155	4156
	4157	4158	4159	4160	4161	4162	4163	4164
	4165	4166	4167	4168				
Volvo Citybus	4654	4655						
Olympian	4478	4480	4481	4486	4487	4491	4492	4493
	4494	4510	4528	4601	4602	4603	4604	4605
	4606	4607	4608	4609	4610	4611	4612	4613

Unallocated

Mercedes	M160		
Fleetline	D305	D309	D313
Olympian	4628	4635	

AUSDEN-CLARKE

Ausden-Clarke Ltd, Wanlip Street, Dysart Way, Leicester, LE1 2JY

Reg	Chassis	Body	Seats	Year	History
HHE348N	Bedford YRT	Plaxton Panorama Elite III	C53F	1975	Cake, Leicester, 1995
VWO995S	Ford R1114	Duple Dominant	C53F	1978	Akeins, Leicester, 1995
TSN585S	Bedford YMT	Duple Dominant	C53F	1978	West End, Leicester, 1998
GNH333T	Bedford YMT	Plaxton Supreme III	C53F	1979	Alec Head, Lutton, 1993
NBF871V	Ford R1114	Plaxton Supreme III	C53F	1979	Croydon, Leicester, 1993
MDG231V	Bedford YMT	Duple Dominant II	C53F	1980	Arle, Shipton Oliffe, 1996
6871RU	Bedford YMT	Plaxton Supreme IV	C53F	1980	Marcus Birr, Syston, 1997
AYA193A	Bedford YNT	Duple Dominant II	C53F	1981	DD Travel, Leicester, 1998
IIL8585	Bedford YNT	Duple Dominant II	C53F	1982	Jackson, Queniborough, 1999
GAZ4503	Volvo B10M-61	Duple Laser	C51F	1983	Smith, Chesham, 1994
PJI6075	Bedford YNT	Plaxton Paramount 3200	C53F	1983	Harrington, Bedworth, 1999
KBZ8726	Bedford YNT	Plaxton Paramount 3200	C53F	1984	Castle, Clanfield, 1996
GIL3122	Scania K112CRS	Jonckheere Jubilee P599	C51FT	1985	Turner, Maidstone, 1998
KAZ4574	Scania K112CRS	Plaxton Paramount 3500	C53F	1985	Elseys, Gosberton, 1996
B49DNY	Bedford YNV	Duple Laser	C53F	1985	Clarkson, Barrow, 1998
B456TVJ	Bedford YNV	Duple Laser	C53F	1985	Measom, Ibstock, 1998
NIL8993	Bedford YNV	Plaxton Paramount 3200	C57F	1985	Mitchell, Plean, 1997
KAZ4523	Bedford YNT	Duple Laser	C53F	1985	Rogers, Cheltenham, 1996
MIW4890	Scania K112CRS	Van Hool Alizée DH	C49FT	1985	Reay, Fletchertown, 1997
GAZ4502	Bedford YNV	Plaxton Paramount 3200 II	C51FT	1985	Perrett, Shipton Oliffe, 1993
NIL8992	Bedford YNV	Plaxton Paramount 3200 II	C57F	1986	George, Hare Street, 1997
GAZ4501	Scania K112CRB	Jonckheere Jubilee P599	C51FT	1987	AJC, Leeds, 1995
D140WCC	Freight Rover Sherpa	Carlyle	B18F	1987	Glover, Birstall, 1997
NIL8991	Bedford YNV	Plaxton Paramount 3200 III	C57F	1988	Cheney, Banbury, 1997

Ausden-Clarke are a new entrant into the tendered bus arena having obtained a number of Leicestershire contracts for shopping services to Leicester, Melton Mowbray and Lutterworth. Tours, private hire and school contracts remain the mainstay of the business. Seen loading at a school in Melton Mowbray is the oldest vehicle in the Ausden-Clarke fleet, HHE348N, a Bedford YRT with a Plaxton Panorama Elite body.
Steve Sanderson

H809RWJ	Scania K93CRB	Plaxton Paramount 3200 III	C57F	1990	Alec Head, Lutton, 1999
NIB8272	Scania K113CRB	Van Hool Alizée HE	C51FT	1991	Hardings of Redditch, 1998
NIB8179	Scania K113CRB	Van Hool Alizée DH	C51FT	1991	Hardings of Redditch, 1998
J911VFS	Mercedes-Benz 609D	Crystals	BC24F	1992	Castle Coaches, Balloch, 1995
L354MKU	Mercedes-Benz 814D	Plaxton Beaver	BC33F	1993	Castell Coaches, Trethomas, 1998
T20ACL	Mercedes-Benz Vario O814	Plaxton	C29F	1999	

Previous Registrations:

6871RU	BBB549V	KAZ4524	687DEW, B226GEW	NIB8272	H2HCR, H633AWP
AYA193A	JAX22W	KBZ8726	B201SWX	NIL8991	E175TWW
GAZ4501	D326VVV	MDG231V	NKX993V, ACH85A	NIL8992	C669TUT
GAZ4502	C154UDD	MIW4890	C408HVH	NIL8993	B90CDS
GAZ4503	ODS467Y, TJT788, WWE349Y	NBF871V	HBF178V, MIB279	PJI6075	A545TLG
GIL3122	B703EOF, MFU383, B357HFW.	NIB8179	H3HCR, H764AWP	VWO995S	D326VVV, UCY125S, FIL8275
KAZ4523	B500OFP	IIL8585	ABH773X		

Livery: White

Depots: Dysart Way, Leicester; New Henry Street, Leicester; Aylkestone Road, Leicester.

AVISDORS

W C Heath, Twingates, Stapleton Lane, Barwell, Leicestershire, LE9 8HE

D41TKA	Freight Rover Sherpa	Dormobile	B16F	1987	Shaw, Werrington, 1992
D163KDN	Volkswagen LT55	Optare CityPacer	B25F	1987	Ross, Dulnais Bridge, 1995
E405BHK	Volkswagen LT55	Optare CityPacer	B25F	1987	Derby Blue Bus, 1995
E738VWJ	Freight Rover Sherpa	Whittaker	M16	1988	
F307EKP	Freight Rover Sherpa	Dormobile	B16FL	1989	

Livery: Various; most vehicles are in former owner's colours

Avisdors is a small minibus operator based in the village of Barwell near Hinckley. The level of operation has reduced in recent times with the loss of some tenders. The fleet is maintained in a variety of colours. Dormobile-bodied Freight Rover Sherpa F307EKP was bought new in 1989 and carries a green and white colour scheme. *Steve Sanderson*

BEAVER BUS / VIRGIN BUS

C & J McDonald, 10 Churchill Close, Oadby, Leicester, LE2 4AJ

w							
	NIL2984	Leyland National 11351/1R/SC		BC48F	1974	Annison, Ilkeston, 1996
	MIL7621	Leyland National 11351A/1R(DAF)		B50F	1974	Arriva North West, 1999
	NIL2985	Leyland National 11351A/1R		B45F	1978	Black Prince, Morley, 1997
	DMS21V	Leyland National 2 NL116L11/1R		B52F	1980	Fife Scottish, 1996
	YOT545V	Leyland National 2 NL116L11/2R		B44D	1980	Leask & Silver, Lerwick, 1997
	E555GFR	Volkswagen LT55	Optare CityPacer	B21F	1987	Greatley, Warminster, 1998

Previous Registrations:

MIL7621	TOE523N	NIL2894	GLJ674N	NIL2894	CUP667S

Livery: Blue and white

Depot: Knighton Junction Lane, Leicester.

The former Virgin Bus operation is in the process of being re-branded Beaver Bus. The current operations consist of a number of school services and a free bus service to a store run by ASDA. Late evening bus services, which were once part of the operations, have now been discontinued. YOT545V is a Leyland National 2, unusual in that it once operated in the Shetland Islands. *Steve Sanderson*

BRYLAINE

B W & E R Gregg, 291 London Road, Boston, Lincolnshire, PE21 7DD

XAZ1413	Ford R1114	Alexander AYS	B53F	1977	Strathtay Scottish, 1987
XAZ1412	Leyland Fleetline FE30AGR	MCW	B43/33F	1978	Merseyline, Garston, 1997
SDA768S	Leyland Fleetline FE30AGR	MCW	B43/33F	1978	Merseyline, Garston, 1997
SDA784S	Leyland Fleetline FE30AGR	MCW	B43/33F	1978	Merseyline, Garston, 1997
WDA994T	Leyland Fleetline FE30AGR	MCW	B43/33F	1978	Fisher, Skegness, 1999
XAZ1409	Leyland National 2 NL116L11/1R		B49F	1979	Arriva North West, 1998
XAZ1403	Leyland National 2 NL116L11/1R		B52F	1980	Filer, Ilfracombe, 1998
XAZ1411	Leyland Fleetline FE30ALR	Northern Counties	B44/31F	1980	City of Nottingham, 1996
JAF208W	Ford R1114	Plaxton Supreme IV Express	C53F	1980	Hambly, Pelynt, 1995
XAZ1294	Bedford VAS5	Plaxton Supreme IV	C29F	1981	Swansdown, Inkpen, 1993
XAZ1410	Leyland Fleetline FE30ALR	Eastern Coach Works	B44/31F	1981	City of Nottingham, 1996
XAZ1427	Leyland National 2 NL116AL11/2R		B48D	1981	Arriva North West, 1998
XAZ1408	Leyland National 2 NL116AL11/2R		B52F	1981	Arriva North West, 1998
XNK199X	Ford R1014	Plaxton Bustler	B47F	1981	Provence, St Albans, 1994
XAZ1346	Ford R1115	Duple Dominant IV	C53F	1982	Long, Freshwater, 1996
XAZ1399	Ford R1114	Duple Dominant IV	C53F	1983	Diamond, Portchester, 1996
XAZ1321	Ford R1115	Plaxton Paramount 3200	C49F	1983	Plastow, Wheatley, 1995
XAZ1398	Ford R1115	Plaxton Paramount 3200	C53F	1983	Dixon, Rock, 1997
IIL6766	Ford R1115	Plaxton Paramount 3200	C53F	1983	Lockwood, Widmer End, 1997
XAZ1310	Ford R1115	Plaxton Paramount 3200	C53F	1983	Springate, Swanley, 1997
XAZ1312	Ford R1115	Plaxton Paramount 3200	C53F	1983	Hill Enterprises, Burnham on Sea, 1997
XAZ1314	Ford R1115	Plaxton Paramount 3200	C53F	1983	Turner, Chulmleigh, 1998
XAZ1315	Ford R1115	Plaxton Paramount 3200	C46FT	1983	Griffiths, South Mimms, 1997
XAZ1316	Ford R1115	Plaxton Paramount 3200	C53F	1983	Griffiths, South Mimms, 1997
XAZ1320	Ford R1115	Plaxton Paramount 3200	C53F	1983	Jones, Meidrim, 1997
XAZ1321	Ford R1115	Plaxton Paramount 3200	C53F	1984	Plastow, Wheatley, 1995
XAZ1311	Ford R1115	Plaxton Paramount 3200	C53F	1984	Fletcher, Malton, 1996
XAZ1301	Quest VM	Plaxton Paramount 3200	C53F	1984	Rees Travel, Llanelly Hill, 1993
E903DRG	Ford R1114	Plaxton Panorama Elite III	C53F	1988	Bob Smith Travel, Langley Park, 1994
XAZ1293	Iveco Daily 49.10	Phoenix	B25F	1989	Stagecoach South, 1997
XAZ1297	Iveco Daily 49.10	Phoenix	B25F	1989	Stagecoach South, 1997

Previous Registrations:

IIL6766	BLJ709Y	XAZ1346	BBY430Y
XAZ1293	G37SSR	XAZ1398	8955RH, OJL345Y, DXI722, PJI1823
XAZ1294	ENP666W	XAZ1399	FDV142Y
XAZ1301	A820LEL	XAZ1403	BUH219V
XAZ1310	A56HAD, KCT638, A41SKL	XAZ1408	FCA7X
XAZ1311	A106EBC	XAZ1409	CCY817V
XAZ1312	CJF109Y	XAZ1410	SCH116X
XAZ1314	ETA101Y	XAZ1411	HNN115V
XAZ1315	UWG951Y, GSU305, RAZ6947	XAZ1412	SDA564S
XAZ1316	BUT49Y, GBZ8912	XAZ1413	USO184S
XAZ1320	XAO134Y	XAZ1427	AFM4W
XAZ1321	YRB652Y		

Named Vehicles: XAZ1320, *Pearl*; A106EBC, *Hannah*

Livery: White and blue

Depots: London Road, Boston; Old Boston Road, Coningsby; Old Bolingbroke; Hassal Road, Skegness.

A number of double deck buses are operated on school services by Brylaine Travel. XAZ1410 was new to South Notts of Gotham and was one of the last Fleetlines to be built. It is seen in the Boston depot yard that is also home to a large number of withdrawn vehicles used to supply the fleet with spare parts. These vehicles are not listed in the fleet list as they will not see service again. *Steve Sanderson*

The majority of the Brylaine operational fleet has been re-registered with XAZ number plates. XAZ1311, once A106EBC, is a Ford R1115 that carries a Plaxton Paramount 3200 body. Ford coaches are used by Brylaine to provide a network of services radiating from the Lincolnshire port of Boston. *Steve Sanderson*

BOWERS

E W Bowers (Coaches) Ltd, Aspincroft Garage, Town End,
Chapel-en-le-Frith, Derbyshire, SK23 0NU

Reg	Chassis	Body		Type	Year	Notes
JOX503P	Leyland National 11351A/1R			B49F	1976	Stagecoach Midland Red, 1999
JOX510P	Leyland National 11351A/1R			B49F	1976	First Midland Red, 1999
PTT80R	Leyland National 11351A/1R			B52F	1976	Ludlows, Halesowen, 1999
VPT586R	Leyland National 11351A/1R			B49F	1977	Ludlows, Halesowen, 1999
NOE587R	Leyland National 11351A/1R			B49F	1977	Stagecoach Midland Red, 1999
PUK628R	Leyland National 11351A/1R (DAF)			B49F	1977	Stagecoach Midland Red, 1999
PUK629R	Leyland National 11351A/1R (DAF)			B49F	1977	Stagecoach Midland Red, 1999
XGR728R	Leyland National 11351A/1R (DAF)			B49F	1977	Stagecoach Midland Red, 1999
HUI4891	Kässbohrer Setra S215H	Kässbohrer		C53F	1982	Falcon Travel, Shepperton, 1997
MIL4685	DAF MB200DKFL600	Van Hool Alizée		C48FT	1983	Mellor, Harrow, 1997
D959WJH	Freight Rover Sherpa	Dormobile		B16F	1986	Hardings, Redditch 1999
D930ARE	Mercedes-Benz L608D	PMT Hanbridge		B17F	1986	
IUI9144	Scania K112CRB	Plaxton Paramount 3200 II		C53F	1986	Luckett, Fareham, 1996
LIL7568	Mercedes-Benz 609D	Reeve Burgess Beaver		BC25F	1988	
LIL3068	Mercedes-Benz 709D	Reeve Burgess Beaver		BC25F	1988	Stagecoach Oxford, 1999
E308BWL	Mercedes-Benz 709D	Reeve Burgess Beaver		BC25F	1988	Stagecoach Oxford, 1999
F411KOD	Mercedes-Benz 709D	Reeve Burgess Beaver		BC25F	1988	Stagecoach Devon, 1999
NIL8163	Mercedes-Benz 811D	Wadham Stringer Wessex		B31F	1989	Brighton & Hove, 1999
LIL2612	Leyland Swift ST2R44C97T5	Reeve Burgess Harrier		BC37F	1989	AMR, Bedfont, 1995
LIL7910	Mercedes-Benz 814D	Reeve Burgess Beaver		BC33F	1991	
LIL7912	Mercedes-Benz 811D	Reeve Burgess Beaver		BC25F	1991	
NIL9936	Toyota Coaster HDB30R	Caetano Optimo II		C21F	1993	Hardings, Redditch, 1997
B8WER	Scania K113CRB	Van Hool Alizée HE		C51F	1994	Holmeswood Coaches, Rufford, 1996
PRD34	Scania K113CRB	Van Hool Alizée HE		C49FT	1994	Rambler, Hastings, 1998
V	Optare	Optare Solo		N	On order	
V	Optare	Optare Solo		N	On order	

Previous Registrations:

B8WER	L839KHD, L4HWD, L749NEO	LIL7910	J281YWJ
HUI4891	VWX360X,146WAL,YNA484X,FSK867	LIL7912	J282YWJ
IUI9144	D662YRP,SJI5027,D419HPO	MIL4685	UHL935Y,4233FM,3523FM,4543VC
LIL2612	G341VHU	NIL8163	G52BEL
LIL3068	E305BVL	NIL9936	K4HCR, K429JDT
LIL7568	E468AWF	PRD34	M222CDY, M134GAD

Livery: Red

Opposite, top: **The relatively rare Reeve Burgess Harrier bodywork can be found with only a few operators in Britain. However, one is operated by Bowers Coaches of Chapel-en-le-Frith in the north west corner of Derbyshire. Mounted on a Leyland Swift chassis, LIL2612 negotiates the village of Hartington as it pulls onto the stop in the centre of the village in June 1999.** *Tony Wilson*
Opposite, bottom: **Since the last edition of this Bus Handbook, Bowers has acquired a number of Leyland Nationals. Amongst them is this former Stagecoach Midland Red South example. Rural Grant funding has benefited a number of services in the Peak District, not withstanding the 442 on the western fringes of the National Park. JOX510P approaches Hartington from the hills above the village, on a school-timed journey on the route from Ashbourne to Buxton.** *Tony Wilson*

BUTLER BROS

R & R Butler, 60 Vernon Road, Kirkby-in-Ashfield, Nottinghamshire, NG17 8ED

BUT2B	DAF MB200DKFL600	Van Hool Alizée	C53FT	1984	
68BUT	DAF MB200DKTL600	Van Hool Alizée	C53F	1984	
83BUT	Leyland Tiger TRCTL11/3RZ	Duple 340	C57F	1986	
PIL2750	DAF MB230DKFL615	Duple 320	C57F	1987	Go-Ahead (OK), 1998
E393HNR	Dennis Javelin 12SDA1907	Duple 320	C55F	1988	
E562MAC	Peugeot-Talbot Pullman	Talbot	B22F	1988	Filer, Ilfracombe, 1995
G701AEF	DAF MB230LB615	Duple 320	C53F	1989	Go-Ahead (OK), 1998
F232RNR	Toyota Coaster HB31R	Caetano Optimo	C21F	1989	Dale Hire, Astwood Bank, 1994
G440NET	Leyland DAF400	Whittaker	M16	1990	
179BUT	Volvo B10M-60	Plaxton Paramount 3200 III	CxxF	1990	Southern, Barrhead, 1998
J626JNP	MAN 10.180 HOCLR	Caetano Algarve II	C35F	1991	Cresswell, Evesham, 1999
K550RJX	DAFSB3000DKV601	Van Hool Alizée HE	C49FT	1992	Boon's, Boreham, 1996
M784NBA	Dennis Javelin 12SDA2131	Plaxton Premiére 320	C57F	1995	Bullock, Cheadle, 1998

Previous Registrations:

68BUT	A482FAU	BUT2B	From new	PIL2750	D905EAJ, EIB8955, D905EAJ
83BUT	From new	G701AEF	G701AEF, MCT612		
179BUT	H990YGG	J626JNP	J2NNC		

Livery: Turquoise, blue and red

Butler Bros operate a local bus service between Annesley, Kirkby-in-Ashfield, Sutton-in-Ashfield and Mansfield. The route is numbered B4 which echoes the numbering scheme used by Mansfield and District when that operator ran the majority of services in the area. The fleet carries a distinctive turquoise, blue and red livery as seen on E393HNR. This Dennis Javelin was bodied by Duple with the 320 type of coachwork.
Paul Hill

CAMMS

Camms of Nottingham Ltd, 273 Ilkeston Road, Radford, Nottingham, NG7 3FY

Part of Dunn-Line Holdings

100	A100AVO	Leyland Tiger TRCTL11/3R	Duple Laser	C53FT	1983	
114	RJI1656	Volvo B10M-61	Plaxton Paramount 3500	C49FT	1983	Watson, Annfield Plain, 1985
145	TFJ61X	AEC Reliance 6U2R	Duple Dominant IV	C53F	1981	Watson, Annfield Plain, 1987
147	OGR51T	Leyland Leopard PSU3E/4R	Plaxton Supreme IV Express	C53F	1979	Watson, Annfield Plain, 1987
148	WBR5V	Leyland Leopard PSU3E/4R	Plaxton Supreme IV	C53F	1980	Watson, Annfield Plain, 1987
165	NNU128M	Daimler Fleetline CRL6-30	Roe	B42/29D	1973	Chesterfield, 19??
178	XBF54S	Leyland Leopard PSU3E/4R	Duple Dominant I	C49F	1978	PMT, 1992
180	XPK52T	AEC Reliance 6U2R	Duple Dominant II Express	C53F	1978	Lively Marple, 1992
184	GHR302W	Leyland Leopard PSU3F/4R	Duple Dominant II Express	C53F	1981	Thamesdown, 1993
185	RJI1657	Leyland Royal Tiger RT	Van Hool Alizée	C49F	1986	Cosey, East Molesey, 1993
186	RJI1658	Leyland Royal Tiger RT	Van Hool Alizée	C49F	1986	Cook, Biggleswade, 1993
187	TJI4698	Neoplan N722/3	Plaxton Paramount 4000	C55/20DT	1984	Grey Green, 1995
188	TJI4699	Neoplan N722/3	Plaxton Paramount 4000	C55/20DT	1985	Grey Green, 1995
189	LRB405W	Leyland Atlantean AN68A/1R	East Lancashire	B47/33D	1980	City of Nottingham, 1995
190	LRB407W	Leyland Atlantean AN68A/1R	East Lancashire	B47/33D	1980	City of Nottingham, 1995
191	LRB409W	Leyland Atlantean AN68A/1R	East Lancashire	B47/31D	1980	City of Nottingham, 1995
192	YPL80T	AEC Reliance 6U2R	Duple Dominant II Express	C53F	1978	Smithyman, Maltby, 1996
193	RKA886T	Leyland National 11351A/1R/SC		BC45F	1978	Delta, Kirkby in Ashfield, 1996
194	GNN222N	Leyland Leopard PSU3B/4R	Plaxton Elite III Express	C53F	1974	Bestwick, Tibshelf, 1998
195	GNN218N	Leyland Leopard PSU3B/4R	Plaxton Elite III Express	C53F	1974	Gotham British Legion, 1997
196	LUG96P	Leyland Atlantean AN68/1R	Roe	B45/33F	1975	Stagecoach East Midland, 1997
197	MOD816P	Leyland National 11351/1R		B52F	1976	Delta, Kirkby in Ashfield, 1996
198	FGE438X	Dennis Dominator DD137B	Alexander RL	B45/34F	1982	Delta, Kirkby in Ashfield, 1996

Previous Registrations:

RJI1656	ANA403Y		TJI4698	B101XYH
RJI1657	D40HMT, RJI1656		TJI4699	B102XYH
RJI1658	C51CWX, HIL3474			

Livery: Orange and cream (buses); white, orange and red (coaches)

Camms of Nottingham provide tendered journeys on service 331 from the operator's home city to Alfreton. The bus station in Alfreton is the location of this view of Leyland Leopard OGR51T. As this book was being prepared it was announced that Camms had become part of Dunn-Line holdings.
Tony Wilson

CARNELL'S

Carnell Coaches, 72 Bridge Street, Sutton Bridge, Lincolnshire, PE12 9UA

PAK690R	Bedford YMT	Plaxton Supreme III	C53F	1976	Drabble, Sheffield, 1981
STA381R	Bedford YMT	Duple Dominant	C53F	1977	National Travel (South West) 1980
AWE113T	Bedford YMT	Duple Dominant II	C45F	1979	Bryan A Garratt, Syston, 1984
BGY595T	Bedford YMT	Duple Dominant II	C53F	1979	National Travel (London) 1982
BOK17V	MCW Metrobus DR102/12	MCW	B43/30F	1979	Travel West Midlands, 1998
GTX755W	Bristol VRT/SL3/501	Eastern Coach Works	B43/31F	1980	Red & White, 1994
ORJ95W	MCW Metrobus DR102/31	MCW	B43/30F	1981	Stagecoach Manchester, 1998
KJW284W	MCW Metrobus DR102/31	MCW	B43/30F	1981	Travel West Midlands, 1998
SMY631X	Leyland Tiger TRCTL11/3R	Plaxton Supreme V	C50F	1982	The Beeline, 1996
SMY632X	Leyland Tiger TRCTL11/3R	Plaxton Supreme V	C51F	1982	The Beeline, 1996
SMY637X	Leyland Tiger TRCTL11/3R	Plaxton Supreme V	C50F	1982	The Beeline, 1996
OHE270X	Volvo B10M-61	Duple Dominant IV	C50F	1982	SUT 1987
PNL163Y	Bedford YMP	Duple Dominant IV	C35F	1982	Red Arrow, Huddersfield, 1990
YPD121Y	Leyland Tiger TRCTL11/2R	Duple Dominant IV	C53F	1983	Richardson, Midhurst, 1996
ENF572Y	Volvo B10M-61	Duple Dominant IV	C53F	1983	Smith Shearings, 1989
ENF574Y	Volvo B10M-61	Duple Dominant IV	C53F	1983	Smith Shearings, 1989
RDZ4275	DAF SB2300DHTD585	Plaxton Paramount 3200	C53F	1984	AMR, Bedfont, 1995
FDZ4731	Volvo B10M-61	Van Hool Alizée	C53F	1984	Shearings, 1990
NJI9487	Leyland Tiger TRCTL11/3R	Duple Caribbean	C51F	1984	Swansdown, Inkpen, 1997
129SDV	Leyland Tiger TRCTL11/3R	Duple Laser	C57F	1985	Hedingham & District, 1998
B290TCT	DAF MB2000DKVL600	Duple Caribbean	C55F	1985	
B526AHD	Mercedes-Benz L608D	Reeve Burgess	C19F	1985	Euro Academy, Croydon, 1985
C210VCT	Bedford YNV Venturer	Plaxton Paramount 3200 II	C57F	1985	
C136DWT	Volvo B10M-61	Duple 340	C53F	1986	Wallace Arnold, 1990
D721PTU	Freight Rover Sherpa	Dormobile	B16F	1986	Talbot, Huntingdon, 1996
D811SGB	Volvo B10M-61	Plaxton Paramount 3500 III	C53F	1987	Park's of Hamilton, 1988
JIL3964	Leyland Tiger TRCL10/3ARZM	Plaxton Panorama 3500 III	C49FT	1990	Armchair, Brentford, 1997
K702RNR	Toyota Coaster HDB30R	Caetano Optimo II	C18F	1992	Avis, Heathrow, 1998
H917DFG	Toyota Coaster HDB30R	Caetano Optimo II	C21F	1992	

Previous Registrations:

129SDV	B288OGV	NJI9487	A134RMJ
FDZ4731	A178MNE	RDZ4275	A80WHS
JIL3964	G608XMD, G406XMK		

Livery: Silver, red and orange; **Depot:** Dockings Holt, Long Sutton

Carnell's operate a service from Sutton Bridge to Boston. Seen emerging onto the main road at Fosdyke while on a Saturday journey, is SMY632X, one of three Plaxton Supreme-bodied Leyland Tigers purchased from The Beeline in 1996.
Steve Sanderson

CAVALIER

A D Ladbrook & C J Boor, Seagate Road, Long Sutton, Spalding, Lincolnshire, PE12 9AD

ADL72B	Ford Transit	Ford	M8	19xx	?, 1997
A20PSV	Mercedes-Benz 609D	?	C24F	1988	?, 1996
E307BWL	Mercedes-Benz 709D	Reeve Burgess Beaver	BC25F	1988	Thames Transit, 1997
F315EJO	Mercedes-Benz 709D	Reeve Burgess Beaver	BC25F	1988	Thames Transit, 1997
F43CWY	Mercedes-Benz 811D	Optare StarRider	B32F	1989	London Central, 1999
F165FWY	Mercedes-Benz 811D	Optare StarRider	B32F	1989	Stagecoach London, 1999
F172FWY	Mercedes-Benz 811D	Optare StarRider	B32F	1989	Stagecoach London, 1999
H181DHA	Ford Transit VE6	Dormobile	B18F	1990	Arriva Midlands North, 1998
H182DHA	Ford Transit VE6	Dormobile	B18F	1990	Arriva Midlands North, 1998
H183DHA	Ford Transit VE6	Dormobile	B18F	1990	Arriva Midlands North, 1998
H184DHA	Ford Transit VE6	Dormobile	B18F	1990	Arriva Midlands North, 1998
H742VHS	Mercedes-Benz 609D	Sparshatt	C24F	1990	Staffordian, Stafford, 1996
K3CAV	Renault Master T35D	Cymric	M16	1992	
K2CAV	Volkswagen	Volkswagen	M8	1993	Private owner, 1997
T405BGB	Mercedes-Benz Vario O814	Marshall	B31F	1999	

Previous Registrations:

A20PSV	?	ADL72B	?	K2CAV	K517LPW

Livery: White and blue

In common with many operators of small buses, Cavalier started with a fleet of 16 seaters. 1999 saw the addition of a trio of Optare StarRiders obtained from London operators. All three of these Mercedes-Benz 811D midibuses are seen in this depot line up.
Steve Sanderson

CONFIDENCE

K M Williams, 105 Coombe Rise, Oadby, Leicestershire, LE2 5TJ

15	WLT655	AEC Routemaster R2RH	Park Royal	H36/28R	1961	London Buses, 1985
18	VWM83L	Leyland Atlantean AN68/1R	Alexander AL	B45/29D	1973	Merseybus, 1988
19	VWM89L	Leyland Atlantean AN68/1R	Alexander AL	B45/29D	1973	Merseybus, 1988
20	OTO540M	Leyland Atlantean AN68/1R	East Lancashire	B47/30D	1974	City of Nottingham, 1990
21	GVO717N	Leyland Atlantean AN68/1R	East Lancashire	B47/31D	1974	City of Nottingham, 1990
22	OTO570M	Leyland Atlantean AN68/1R	East Lancashire	B47/30D	1974	City of Nottingham, 1990
23	HOR305N	Leyland Atlantean AN68/1R	Alexander AL	B45/30D	1975	Portsmouth, 1991
24	HOR306N	Leyland Atlantean AN68/1R	Alexander AL	B45/30D	1975	Portsmouth, 1991
25	KSA183P	Leyland Atlantean AN68A/1R	Alexander AL	B45/29D	1976	Portsmouth Transit, 1991
26	OTO557M	Leyland Atlantean AN68/1R	East Lancashire	B47/30D	1974	City of Nottingham, 1992
27	OTO551M	Leyland Atlantean AN68/1R	East Lancashire	B47/30D	1974	City of Nottingham, 1993
28	OTO562M	Leyland Atlantean AN68/1R	East Lancashire	B47/30D	1974	City of Nottingham, 1993
29	MNU625P	Leyland Atlantean AN68A/1R	East Lancashire	B47/31D	1976	City of Nottingham, 1994
30	MNU631P	Leyland Atlantean AN68A/1R	East Lancashire	B47/31D	1976	City of Nottingham, 1994
31	XRR616M	Leyland Leopard PSU3B/4R	Plaxton Elite III Express	C53F	1973	Trent (Barton), 1994
33	MNU632P	Leyland Atlantean AN68A/1R	East Lancashire	B47/31D	1976	City of Nottingham, 1994
34	KAU564V	Leyland Leopard PSU3E/4R	Plaxton Supreme IV Express	C53F	1980	Trent (Barton), 1996
35	LNU569W	Leyland Leopard PSU3E/4R	Plaxton Supreme IV Express	C53F	1980	Trent (Barton), 1996
36	VRC611Y	Leyland Leopard PSU3G/4R	Plaxton Supreme V Express	C53F	1982	Trent (Barton), 1996
37	PTV591X	Leyland Leopard PSU3F/4R	Plaxton Supreme IV Express	C53F	1981	Cygnet, Darton, 1997
38	A511VKG	Leyland Olympian ONLXB/1R	East Lancashire	B43/31F	1984	Cardiff Bus, 1998
39	RBO510Y	Leyland Olympian ONLXB/1R	East Lancashire	B43/29F	1983	Cardiff Bus, 1999
40	BWT199X	Volvo B10M-61	Van Hool Alizée	C48FT	1981	Pilusa, Harrogate, 1999

Previous Registrations: BWT199X   STT611X, 735JVO

Livery: Grey, black and red; **Depots:** Spalding Street, Leicester and Harrison Close, South Wigston

The Confidence fleet contains a number of former Nottingham Atlanteans. OTO551M, numbered 27 in the fleet, was bodied with the distinctive Nottingham style by East Lancashire. In the background is No 15, an AEC Routemaster which has now been in this fleet for fourteen of its thirty-eight years.
Steve Sanderson

CROPLEY

Cropley Bros Tours (Fosdyke) Ltd, The Laurels, Old Main Road, Fosdyke, Lincolnshire, PE20 7BU

FLD634Y	Volvo B10M-61	Jonckheere Jubilee	C51FT	1982	Hughes, Slough, 1997
BAO104Y	Volvo B10M-61	Duple Laser	C57F	1983	Bowman, Birthwaite, 1996
4506UB	Volvo B10M-61	Plaxton Paramount 3500	C53F	1984	Ralph, Langley, 1993
B521YTC	Volvo B10M-61	Plaxton Paramount 3200 II	C57F	1984	Gilmour, Kilmarnock, 1996
EAZ4709	Volvo B10M-61	Plaxton Paramount 3200 II	C53F	1985	Epsom Coaches, 1994
EAZ5347	Volvo B10M-61	Plaxton Paramount 3200 II	C53F	1985	Epsom Coaches, 1994
8302NF	Volvo B10M-61	Plaxton Paramount 3500 II	C53F	1985	Epsom Coaches, 1994
VSK207	Volvo B9M	Plaxton Paramount 3200 II	C35F	1985	Capital, West Drayton, 1996
CLZ1860	Volvo B10M-61	Plaxton Paramount 3200 II	C53F	1986	Dereham Coaches, 1998
610LYB	Volvo B10M-61	Plaxton Paramount 3500 III	C50F	1988	Gold Star, Llandudno Junction, 1998
XSV839	Volvo B10M-61	Jonckheere Jubilee	C57F	1988	Dereham Coaches, 1998
WUY713	Volvo B10M-60	Plaxton Paramount 3500 III	C46FT	1990	Birmingham Coach Company 1998

Previous Registrations:

4506UB	A518NCL	EAZ4709	B505CGP
610LYB	E909UNW	EAZ5347	B506CGP
8302NF	B508CGP	FLD634Y	JNV629Y, GSU382
B521YTC	432CYA	VSK207	C157TJF
BAO104Y	MSU599Y, GPV516	WUY713	H595SWY
CLZ1860	C176EMU	XSV839	E505KNV

Livery: White and turquoise

Depot: Main Road, Fosdyke.

The Volvo B10M is the standard vehicle in the fleet of Cropley Bros of Fosdyke. EAZ5347 is one of a trio of Plaxton Paramount-bodied examples acquired from Epsom Coaches in 1994. As well as school contracts and private hire work, the company now operate a number of tendered services in the South Holland area of Lincolnshire. *Steve Sanderson*

The Mid-Derbyshire village of Heage is served by Doyle Minicoaches who have taken over the route from Albert Wilde Coaches. Route 137 links the village with nearby towns of Ripley and Belper. The service is operated with minibuses represented here by G697NUB, seen departing Ripley. This Renault-Dodge S56 was bodied by Optare of Leeds and supplied new to that city's council. *Tony Wilson*

Doyles Minicoaches, based in Ripley, have won the tenders for a number of services in the area around the company's home base. These routes are all supported by Derbyshire County Council, though the company also operates a number of contracts for other organisations, some requiring wheelchair access. A wheelchair lift is fitted to the rear of G606JUG, one of three Ford Transits purchased in 1998. *Tony Wilson*

D D TRAVEL

D C Dixon, 56 Windley Road, Leicester, LE2 6QX

| A69XEP | Bedford YNT | Duple Laser | C53F | 1983 | Kirby, Birmingham, 1995 |
| D171LTA | Renault-Dodge S56 | Reeve Burgess | B23F | 1986 | Woods, Wigston, 1998 |

Previous Registrations:
A69XEP   A720OCJ, 99KMH

Depot: Premier Warehousing, Western Boulevard, Leicester

DOYLE MINICOACHES

K J Doyle, 190 Nottingham Road, Ripley, Derbyshire, DE55 3AY

A275KVU	Ford Transit	Taurus	M10L	1984	Zamir, Burton-on-Trent, 1993
A802JLT	Mercedes-Benz L310D	Devon Conversions	M12L	1984	CDS, Nottingham, 1995
B169NAJ	Bedford CF	Dormobile	M6L	1985	private owner, 1994
C270CBU	Freight Rover Sherpa	Cunliffe	M15L	1988	Manchester MDC, 1995
D481CKV	Freight Rover Sherpa	Rootes	B16F	1986	Omega, Hasland, 1996
D129WTL	Freight Rover Sherpa	Dormobile	B16FL	1987	TransLinc, Lincoln, 1996
E228FLD	Scania N112DRB	Van Hool Alizée	C30D	1987	Capital, West Dayton, 1999
E381TUB	Volkswagen LT55	Optare CityPacer	B13FL	1988	Leeds MDC, 1998
E924VUG	Volkswagen LT55	Optare CityPacer	B13FL	1988	Leeds MDC, 1998
F433AYG	Volkswagen LT55	Optare CityPacer	B13FL	1988	Leeds MDC, 1998
F433AYG	Volkswagen LT55	Optare CityPacer	B13FL	1988	Leeds MDC, 1998
F368HTY	Renault Trafic	Holdsworth	M14	1988	Smith, Bedlington, 1996
F901HAU	Renault Trafic	Holdsworth	M8	1989	
F640HDB	Freight Rover Sherpa	Cunliffe	M12	1989	Manchester MDC, 1997
F642HDB	Freight Rover Sherpa	Cunliffe	M12	1989	Manchester MDC, 1997
F462KKE	Ford Transit VE6	Dormobile	M12L	1989	Wirral MDC, 1997
F240PAC	Freight Rover Sherpa	Freight Rover	M16	1989	Lanchester Polytechnic, Coventry, 1992
G605JUG	Ford Transit VE6	Dormobile	M14L	1989	Wakefield MDC, 1998
G606JUG	Ford Transit VE6	Dormobile	M14L	1989	Wakefield MDC, 1998
G608JUG	Ford Transit VE6	Dormobile	M14L	1989	Wakefield MDC, 1998
G697NUB	Renault-Dodge S56	Optare	B9FL	1990	Leeds MDC, 1999
H976CAY	Leyland-DAF 400	Dormobile	B16FL	1990	Service Team, Wandsworth, 1996

Livery: Beige

Depot: Prospect Court, Nottingham Road, Ripley.

DELAINE

Delaine Buses Ltd, 8 Spalding Road, Bourne, Lincolnshire, PE10 9LE

45	KTL780	Leyland Titan PD2/20	Willowbrook	B35/28R	1956	privately preserved 1979-90
50	RCT3	Leyland Titan PD3/1	Yeates	B39/34R	1960	
72	ACT540L	Leyland Atlantean AN68/2R	Northern Counties	B47/35F	1973	
93	KTL27Y	Leyland Tiger TRCTL11/2RZ	Duple Dominant	B59F	1983	
94	A24OVL	Leyland Tiger TRCTL11/2RZ	Duple Dominant	B59F	1983	
98	C426MFE	Leyland Tiger TRCTL11/2RZ	Duple Dominant	B59F	1986	
100	E100AFW	Leyland Tiger TRCTL11/2RZ	Duple Dominant	B59F	1987	
103	F603VEW	Leyland Tiger TRCTL11/2R	Duple 300	B59F	1988	
115	OTL3	Leyland Tiger TRBTL11/2R(Z)	East Lancashire EL2000 (1994)	B59F	1983	Smith, Blairgowrie, 1992
116	M1OCT	Volvo Olympian YN2RV18Z4	East Lancashire	B51/35F	1995	
117	M2OCT	Volvo Olympian YN2RV18Z4	East Lancashire	B51/35F	1995	
118	N3OCT	Volvo Olympian YN2RV18Z4	East Lancashire	B51/35F	1995	
119	ANA224T	Leyland Atlantean AN68A/1R	Northern Counties	B43/32F	1978	GM North, 1996
120	FVR256V	Leyland Atlantean AN68A/1R	Northern Counties	B43/32F	1979	GM North, 1996
121	P1OTL	Volvo Citibus B10M-55	East Lancashire	B53F	1996	
122	P2OTL	Volvo Citibus B10M-55	East Lancashire	B53F	1996	
123	ORJ384W	Leyland Atlantean AN68A/1R	Northern Counties	B43/32F	1981	GM North, 1996
124	ORJ365W	Leyland Atlantean AN68A/1R	Northern Counties	B43/32F	1981	GM South, 1996
125	ORJ380W	Leyland Atlantean AN68A/1R	Northern Counties	B43/32F	1981	GM South, 1996
126	ORJ362W	Leyland Atlantean AN68A/1R	Northern Counties	B43/32F	1981	GM South, 1997
127	R4OCT	Volvo Olympian	East Lancashire	B51/35F	1997	
128	S5OCT	Volvo Olympian	East Lancashire	B47/33F	1998	
129	T6OCT	Volvo Olympian	East Lancashire	B47/33F	1999	

Previous Registrations:

KTL780	From new	OTL3	YPD125Y
RCT3	From new	ACT540L	ACT540L, YCT3

Livery: Blue and cream

Opposite: **Delaine is a long-established operator based in the Lincolnshire town of Bourne whose main route links it to Peterborough passing through The Deepings. The fleet comprises chassis entirely sourced from Leyland, and its sucessor, Volvo. The upper picture, taken in Peterborough, shows Leyland Tiger 94, A24OVL. One of five Tigers bodied for the company by Duple over a number of years. The lower picture shows Volvo Olympian 118, N3OCT. All the Volvo Olympians have been bodied by East Lancashire who have supplied all the bodywork requirements for the fleet since 1994.** *Tony Wilson/Richard Godfrey.*

DENT

R H Dent & L C Horstwood, The Poplars, South Street, North Kelsey, Market Rasen, Lincolnshire, LN7 6ET

	LVS449P	AEC Reliance 6U3ZR	Plaxton Supreme III	C55F	1976	Hilo, Sandy, 1997
	OSJ747R	Leyland Leopard PSU3C/4R	Plaxton Supreme III	C53F	1977	Pulfrey, Foston, 1997
	WUM100S	Leyland Fleetline FE30AGR	Roe	B43/33F	1977	Yorkshire Rider, 1996
	CWU136T	Leyland Fleetline FE30AGR	Roe	B43/33F	1978	Yorkshire Rider, 1996
	BUR437T	Bedford YMT	Plaxton Supreme IV	C53F	1978	Turner, Maidstone, 1999
	JEC557T	Bedford YMT	Plaxton Supreme IV	C53F	1979	Browne, Brabourne, 1996
	ELR109T	Bedford YMT	Plaxton Supreme IV	C53F	1979	Stephensons, Easingwold, 1997
	MFE414V	Bedford YMT	Plaxton Supreme IV	C53F	1979	Parker, Kirton in Lindsey, 1998
	KVF249V	Bristol VRT/SL3/6LXB	Eastern Coach Works	B43/31F	1980	Circle Line, Gloucester, 1999
w	VNH155W	Leyland Leopard PSU3F/4RT	Duple Dominant IV	C53F	1981	Emmersons, Immingham, 1999
	CKA951X	Bedford YMT	Duple Dominant III	C53F	1981	Samuda & Hall, Birmingham, 1997
	20AAX	Leyland Tiger TRCTL11/3R	Duple Caribbean	C46FT	1983	Trent Motors, Scunthorpe, 1997
	XRM623Y	DAF MB200DKFL600	Plaxton Paramount 3200	C57F	1983	Barnes, Eastwood, 1995
	UXI8651	Bedford YNT	Plaxton Paramount 3200	C49F	1984	Gunter, Ongar, 1997
	C988MWJ	Neoplan N722/3	Plaxton Paramount 4000	C53/18DT	1986	Yorkshire Traction, 1997
	C35FEC	Bedford YNT	Plaxton Paramount 3200 II	C53F	1986	Everett, Atterby, 1998
	J299KFP	DAF MB230LB615	Caetano Algarve X-NDH	C49FT	1991	

Previous Registrations:

20AAX	SDW911Y	LVS449P	LVS449P, 173KKH
C35FEC	C211DEC, BIB7670	UXI8651	A709GLD
C988MWJ	C92KET, HE5632		

Livery: varies; **Depot:** Old Air Ministry Site, Caistor Road, Holton le Moor.

Since the last edition of this publication, the proprietor of Everetts has retired and the business discontinued. Some of the operation has been picked up by Dent. Seen on the outskirts of Lincoln on one of these services is MFE414V. This Plaxton-bodied Bedford has always been based in Lincolnshire having been purchased from Parker of Kirton-in-Lindsey. *Steve Sanderson*

DUNN-LINE

Dunn-Line Holdings Ltd; Dunn-Line (Derby) Ltd; Dunn-Line (West Midlands) Ltd
The Coach Station, Dunn-Line Corporation House,
Park Lane, Basford, Nottingham, NG6 0DW

B1	J6BOB	Volvo B10M-60	Jonckheere Deauville P599	C8FT	1991	
B2	A4BOB	Volvo B10M-53	Plaxton Paramount 4000 III	C(16)DT	1989	Flights, Birmingham, 1994
B3	A5BOB	Volvo B10M-53	Plaxton Paramount 4000 III	C(16)DT	1989	Flights, Birmingham, 1995
B4	MIL8334	DAF SBR3000DKZ570	Van Hool Astrobel	C(16)CT	1988	Holmeswood Coaches, 1997
1	A3BOB	Scania K124IB6	Irizar Century 12.37	C32FT	1999	
2	R902TCH	Bova FHD12.340	Bova Futura	C33FT	1997	
3	R901TCH	Bova FHD12.340	Bova Futura	C33FT	1997	
15	N781SJU	Toyota Coaster HZB30R	Caetano Optimo III	C18F	1996	MTL London Northern, 1997
16	N997BWJ	Toyota Coaster HZB50R	Caetano Optimo III	C21F	1996	
17	N67NDW	Mercedes-Benz 811D	Autobus Classique	B33F	1996	Bebb, Llantwit Ffardre, 1998
18	N69MDW	Mercedes-Benz 811D	Autobus Classique	B33F	1996	Bebb, Llantwit Ffardre, 1998
D19	MIL8325	Mercedes-Benz 811D	Optare StarRider	B25F	1989	HMB, Gateshead, 1997
20	MIL8337	Mercedes-Benz 811D	Optare StarRider	B25F	1989	HMB, Gateshead, 1997
21	F47CWY	Mercedes-Benz 811D	Optare StarRider	B26F	1989	London Central, 1998
22	F53CWY	Mercedes-Benz 811D	Optare StarRider	B26F	1989	London Central, 1998
30	P351EAU	Dennis Dart SLF	East Lancashire Spryte	N43F	1996	
31	P352EAU	Dennis Dart SLF	East Lancashire Spryte	N43F	1996	
32	P353EAU	Dennis Dart SLF	East Lancashire Spryte	N43F	1996	
34	R903TCH	Dennis Dart SLF	East Lancashire Spryte	N43F	1998	
40	WJI9361	Volvo B10M-55	East Lancs Flyte (1998)	B53F	1987	Hutchison, Overtown, 1995
41	WJI9362	Volvo B10M-61	East Lancs Flyte (1998)	BC53F	1987	Stagecoach South, 1998
D42	D498NYS	Volvo B10M-61	East Lancs Flyte (1998)	B53F	1986	Hutchison, Overtown, 1992
D50	MIL8330	Volvo B10M-60	Plaxton Paramount 3200 III	C53F	1991	Westbus, Hounslow, 1998
D51	7822VW	Volvo B10M-60	Plaxton Paramount 3200	C57F	1989	Woodstones, Kidderminster, 1996
D52	E445FNU	Volvo B10M-61	Van Hool Alizée L	C53F	1988	Park's of Hamilton, 1995
D53	E648CHS	Volvo B10M-61	Duple 340	C55F	1988	Hutchinson, Overtown, 1999
60	S374SET	Scania L94IB	Irizar InterCentury 12.32	C57F	1999	
61	T34CNN	Scania L94IB	Irizar InterCentury 12.32	C57F	1999	
62	T35CNN	Scania L94IB	Irizar InterCentury 12.32	C57F	1999	
63	T36CNN	Scania L94IB	Irizar InterCentury 12.32	C57F	1999	
80	N97ACH	Bova FHD12.340	Bova Futura	C51FT	1996	
81	N751DAK	Bova FHD12.340	Bova Futura	C51FT	1996	
90	MIL9765	DAF SBR3000DKZ570	Plaxton Paramount 4000 III	C55/19CT	1990	Flights, Birmingham, 1997
D91	WLT702	DAF SBR3000DKZ570	Plaxton Paramount 4000 III	C55/19CT	1990	Flights, Birmingham, 1997
92	IIL2948	DAF SBR3000DKZ590	Plaxton Paramount 4000 III	C55/17CT	1988	Bailey, Biddisham, 1996
WM92	DXI92	Renault Master	Jubilee	M10	1994	Executive Travel, 1999
93	L6BOB	Volvo B12T	Jonckheere Monaco	C55/16CT	1995	Impact, Carlisle, 1999

| 100-104 | | Volvo B10M-62 | | Jonckheere Mistral 50 | | C51FT | | 1998 | |
| 100 | S595CJF | 101 | S596CJF | 102 | S597CJF | 103 | S598CJF | 104 | S599CJF |

105	P251AUT	Volvo B10M-66SE	Jonckheere Mistral 50	C51FT	1997	
106	P252AUT	Volvo B12T	Plaxton Excalibur	C49FT	1997	
107	P253AUT	Volvo B10M-66SE	Jonckheere Mistral 50	C51FT	1997	
108	P354EAU	Volvo B10M-66SE	Jonckheere Mistral 50	C39FT	1997	
109	P2DFC	Volvo B10M-66SE	Jonckheere Mistral 50	C51FT	1996	
110	N655EWJ	Volvo B10M-62	Van Hool Alizée HE	C48FT	1996	MTL London Northern, 1997
111	N656EWJ	Volvo B10M-62	Van Hool Alizée HE	C48FT	1996	MTL London Northern, 1997
112	N657EWJ	Volvo B10M-62	Van Hool Alizée HE	C48FT	1996	MTL London Northern, 1997
114	N658EWJ	Volvo B10M-62	Van Hool Alizée HE	C48FT	1996	MTL London Northern, 1997
115	N998MJW	Volvo B10M-62	Van Hool Alizée HE	C39FT	1996	
116	M732KJU	Volvo B10M-62	Jonckheere Deauville 45	C49FT	1995	
117	M733KJU	Volvo B10M-62	Jonckheere Deauville 45	C49FT	1995	
118	M734KJU	Volvo B10M-62	Jonckheere Deauville 45	C49FT	1995	
119	M735KJU	Volvo B10M-62	Jonckheere Deauville 45	C49FT	1995	
120	K574EKY	Volvo B10M-60	Ikarus Blue Danube	C49FL	1992	Walton, Stockton, 1996
122	J421HDS	Volvo B10M-60	Plaxton Premiere 350	C49FT	1992	Bellamy, Nottingham, 1998
123	JIL8813	Volvo B10M-60	Plaxton Premiere 350	C48FT	1992	Cairngorm Chairlift, Aviemore, 1997
123	T37CNN	Volvo B10M-62	Plaxton Excalibur	C49FT	1999	
124	T38CNN	Volvo B10M-62	Plaxton Excalibur	C49FT	1999	

D124	MIL8336	Volvo B10M-60	Plaxton Paramount 3500 III	C49F	1991	South Yorkshire Coachline, 1998
125	H946DRJ	Volvo B10M-60	Plaxton Paramount 3500 III	C49FT	1991	Park's of Hamilton, 1998
125	T39CNN	Volvo B10M-62	Plaxton Excalibur	C49FT	1999	
126	MIL8342	Volvo B10M-60	Plaxton Paramount 3500 III	C49FT	1991	Park's of Hamilton, 1998
D127	MIL8332	Volvo B10M-60	Plaxton Paramount 3500 III	C49F	1991	?????, 1998
128	MIL8339	Volvo B10M-60	Plaxton Paramount 3500 III	C49F	1991	City of Oxford, 1998
129	M321VET	Scania K113CRB	Van Hool Alizée	C49FT	1995	Ambassador, Norwich, 1999
130	M325VET	Scania K113CRB	Van Hool Alizée	C49FT	1995	Ambassador, Norwich, 1999

130-139

Scania L94IB — Irizar Century 12.35 — C49FT — 1999

130	T41CNN	132	T43CNN	134	T46CNN	136	T48CNN	138	T51CNN
131	T42CNN	133	T45CNN	135	T47CNN	137	T49CNN	139	T52CNN

140	J261NNC	Volvo B10M-60	Plaxton Premiére 350	C49FT	1992	Shearings,1999
141	J264NNC	Volvo B10M-60	Plaxton Premiére 350	C49FT	1992	Shearings,1999
D142	J265NNC	Volvo B10M-60	Plaxton Premiére 350	C49FT	1992	Shearings,1999
D143	J267NNC	Volvo B10M-60	Plaxton Premiére 350	C49FT	1992	Shearings,1999
145	T32CNN	Volvo B12(T)	Jonckheere Monaco	C57/14CT	1999	
220	WJI9363	Volvo B10M-55	East Lancs Pyoneer (1998)	BC45/35F	1986	Hutchison, Overtown, 1995
221	PJI5631	Volvo B10M-61	East Lancs Pyoneer (1998)	BC45/35F	1983	ABC, Leicester, 1997
222	MIL8341	Volvo B10M-56	East Lancs Pyoneer (1998)	BC45/35F	1982	Tillingbourne, Cranleigh, 1997
223	MIL8340	Volvo B10M-61	East Lancs Pyoneer (1997)	BC45/35F	1981	Webster, Rayleigh, 1997
224	WSV535	Volvo B10M-61	East Lancs Pyoneer (1999)	BC45/35F	1982	Tracks, Brooklands, 1999
225	T399OWA	Scania N113DRB	East Lancs Cityzen (1999)	BC43/35F	1999	
D280	A620THV	Leyland Titan TNLXB2RR	Leyland	B44/32F	1984	London Central, 1997
281	A649THV	Leyland Titan TNLXB2RR	Leyland	B44/26D	1984	London Central, 1997
282	MIL8326	Leyland Titan TNLXB2RR	Leyland	B44/32F	1982	Metroline, 1997
283	MIL8327	Leyland Titan TNLXB2RR	Leyland	B44/24D	1982	Metroline, 1997
284	MIL8328	Leyland Titan TNLXB2RR	Leyland	B44/24D	1982	Metroline, 1997
285	MIL8329	Leyland Titan TNLXB2RR	Leyland	B44/24D	1982	Metroline, 1997
D400	HSV781	Bova EL26/581	Bova Europa	C53F	1983	Ascot, Derby, 1999
D401	HIL2393	Bova EL26/581	Bova Europa	C53F	1983	Ascot, Derby, 1999
WM300	R866SDT	Scania K113TRB	Irizar Century 12.37	C51FT	1998	Executive Travel, 1999
WM301	R865SDT	Scania K113TRB	Irizar Century 12.37	C51FT	1997	Executive Travel, 1999
WM302	N697AHL	Scania K113TRB	Irizar Century 12.37	C51FT	1996	Executive Travel, 1999
WM303	N696AHL	Scania K113CRB	Irizar Century 12.35	C49FT	1995	Executive Travel, 1999
WM304	N695AHL	Scania K113TRB	Irizar Century 12.37	C51FT	1996	Executive Travel, 1999
WM305	M76HOV	Scania K113CRB	Irizar Century 12.35	C49FT	1995	Executive Travel, 1999
WM312	DXI84	MAN 11.220HOCLR	Caetano Algarve II	C26FT	1992	Executive Travel, 1999

Previous Registrations:

7822VW	F466WFX	MIL8327	KYV475X	MIL8341	FGD827X
A4BOB	F704COA	MIL8328	KYV479X	MIL8342	H947DRJ
A5BOB	F701COA	MIL8329	KYV518X	MIL9765	G778HOV, 245DOC
DXI84	J513LRY, WCT476, J996NLL	MIL8330	H933DRJ	P251AUT	P253AUT
DXI92	question	MIL8332	H948DRJ	P253AUT	P251AUT
E445FNU	E965CGA, LSK965, E648UNE, A3BOB	PJI5631	BDV866Y, KSV832, RBD46Y		
E648CHS	E154XHS, KSK935	MIL8334	F626OHD	UES274S	BGS160S, BSK744
HIL2393	VWX357X	HSV781	FUA399Y	WJI9361	D391PYS
IIL2948	E312AGA	MIL8336	H953DRJ, 220AWY, N442VHE		
JIL8813	J700CWT	MIL8337	G90KUB	WJI9362	GGE131X, GSU950, TOS757X
KSK932	E153XHS	MIL8338	WRJ448X	WJI9363	D390PYS
L6BOB	XFV257, M724VAO	MIL8339	H951DRJ	WLT702	G776HOV
MIL8325	F181FWY	MIL8340	NCS123W, WLT439, WGB853W	WSV535	ADV145Y
MIL8326	KYV399X				

Livery: White, purple, pink and turquoise; **Depots:** Derby (Shaftesbury Street) - D prefix; Nottingham (Park Lane, Basford); Wednesbury (Patrick Gregory Road) - WM prefixed numbers.

Opposite: **The attractive Jonckheere Mistral body is applied to P354EAU, a Volvo B10M and one of the high quality coaches operated by Dunn-Line. It is shown here leaving the Beetwell Street bus station in Chesterfield during September 1998, having deposited passengers from a week-long tour. The lower picture illustrates the diversity of Dunn-Line operation, route 304 that links Nottingham City Centre with one of the four Park and Ride sites. The Racecourse site is situated to the east of the city, and normally requires three vehicles to run the service. As this is a council tendered service, new vehicles were acquired, being a small number of SLF Dennis Darts bearing the East Lancashire Spryte bodywork. P351EAU departs from the P&R park during October 1996, when the service first started. In August 1999 Dunn-Line acquired CAMMS. This operation is to be named Nottingham Coach Company, aimed at a different market sector.** *Tony Wilson*

EAGRE

R H Eaglen, Crooked Billet Street, Morton, Gainsborough,
Lincolnshire, DN21 3AG

Reg	Chassis	Body	Seating	Year	History
AFE610A	Leyland National 1151/1R/0402		B49F	1974	Alder Valley South, 1988
AFE595A	Leyland National 11351/1R		B49F	1974	Alder Valley South, 1988
HHH272N	Bristol VRT/SL2/6G	Eastern Coach Works	B43/34F	1974	Cumberland, 1990
1878R	Leyland Leopard PSU3D/4R	Duple 320 (1987)	C53F	1977	National Travel East, 1987
RAZ8974	Leyland Atlantean AN68A/2R	Alexander AL	B49/40F	1978	Fife Scottish, 1996
UNA864S	Leyland Atlantean AN68A/1R	Park Royal	B43/32F	1978	GM Buses, 1991
BOK22V	MCW Metrobus DR102/12	MCW	B43/30F	1979	Travel West Midlands, 1999
RAZ8973	Leyland Atlantean AN68A/2R	Alexander AL	B49/37F	1980	Wilson, Carnwath, 1996
RFS582V	Leyland National 2 NL116L11/1R		B52F	1980	Stagecoach Ribble, 1998
GFV155W	Leyland Atlantean AN68D/2R	East Lancashire	B50/36F	1981	Preston Bus, 1998
KSU479	Leyland Leopard PSU5C/4R	Duple Dominant IV	C53FT	1981	Hallam, Newthorpe, 1994
LAZ2445	Dennis Dominator DD137B	Alexander RL	B45/34F	1982	KCB, 1996
WCK215Y	Leyland Atlantean AN68D/2R	East Lancashire	B50/36F	1982	Stagecoach Ribble, 1998
2160RE	Van Hool T815	Van Hool Acron	C48FT	1982	Belmont, Askern, 1983
9962R	Leyland Leopard PSU3E/4R	Plaxton Paramount 3200	C49F	1983	
KAZ3253	Dennis Falcon HC SDA406	East Lancashire	B51F	1983	Ipswich, 1996
KAZ3254	Dennis Falcon HC SDA406	East Lancashire	B51F	1983	Ipswich, 1996
KSU477	Leyland Tiger TRCTL11/2R	Alexander TE	BC53F	1983	Eastern National, 1995
TFE1R	Dennis Dorchester SDA805	Berkhof Everest 370	C53F	1983	R Bullock, Cheadle, 1997
ROI876	Leyland Tiger TRCTL11/3RH	Berkhof Everest 370	C51FT	1985	Mackay, Dalbeg, 1995
3064RE	Van Hool T815	Van Hool Alicron	C53F	1984	Lock, Surrey Docks, 1989
HFU531	Leyland Tiger TRCTL11/3RZ	Wadham Stringer Vanguard	BC54F	1986	MoD, 1996 (64KD86)
A10RHE	Leyland Tiger TRCTL11/3RZ	Plaxton Paramount 3200 II	C51F	1987	Thamesway, 1996
7126RE	Leyland LX1126LXCTFR1S	Leyland Lynx	B49F	1987	Arriva Yorkshire, 1999
6077RE	LAG G355Z	LAG Panoramic	C49FT	1988	Silver Coach Lines, Edinburgh, 1990
7980R	Mercedes-Benz 811D	Optare StarRider	BC33F	1988	Yorkshire Coastliner, 1998
B10RJE	EOS E180Z	EOS 90	C53FT	1990	Stratos, Newtown, 1996
N10DME	Iveco EuroRider 391.12.37	Beulas Stergo E	C49FT	1996	Channel Coachways, Bow, 1998
T100ANN	Iveco EuroRider 391.12.29	Beulas Stergo E	C49FT	1999	
V	MAN 18.310	Marcopolo Continental 340	C49FT	1999	

Previous Registrations:

1878R	OKY57R	AFE610A	NRD148N	KSU479	SAL921X
2160RE	PWG148X, AFE80A	A10RHE	D597MVR	LAZ2445	FGE435X
3064RE	ROI876, A501VGP	B10RJE	G810LVV, KSU477	RAZ8973	AVK178V
6077RE	E673NNV	HFU531	D121ODO	RAZ8974	SCN244S
7126RE	E259TUB	KAZ3254	YDX105Y	ROI876	B123KPF, YFN251
7980R	E283TWW	KAZ3253	YDX103Y	TFE1R	KNO224Y, BUI1424
9962R	LVL727Y, TFE1R	KSU477	HHJ380Y		
AFE595A	TBL177N				

Livery: Red and cream (buses); white, red and yellow (coaches); maroon, purple and silver (new coaches)

Opposite, top: **A couple of Dennis Falcon buses were acquired by Eagre from Ipswich Borough Transport during 1996. Based in Gainsborough, these vehicles can frequently be found operating local town services. Their dual-door bodies were converted to single-door configuration, the result is seen on KAZ3254 pictured as it pulls away from the bus station during April 1999. The livery shows off the stepped window line, which in turn accentuates the rearward rising floor and bus seating.** *Tony Wilson*
Opposite, bottom: **The first new purchase by Eagre for some time is T100ANN, an Iveco EuroRider bodied by Spanish coachbuilder, Beulas. The coach was purchased after the successful operation of a similar, more highly-powered, vehicle acquired in 1998. Both of the EuroRiders carry a livery of silver fading to maroon rather than the usual Eagre coach livery of white, red and yellow.** *Paul Hill*

ELSEYS

A & W Elsey Ltd, 119 High Street, Gosberton, Spalding, Lincolnshire, PE11 4NA

JJL390F	Bedford SB5	Duple Bella Vega	C41F	1968	
WSV418	Leyland Leopard PSU3E/4R	Plaxton Supreme IV	C53F	1980	Bailey, Toton, 1992
E333EVH	DAF MB230LB615	Van Hool Alizée H	C55F	1988	
E112YNM	Scania K112CRS	Van Hool Alizée H	C49FT	1987	Ace, Enfield, 1992
G849VAY	Dennis Javelin 11SDL1905	Duple 300	B55F	1989	
G997KJX	DAF SB2305DHS585	Duple 320	C57F	1990	
G998KJX	DAF SB2305DHS585	Duple 320	C53F	1990	
H380TNG	Leyland Tiger TRCL10/3ARZH	Plaxton Paramount 3500 III	C51F	1991	Ambassador, Gt Yarmouth, 1997
K120OCT	Kässbohrer Setra S215HD	Kässbohrer	C49F	1992	Ebdon, Sidcup, 1996
K519RJX	DAF SB3000DKVF601	Van Hool Alizée HE	C49FT	1993	
K529EHE	Scania K113CRB	Van Hool Alizée HE	C53F	1993	
L907RDO	Ford Transit VE6	Ford	M8	1994	
M290OUR	Iveco Turbo City 480-10-21	Wadham Stringer Vanguard	B47F	1994	
N981FWT	DAF DE33WSSB3000	Ikarus Blue Danube 350	C55F	1996	

Previous Registrations:
WSV418   KBH847V

Livery: White, red and grey

Depot: High Street, Gosberton and Bicker Road, Donington.

Elseys of Gosberton have operated a bus service between Boston and Spalding since deregulation though in 1999 they suspended service leaving the route to Brylaine and Kime's. Now concentrating on coaching, the company has a number of modern types including Setra K120OCT shown here at Ascot races. *David Heath*

EMMERSONS

OM & AG Stocks and A Brumby, 91 Bluestone Lane, Immingham,
North East Lincolnshire, DN40 2EL

	NLO857V	Bedford YMT	Plaxton Supreme IV	C53F	1980	McLernon, Grimsby, 1985
	173LYB	DAF MB200DKTL550	Plaxton Supreme IV	C53F	1980	McLernon, Grimsby, 1985
	WFU561V	Ford R1114	Duple Dominant II	C53F	1980	
	VBH50W	Ford R1114	Duple Dominant IV	C53F	1981	The Londoners, Nunhead, 1986
	EFU613Y	Ford R1114	Duple Dominant IV	C53F	1983	
	MIB648	Volvo B10M-61	Duple Laser	C57F	1983	Coachman, Cowplain, 1995
w	XFC486	Bova EL28/581	Duple Calypso	C53F	1984	Supreme, Coventry, 1987
	NSU180	Scania K112CRS	Plaxton Paramount 3200 II	C53F	1985	Supreme, Hadleigh, 1993
	XFK173	Volvo B10M-61	Ikarus Blue Danube	C49F	1988	
	F701PAY	Mercedes-Benz 0303/15R	Mercedes-Benz	C53F	1988	Comfort Travel, Chesterfield, 1997
	F702PAY	Mercedes-Benz 0303/15R	Mercedes-Benz	C53F	1988	Redwing, London, 1997
	H10SUP	MAN 16.290	Jonckheere Deauville P50	C51FT	1991	Supreme, Hadleigh, 1999
	L340YAC	Volvo B10M-62	Plaxton Premiere 350	C53F	1994	Kikby Coach & Bus

Previous Registrations:

173LYB	JDU902V	XFC486	A313JRW
MIB648	MCR333Y, 710VCV, 800GTR	XFK173	From new
NSU180	B546CHJ		

Livery: Orange, black and white

Depots: Gilbey Road, Pyewipe, Grimsby & Bluestone Lane, Immingham.

Emmersons of Immingham has one of a small number of Bova coaches bodied by Duple. XFC486 carries the Calypso body which was derived from the Caribbean. New to a Coventry operator in 1984, this coach has now been with Emmersons for 12 years though it has recently been withdrawn. *Steve Sanderson*

EXPRESS MOTORS

P Brown, 3 Wild Park Lane, Brailsford, Derbyshire, DE6 3BN

1	S376TMB	Mercedes-Benz Vario O814	Plaxton Beaver 2	B31F	1998	
2	R477GFM	Mercedes-Benz Vario O814	Plaxton Beaver 2	B31F	1998	Pete's Travel, West Bromwich, 1998
10	F109YVP	MCW MetroRider MF158/16	MCW	B28F	1988	Stagecoach East London, 1996
11w	F197YDA	MCW MetroRider MF158/18	MCW	B28F	1988	Pete's Travel, West Bromwich, 1997
12	F120YVP	MCW MetroRider MF158/16	MCW	B31F	1988	Aston Express, 1997
31	UPB311S	Leyland National 10351A/1R		B44F	1977	London & Country, 1995
71	FBV271W	Bristol LHS6L	Eastern Coach Works	B35F	1980	Bluebird Buses, 1993
73w	OJD89R	Bristol LH6L	Eastern Coach Works	B45F	1977	Coombs, Weston-super-Mare, 1994
74	OJD66R	Bristol LH6L	Eastern Coach Works	B45F	1977	Shaftesbury & District, 1995

Livery: Blue and white

Depot: Hulland Motors, Hulland, Derbyshire

An acquisition by Express Motors during Spring 1999 was that of a Mercedes-Benz Vario with a Plaxton Beaver 2 body. S376TMB is run by the company that operates from a base in the Derbyshire village of Hulland Ward. Rural Aid Grant increased operation of the Ashbourne to Matlock route 411, which passes along the edge of the Peak District National Park. The vehicle is illustrated here pulling up the sharp incline leading to Middleton Top after which it will head across the hill-tops to Ashbourne. *Tony Wilson*

FELIX

Felix Bus Services Ltd, 157 Station Road, Stanley, Ilkeston, Derbyshire, DE7 6FJ

WRC826S	Bedford YMT	Duple Dominant II	C53F	1978	
GRF264V	Leyland Leopard PSU3E/4R	Duple Dominant II Express	C53F	1979	Tillingbourne, 1988
BES270V	Leyland Leopard PSU3E/4R	Plaxton Supreme IV Express	C53F	1978	Earnside, Glenfarg, 1987
DTN958W	Leyland Leopard PSU3E/4R	Plaxton Supreme IV Express	C53F	1980	Holmes, Clay Cross, 1986
F697HNU	Leyland Tiger TRBTL11/2R	Plaxton Derwent	B54F	1988	
J564URW	Leyland Lynx LX2R11C15245	Leyland Lynx 2	B51F	1992	Volvo demonstrator, 1992
M21UUA	Dennis Lance 11SDA3113	Optare Sigma	B47F	1994	Optare demonstrator, 1995
M301KRY	Volvo B10B-58	Alexander Strider	B51F	1995	
N703AAL	Dennis Javelin 12SDA2117	Plaxton Premiére 320	C53F	1996	
R704RNN	Volvo B10M-62	Plaxton Premiére 320	C57F	1997	
R705MNU	Volvo B10M-62	Plaxton Premiére 320	C57F	1997	
R706MNU	Volvo B10M-62	Plaxton Premiére 320	C53F	1998	
S590KJF	Volvo B10BLE	Alexander ALX300	N45F	1998	

Livery: Red and maroon or red and white (buses); white and gold (coaches).

One of the first **Volvo B10BLE** vehicles to sport the Alexander ALX300 body design, was S590KJF. Felix of Ilkeston purchase single examples of vehicle types for its local service vehicle needs. The company base is located between the home town and Derby along route 12 which provides an hourly service. Bearing a eponymous cat motif, company name and route branding on the red and white livery, the newest vehicle in the fleet lays over in Derby bus station in March 1998. *Tony Wilson*

FLEETLINE BUSES

M Franks, 22 Chitterman Way, Markfield, Leicestershire, LE6 0WU

KSA178P	Leyland Atlantean AN68A/1R	Alexander AL	B45/29D	1976	Portsmouth Transit, 1991
MNU623P	Leyland Atlantean AN68A/1R	East Lancashire	B47/31D	1976	City of Nottingham, 1994
MNU630P	Leyland Atlantean AN68A/1R	East Lancashire	B47/31D	1976	City of Nottingham, 1994
UTV218S	Leyland Fleetline FE30AGR	Northern Counties	B47/31D	1977	City of Nottingham, 1994
UTV219S	Leyland Fleetline FE30AGR	Northern Counties	B47/31D	1977	City of Nottingham, 1994
XTV667S	Leyland Atlantean AN68A/1R	Northern Counties	B47/31D	1978	City of Nottingham, 1996
BTV655T	Leyland Atlantean AN68A/1R	East Lancashire	B47/31D	1979	City of Nottingham, 1996
RNU430X	Leyland Atlantean AN68C/1R	Northern Counties	B47/31D	1981	City of Nottingham, 1999
RNU434X	Leyland Atlantean AN68C/1R	Northern Counties	B47/31D	1981	City of Nottingham, 1999
RNU442X	Leyland Atlantean AN68C/1R	Northern Counties	B47/31D	1981	City of Nottingham, 1999
SNU456X	Leyland Atlantean AN68C/1R	East Lancashire	B47/33D	1982	City of Nottingham, 1997

Livery: Green and cream

Depot: Broad Lane, Markfield and c/o WS Group, Ratby

Fleetline Buses run two peak hour-only services from Markfield to Leicester in addition to a number of school services. KSA178P is an Alexander-bodied Leyland Atlantean which was new to Grampian Regional Transport. It is seen entering St Margaret's bus station in Leicester on a F2 evening journey from Leicester Royal Infirmary to Markfield. *Steve Sanderson*

FIRST LEICESTER

Leicester CityBus Ltd, Abbey Park Road, Leicester, LE4 5AH

2	P176NAK	Volvo B10M-62		Plaxton Première 350	C53F	1997	Waugh, Greenhead, 1998
3	P177NAK	Volvo B10M-62		Plaxton Première 350	C53F	1997	Waugh, Greenhead, 1998
7	N378EAK	Volvo B10M-62		Plaxton Première 350	C53F	1996	Yorkshire Rider, 1998
11	SSU837	Volvo B10M-60		Plaxton Paramount 3500 III	C53F	1990	Yorkshire Rider, 1998

42-52

Dennis Dominator DDA142*   East Lancashire   B43/33F   1981-82 *49-52 are DDA141

42	TBC42X	45	TBC45X	49	TBC49X	50	TBC50X	52	TBC52X
43	TBC43X	46	TBC46X						

58-78

Dennis Dominator DDA155*   East Lancashire   B43/33F   1982-83 *70 is DDA160,
71-4 are DDA173, 75-8 are DDA168

58	VAY58X	64	XJF64Y	68	XJF68Y	72	A72FRY	76	A76FRY
61	XJF61Y	65	XJF65Y	69	XJF69Y	73	A73FRY	77	A77FRY
62	XJF62Y	66	XJF66Y	70	AUT70Y	74	A74FRY	78	A78FRY
63	XJF63Y	67	XJF67Y	71	A71FRY	75	A75FRY		

79-86

Dennis Dominator DDA1102*   East Lancashire   B43/33F   1984-85 *81-3 are DDA1002
*84-86 are DDA901 and B46/33F

79	B79MJF	81	B81MJF	83	B83MJF	85	B85MRY	86	B86MRY
80	B80MJF	82	B82MJF	84	B84MRY				

87-99

Dennis Dominator DDA1015   East Lancashire   B46/33F   1988

87	E87HNR	90	E90HNR	93	E93HNR	96	E96HNR	98	E98HNR
88	E88HNR	91	E91HNR	94	E94HNR	97	E97HNR	99	E99HNR
89	E89HNR	92	E92HNR	95	E95HNR				

143	F143MBC	Dennis Dominator DDA1024	East Lancashire	B46/33F	1989	
144	F636BKD	Dennis Dominator DDA1025	East Lancashire	B45/31F	1989	North Western, 1997
145	F637BKD	Dennis Dominator DDA1025	East Lancashire	B45/31F	1989	North Western, 1997
146	F146MBC	Dennis Dominator DDA1024	East Lancashire	B46/33F	1989	
147	G629EKA	Dennis Dominator DDA1031	East Lancashire	B45/31F	1990	North Western, 1997
148	G667FKA	Dennis Dominator DDA1031	East Lancashire	B47/29F	1990	North Western, 1997
149	F149MBC	Dennis Dominator DDA1024	East Lancashire	B46/33F	1989	
150	F150MBC	Dennis Dominator DDA1024	East Lancashire	B46/33F	1989	
151	F151MBC	Dennis Dominator DDA1024	East Lancashire	B46/33F	1989	
152	F152MBC	Dennis Dominator DDA1024	East Lancashire	B46/33F	1989	Northampton, 1998
184	FUT184V	Dennis Dominator DDA120	East Lancashire	B43/33F	1980	Northampton, 1998
179	FUT179V	Dennis Dominator DDA120	East Lancashire	B43/33F	1979	
205	NFP205W	Dennis Dominator DDA131	East Lancashire	B43/33F	1980	
206	MUT206W	Dennis Dominator DDA131	East Lancashire	B43/33F	1980	
250	FUT250V	Dennis Dominator DDA120	East Lancashire	B43/33F	1979	
257	MUT257W	Dennis Dominator DDA120	East Lancashire	B43/33F	1981	
269	BLS443Y	MCW Metrobus DR102/33	Alexander RL	B45/33F	1983	Midland Bluebird, 1994
282	LSU717	Volvo Citybus B10M-50	Alexander RV	BC47/35F	1989	Northampton, 1997

301-310

Optare L1070   Optare Excel   N38F   1997

301	R1LCB	303	R3LCB	305	R5LCB	307	R7LCB	309	R9LCB
302	R2LCB	304	R4LCB	306	R6LCB	308	R8LCB	310	R10LCB

344	R344SUT	Scania L113CRL	Wright Axcess-ultralow	N40F	1998
345	R345SUT	Scania L113CRL	Wright Axcess-ultralow	N40F	1998
346	R346SUT	Scania L113CRL	Wright Axcess-ultralow	N40F	1998

A batch of ten Optare Excels were purchased for Leicester-based services in 1997. These carry Select index marks for the Leicester City bus operation which was renamed First Leicester in 1998. The batch has been repainted from Leicester City bus livery into First Group's *'willowleaf'* colours and is represented here by 304, R4LCB. *Steve Sanderson*

347-358

Scania L113CRL — Wright Axcess-ultralow — N40F — 1998

347	S347MFP	**350**	S350MFP	**353**	S353MFP	**355**	S355MFP	**357**	S357MFP
348	S348MFP	**351**	S351MFP	**354**	S354MFP	**356**	S356MFP	**358**	S358MFP

501-510

Mercedes-Benz O405 — Optare Prisma — B49F — 1995

501	M501GRY	**503**	M503GRY	**506**	M506GRY	**508**	M508GRY	**510**	M510GRY
502	M502GRY	**504**	M504GRY	**507**	M507GRY	**509**	M509GRY		

611-619

Dennis Falcon HC SDA422 — East Lancashire EL2000 — B48F — 1991-92

611	H611EJF	**613**	H613EJF	**615**	H615EJF	**617**	K617SBC	**619**	K619SBC
612	H612EJF	**614**	H614EJF	**616**	H616EJF	**618**	K618SBC		

620-626

Dennis Falcon HC SDA422 — Northern Counties Paladin — B48F — 1993

620	K620SBC	**622**	K622SBC	**624**	L624XFP	**625**	L625XFP	**626**	L626XFP
621	K621SBC	**623**	L623XFP						

627	C107SDX	Dennis Falcon HC SDA416	Northern Counties	B45F	1985	Ipswich, 1997
628	C108SDX	Dennis Falcon HC SDA416	Northern Counties	B45F	1985	Ipswich, 1997
629	C109SDX	Dennis Falcon HC SDA416	Northern Counties	B45F	1986	Ipswich, 1997
630	C111SDX	Dennis Falcon HC SDA416	Northern Counties	B45F	1986	Ipswich, 1997
631	YDX100Y	Dennis Falcon HC SDA408	East Lancashire	B44D	1983	Ipswich, 1997

The latest low floor single-deck buses for First Leicester are Scania L113CRL vehicles. They were bodied in Northern Ireland by Wright of Ballymena using their Axcess-ultralow design. Shown here is 347, S347MFP which, like the entire order of this type has been built to the corporate FirstGroup layout for new buses and carries the colours the Group introduced in 1997 to identify their new high-specification buses. It is used throughout the country, except London, for all FirstGroup's high quality vehicles. *Steve Sanderson*

701	HDZ5459	Renault S75	Wright NimBus	B28F	1990	The Bee Line, 1998
702	HDZ5462	Renault S75	Wright NimBus	B28F	1990	The Bee Line, 1998
703	HDZ5475	Renault S75	Wright NimBus	B28F	1990	The Bee Line, 1998
704	HDZ5479	Renault S75	Wright NimBus	B28F	1990	The Bee Line, 1998
705	HDZ5477	Renault S75	Wright NimBus	B28F	1990	CentreWest, 1998
707	HDZ5466	Renault S75	Wright NimBus	B28F	1990	CentreWest, 1998
708	HDZ5488	Renault S75	Wright NimBus	B28F	1990	CentreWest, 1998
710	HDZ5471	Renault S75	Wright NimBus	B28F	1990	Northampton, 1998
711	HDZ5472	Renault S75	Wright NimBus	B28F	1990	Northampton, 1998

746-761
Renault-Dodge S56   Northern Counties   B25F*   1991-93   *753/4 are BC25F

746	K746VJU	750	K750VJU	753	J753MFP	756	J756MFP	759	J759NNR
748	K748VJU	751	H751ENR	754	J754MFP	757	J757MFP	760	K760SBC
749	K749VJU	752	H752ENR	755	J755MFP	758	J758NNR	761	K761SBC

| 776 | G259LWF | Renault-Dodge S56 | Reeve Burgess Beaver | B23F | 1989 | Yorkshire Rider, 1996 |

781-795
Renault S75   Wright TS303 Citybus   B28F   1990   CentreWest, 1997

781	HDZ5481	784	HDZ5484	787	HDZ5487	790	HDZ5490	793	HDZ5469
782	HDZ5482	785	HDZ5485	788	HDZ5464	791	HDZ5465	794	HDZ5440
783	HDZ5463	786	HDZ5457	789	HDZ5489	792	HDZ5467	795	HDZ5441

Special event vehicle:

| 154 | FJF193 | Leyland Titan PD2/1 | Leyland | B33/29R | 1950 | |
| 233 | UFP233S | Dennis Dominator DDA101 | East Lancashire | B43/31F | 1977 | |

Ancilliary vehicle:

| 240 | FUT240V | Dennis Dominator DDA120 | East Lancashire | | TV | 1979 |

Previous Registrations:

HDZ5440 etc   From new   LSU717   F87DVV

Allocations:-

Leicester (Abbey Park Road)

Renault-Dodge	701	702	703	704	705	707	708	710
	711	746	748	750	753	760	761	781
	782	783	784	785	786	787	788	789
	790	791	792	793	794	795		
Volvo B10M Coach	2	3	7	11				
Excel	301	302	303	304	305	306	307	308
	309	310						
Dennis Falcon	611	612	613	614	615	616	617	618
	619	620	621	622	623	624	625	626
	627	628	629	630	631			
Scania	344	345	346	347	348	350	351	353
	354	355	356	357	358			
Mercedes-Benz O405	501	502	503	504	506	507	508	509
	510							
Metrobus	269							
Dominator	42	43	45	46	49	50	52	58
	61	62	63	64	65	66	67	68
	69	70	71	72	73	74	75	76
	77	78	79	80	81	82	83	84
	85	86	87	88	89	90	91	92
	93	94	95	96	97	98	99	143
	144	145	146	147	148	149	150	151
	152	206						
Volvo Citybus	282							

Unallocated:-

Renault-Dodge	749	751	752	754	755	756	757	758
	759	776						
Dominator	179	184	205	233	250	257		

Opposite, top: **The Dennis Falcon was supplied new to the Leicester fleet between 1991-93. In 1997 a need for further single deck buses was fulfilled by purchasing additional examples of this chassis type from Ipswich Buses. Now numbered 627, C107SDX is fitted with a Northern Counties body and is seen in the centre of Leicester.** *Paul Wigan*

Opposite, bottom: **For many years the Leicester Citybus double deck requirements were met by purchasing substantial numbers of Dennis products, in this case the Dominator. Mr Geoffrey Hilditch, the erstwhile Managing Director of the then municipal operator, was instrumental in the design of this chassis. An East Lancashire-bodied example is shown here: 80, B80MJF.** *Paul Wigan*

FOWLERS TRAVEL

W H Fowler & Sons (Coaches) Ltd, Dog Drove, Holbeach Drove, Lincolnshire, PE12 0SD

Reg	Chassis	Body	Seating	Year	History
FRA521L	AEC Reliance 6U3ZR	Plaxton Panorama Elite III	C51F	1973	Butler, Kirkby-in-Ashfield, 1990
LUG88P	Leyland Atlantean AN68/1R	Roe	B43/33F	1975	Yorkshire Rider, 1993
EAD122T	Leyland Fleetline FE33ALR	Northern Counties	B47/36F	1979	Cottrell, Mitcheldean, 1997
NUB93V	AEC Reliance 6U2R	Plaxton Supreme IV	C53F	1980	Kemp, Chillenden,1996
LMS169W	Leyland Fleetline FE30AGR	Alexander AL	B44/31F	1980	Clydeside Buses, 1996
FBV510W	Leyland Atlantean AN68B/1R	Eastern Coach Works	B43/31F	1981	Clydeside Buses, 1996
PAD806W	Leyland Leopard PSU3E/4R	Plaxton Supreme IV Express	C51F	1982	Cottrell, Mitcheldean, 1997
JDO241W	Bedford YMT	Plaxton Supreme IV Express	C53F	1981	
VXI4453	Bedford YNT	Plaxton Supreme VI Express	C53F	1982	Flintham, Metheringham, 1997
XEF11Y	Leyland Tiger TRCTL11/2R	Plaxton Supreme VI Express	C53F	1983	Go-Ahead Northern, 1998
D77HRU	Bedford YNT	Plaxton Paramount 3200 III	C53F	1987	AWRE, Aldermaston, 1999
F312PEV	Scania N113DRB	Alexander RH	B47/33F	1989	Harris, West Thurrock, 1998
F314RHK	Scania N113DRB	Alexander RH	B47/33F	1989	Harris, West Thurrock, 1998
F259CEW	Scania N113DRB	Alexander RH	B47/33F	1989	
F556NGR	Dennis Javelin 11SDA1909	Duple 300	B55F	1989	Go-Ahead Northern, 1998
G959WNR	Dennis Javelin 11SDA1909	Duple 300	B55F	1989	Go-Ahead Northern, 1998
H447EVK	Dennis Javelin 11SDA1932	Plaxton Derwent II	B55F	1991	Go-Ahead Northern, 1998
L50WHF	Scania K113CRB	Plaxton Premiére 350	C51F	1993	Hanson, Halifax, 1997
N691AHL	Scania L113CRL	Northern Counties Paladin	B51F	1995	
N692AHL	Scania L113CRL	Northern Counties Paladin	B51F	1995	
N693AHL	Scania L113CRL	Northern Counties Paladin	B51F	1995	
A10WHF	Volvo B10M-62	Plaxton Premiére 320	C57F	1996	Bebb, Llantwit Fardre, 1997
P50WHF	Scania K113CRB	Van Hool Alizée HE	C53F	1997	
S333HEB	Scania N113DRB	East Lancs Cityzen	B47/31F	1998	
706STT	Volvo B10M-62	Plaxton Excalibur	C49FT	1999	
T110JBC	Volvo B7R	Plaxton Prima	C53F	1999	
T111JBC	Volvo B7R	Plaxton Prima	C53F	1999	
T744JHE	Scania L94IB	Van Hool Alizée 2	C53F	1999	

Special Event vehicles:

Reg	Chassis	Body	Seating	Year	History
VBT191	AEC Reliance MU3RV	Yeates	C41F	1958	preservation, 1996
GJP197	Bedford SB1	Yeates	C41F	1960	Carter, Foulden, 1995
519SLG	Bedford SB3	Plaxton Embassy	C41F	1961	Miller, Foxton, 1992
8488NU	Bedford VAL14	Plaxton Panorama	C52F	1964	Branson & Howarth, Brampton, 1974
CJN441C	Leyland Titan PD3/6	Massey	B38/32R	1965	Lincoln City, 1993

Previous Registrations:

519SLG	From new	A10WHF	N54MDW	L50WHF	L445FHD
706STT	S577KJF	FRA521L	VWA290L, 20VWC	VBT191	From new
8488NU	From new	GJP197	From new	VXI4453	VDF300X

Named Vehicles: F312PEV, *Betty Boop*; G959WNR , *Macauley John*; H447EVK, *Amy II*; JDO241W, *Ross*; L50WHF, *Melanie*; NUB93V, *Tabatha*; PAD806W , *Paddy*; S333HEB, *Fenland Queen*, T110EBC, *Ella May II.*; 706STT - *Louise*

Livery: Cream and orange

Opposite, top: **XEF11Y is one of a batch of Leyland Tigers purchased new by OK Travel of Bishop Auckland. Sold by OK's new owners in 1998, the coach joined Fowlers Travel fleet. Spalding bus station is the location of this view, seen in the summer of 1999.** *Steve Sanderson*
Opposite, bottom: **Having gained sole operation of the Spalding to Kings Lynn service following from the withdrawal of RoadCar from south of Boston, Fowlers Travel have developed the route. A new purchase for service 505 in 1998 was S333HEB. Named *Fenland Queen*, this Scania N113DRB was bodied by East Lancashire and continues the long tradition of double deck operation on this route.** *Steve Sanderson*

FRED'S

F Hancox, 63 Bridge Road, Cotmanhay, Derbyshire, DE7 8RD

w	C538TJF	Ford Transit 190D	Rootes	B16F	1986	Lamcote, Radcliffe-on-Trent, 1996
	D737JUB	Freight Rover Sherpa	Carlyle	B16F	1986	Phil Anslow, Garndiffaith, 1995
w	D114TFT	Freight Rover Sherpa	Carlyle	B18F	1986	Lutonian, Luton, 1998
	D510NDA	Freight Rover Sherpa	Carlyle	B19F	1986	Lutonian, Luton, 1998
	D231OOJ	Freight Rover Sherpa	Carlyle	B18F	1987	Phil Anslow, Garndiffaith, 1995
w	D64OKG	Freight Rover Sherpa	Carlyle	B18FL	1987	Phil Anslow, Garndiffaith, 1994
	E902GCU	Renault-Dodge S56	Alexander AM	B25F	1988	Go-Ahead Gateshead, 1998
	E907GCU	Renault-Dodge S56	Alexander AM	B25F	1988	Go-Ahead Gateshead, 1998
	E910GCU	Renault-Dodge S56	Alexander AM	B25F	1988	Go-Ahead Gateshead, 1998
	E741VWJ	Ford Transit VE6	Whittaker	M12	1987	
	F364MUT	Mercedes-Benz 609D	Taurus	C26F	1988	
	F721SML	Mercedes-Benz 609D	Reeve Burgess Beaver	BC21F	1989	Adkins, Upper Boddington, 1999
	F510PNR	Mercedes-Benz 609D	Reeve Burgess Beaver	BC19F	1989	
	G274HDW	Freight Rover Sherpa	Carlyle Citybus 2	B20F	1990	Hail & Ride, Skegness, 1998

Livery: White

Fred's now operate a local service from Ilkeston to Cotmanhay Farm in competition with Trent which, previously, Saxton of Langley Mill had provided. A trio of Alexander-bodied Renault-Dodge S56 minibuses were purchased from the Go-Ahead group in 1998 for this route, E902GCU being seen here. *Tony Wilson*

GLOVERS

Glovers Coaches Ltd, 56 Walton Crescent, Ashbourne, Derbyshire, DE6 1FZ

PRR446R	Leyland National 11351A/2R		B50F	1976	Trent, 1997
HRB932V	Bedford YMT	Duple Dominant II	C53F	1980	
KBC4V	Leyland Leopard PSU3E/4R	Plaxton Supreme IV Express	C53F	1980	Blackburn, 1997
NNU71W	Leyland Leopard PSU3E/4R	Duple Dominant IV	C53F	1981	
URA481X	Bedford YMP	Duple Dominant IV	C45F	1982	
YNN396Y	Leyland Tiger TRCTL11/3R	Duple Dominant III	C53F	1983	
A506FSS	Dennis Lancet SDA516	Alexander P	B53F	1984	Northern Scottish, 1991
A281FAL	Mercedes-Benz L307D	Reeve Burgess	M12	1984	
B252KTO	Volvo B10M-61	Plaxton Paramount 3200 II	C53F	1985	
D776WVO	Bedford YNT	Plaxton Paramount 3200 III	C53F	1987	
E964SVU	Freight Rover Sherpa	Made-to-Measure	B18FL	1987	Filer, Ilfracombe, 1991
G700OCH	Mercedes-Benz 609D	Reeve Burgess Beaver	C25F	1989	
N381EAK	Volvo B10M-62	Plaxton Premiére 350	C53F	1996	
N382EAK	Volvo B10M-62	Plaxton Premiére 350	C53F	1996	

Livery: Cream and blue

Depot: Moor Farm Road East, Ashbourne Ind Est.

In 1980, Glovers Coaches of Ashbourne purchased a new Bedford YMT, HRB932V. This vehicle carries the Dominant II style of body produced by Duple at the time and still operates for the company some twenty years later. Glovers operates a number of bus services centred on the Derbyshire town of Ashbourne including routes to Yeaveley, Osmaston, Alkmonton, Derby and Uttoxeter. *Paul Hill*

GO BUS

R Handbury & J L Revell, Incomol Building, Derby Road, Clay Cross,
Derbyshire, S45 9AG

77	E977DNK	MCW MetroRider MF150/81	MCW	B23F	1988	The Shires, 1998
107	YPL407T	Leyland National 10351B/1R		B41F	1978	The Bee Line, 1997
111	AAK111T	Leyland National 10351B/1R		B44F	1979	Northern Bus, Anston, 1998
128	YPL428T	Leyland National 10351B/1R		B41F	1978	The Bee Line, 1997
133w	XPD233N	Leyland National 10351/1R		BC39F	1974	Northumbria, 1999
158	XEU858T	Leyland National 10351B/1R		BC41F	1979	Brewers, 1999
161w	PJT261R	Leyland National 10351A/1R		B44F	1976	Delta, Kirkby in Ashfield, 1996
163	YPF763T	Leyland National 10351B/1R		B41F	1978	The Bee Line, 1997
270	YFB970V	Leyland National 11351A/1R		B52F	1979	Northern Bus, Anston, 1998

Livery: Blue and cream

Go Bus is a small firm operating Leyland Nationals and a minibus on local services in north east Derbyshire. Route 34 is a mainly commercial operation with some county council funding on certain journeys. Here in June 1998, a former London & Country Leyland National 163, YPF763T, bears a deep blue and cream livery reminiscent of the former extant Midland General company. The bus is passing through the community of Holmewood, a small village the inhabitants of which used to be employed in the local coalfields which are too now extinct. *Tony Wilson*

GRAYSCROFT

Grayscroft Bus Services Ltd, 15A Victoria Road, Mablethorpe, Lincolnshire, LN12 2AF

AFE719A	AEC Reliance 2MU3RV	Weymann	O40F	1962	London & Country, 1995
JWW227N	Bristol VRT/SL2/6G	Eastern Coach Works	B43/34F	1975	Dickinson, Wrangle, 1995
NBZ1671	Bristol LHS6L	Plaxton Supreme IV	C33F	1979	Oxon Travel, Bicester, 1995
AVK153V	Leyland Atlantean AN68A/2R	Alexander AL	B49/37F	1980	Stagecoach Busways, 1996
AVK180V	Leyland Atlantean AN68A/2R	Alexander AL	B49/37F	1980	Stagecoach Busways, 1996
MVO414W	Leyland Atlantean AN68C/1R	Northern Counties	B47/33D	1981	City of Nottingham, 1999
NBZ1670	Leyland Leopard PSU5D/5R	Plaxton Supreme IV	C49F	1981	Yelloway, 1987
TJI1679	Leyland Leopard PSU3F/4R	Plaxton Supreme IV	C53F	1981	Wallace Arnold, 1986
WIW6172	Leyland Atlantean AN68B/1R	Roe	B43/30F	1981	Horsham Buses, 1998
RJI1653	Bedford YNT	Plaxton Paramount 3200	C53F	1984	
RJI1655	Leyland Tiger TRCTL11/3RZ	Duple 340	C53F	1986	Shearings, 1992
OIW1608	Leyland Tiger TRCTL11/3RH	Duple	C57F	1986	Chalkwell, Sittingbourne, 1998
D131OWG	Renault-Dodge S56	Reeve Burgess	BC25F	1987	Chesterfield, 1993
TJI1676	Volvo B10M-60	Plaxton Expressliner	C49FT	1992	Stagecoach East Kent, 1999
TJI1677	Volvo B10M-60	Plaxton Expressliner	C49F	1990	Premier Travel, 1996
TJI1678	Dennis Javelin SDA1907	Plaxton Paramount 3200 III	C53F	1990	
H163DVM	Volvo B10M-60	Van Hool Alizée H	C53F	1992	Shearings, 1998

Special Event vehicle

GCC3	Ford 570E	Burlingham	C41F	1958	Creams, Llandudno, 1962

Previous Registrations:

AFE719A	325NKT	RJI1653	A506HBE	TJI1677	G382REG
C308ENA	C308ENA, OIW1608	RJI1654	-	TJI1678	G961WNR
GCC3	From new	RJI1655	C343DND	TJI1679	PNW305W
NBZ1670	MRJ100W	TJI1676	J909NKP	WIW6172	KPJ285W
NBZ1671	FTW133T, 10OOX, ATH108T				
OIW1608	C308ENA				

Livery: White, blue and orange

Having previously been part of the Shearings fleet, H163DVM joined Grayscroft in the spring of 1999. This Volvo B10M is the first Van Hool-bodied coach to run with Grayscroft. As well as bus services centred on Mablethorpe, the company is active in the coaching field. The vehicle is seen in Skegness, departing after unloading most of the passengers.
Steve Sanderson

HAIL AND RIDE

R C & G A Marsh, 28 Seathorne Road, Skegness, Lincolnshire, PE25 1RP

FIL7622	Ford R1014	Plaxton Supreme III	C41F	1977	Bradshaw, Alkrington, 1996
SVM378W	Bedford YMT	Plaxton Supreme IV	C53F	1980	Byley Garage, Byley, 1995
GFO754X	Bedford YMQ	Duple Dominant II Express	C35F	1981	Evans, Prenton, 1993
D404EFA	Ford Transit 150	Ford	M8	1987	private owner, 1993
D758WRR	Ford Transit 150	Ford	M8	1987	private owner, 1993
D323CLB	Ford Transit 150	Ford	M8	1987	private owner, 1993
D552HNW	Iveco Daily 49.10	Robin Hood City Nippy	B16F	1986	Sussex Bus, Pagham, 1996
D627BCK	Iveco Daily 49.10	Robin Hood City Nippy	B25F	1987	Patterson, Birmingham, 1998
D861LWR	Freight Rover Sherpa	Dormobile	B20F	1987	Ambuskill, Tividale, 1994
E90OUH	Freight Rover Sherpa	Carlyle Citybus 2	B20F	1987	Shamrock, Pontypridd, 1994
E402WAM	Renault-Dodge S56	Reeve Burgess	BC25F	1987	Garrington, Hednesford, 1998
E105JPL	Renault-Dodge S56	Northern Counties	B25F	1988	Horsham Buses, 1997
E106JPL	Renault-Dodge S56	Northern Counties	B25F	1988	Horsham Buses, 1997
E326LHN	Renault-Dodge S56	Northern Counties	B23F	1988	Midland Fox, 1998
F218AKG	Freight Rover Sherpa	Carlyle Citybus 2	B20F	1988	Walsh, Alkrington, 1994

Previous Registrations:

SVM378W	62BYL, EDK349W	FIL7622	SEL119R, 292MVT, MIB268

Livery: Blue and white

Depot: Royal Oak Terrace, Winthorpe.

HAINES

N E & F E Haines, Ralphs Lane, Frampton West, Boston, Lincolnshire, PE20 1QU

JPM815V	Volvo B58-61	Plaxton Supreme IV	C53F	1980	Warren, Alton, 1991
OHL912X	Renault-Dodge S46	Rootes	B21F	1982	Ambuskill, Warley, 1991
MMW49X	Bedford YNT	Duple Dominant IV	C53F	1982	Paul Jones, Ratcliffe, 1989
FIL4032	Leyland Leopard PSU5D/5R	Duple Dominant III	C53F	1982	Beeston, Hadleigh, 1994
KAX714	Leyland Tiger TRCTL11/3R	Plaxton Paramount 3500	C49FT	1983	Bryan A Garratt, Leicester, 1992
XSU978	Leyland Tiger TRCTL11/3R	Plaxton Paramount 3500	C49FT	1983	Staffordian, Stafford, 1994
B576DRS	Dennis Dorchester SDA810	Plaxton Paramount 3500 III	C55F	1985	Western Scottish, 1996
KCX304	Leyland Tiger TRCTL11/3R	Duple Caribbean	C49FT	1985	Byley Motors, 1997
D854KWR	Freight Rover Sherpa	Dormobile	B20F	1987	Yorkshire Rider, 1991
E250ADO	Mercedes-Benz 609D	Coachcraft	C21F	1988	
G218EOA	Iveco Daily 49-10	Carlyle Dailybus	BC12F	1989	British Midland, Heathrow, 1995
G232GOJ	Leyland-DAF 400	Crystals	M16	1990	van, 1993
G704EOX	Leyland-DAF 400	Crystals	M16	1990	van, 1990
H633GHA	Leyland-DAF 400	Crystals	M16	1990	van, 1994
J328ONE	Leyland-DAF 400	Jubilee	M16	1991	van, 1992

Previous Registrations:

B576DRS	B200CGA, VLT226	JPM815V	NNS937V, JHF682	KCX304	B207AFV
FIL4032	WGV863X	KAX714	RNY312Y	XSU978	BAJ635Y

Livery: Cream

Hail & Ride operate a variety of minibuses on their service which runs between Skegness and Ingoldmells. A blue and white livery has been adopted illustrated here on E402WAM. Originally in the Thamesdown fleet, this Reeve Burgess-bodied Renault-Dodge S56 now carries holidaymakers at the seaside. *Steve Sanderson*

The Haines fleet carries an all-over cream livery as seen on KAX714. This Leyland Tiger carries a Plaxton Paramount body. The designation 3500 indicates that it was built to an overall height of 3.5 metres. Phil Haines operates a van and minibus self drive hire business as well as operating a PCV fleet. *Steve Sanderson*

HODSONS

Hodson's Coaches Ltd, Chapel Lane, Navenby, Lincolnshire, LN5 0ER.

VTL358	Bedford YMT	Plaxton Supreme IV	C53F	1979	Whittle, Highley, 1982
CIB9152	Kässbohrer Setra S215HD	Kässbohrer	C53F	1986	Chisholm, Swanley, 1995
NIL6469	Kässbohrer Setra S215HD	Kässbohrer	C49FT	1993	Southern Vectis, 1998
L4HOD	Mercedes-Benz 814D	TBP	C29FL	1994	
L5HOD	Mercedes-Benz 410D	Crystals	M15	1994	
A18HOD	Volkswagen Transporter	Volkswagen	M7	1995	
A19HOD	Mercedes-Benz 814D	Autobus Classique Nouvelle	C25F	1996	
P3HOD	Mercedes-Benz 412D	Autobus Classique	M16	1997	
R762NFW	Setra S250 Special	Setra	C48F	1998	
S951RBE	Mercedes-Benz 01120L	Ferqui-Optare Solera	C35F	1999	
S10HOD	Volkswagen Caravelle	Volkswagen	M7	1999	
T7HOD	MAN 18.310	Neoplan Transliner	C49FT	1999	

Previous Registrations:

| CIB9152 | 4777EL | | VTL358 | AUJ744T |
| NIL6469 | J902LDL, WDL778, J902LDL | | | |

Livery: Cream, pink and maroon

Hodsons of Navenby operate a number of shopping services from the company's home village to Lincoln, Boston and Newark. Midicoach A19HOD was registered in 1996 with a mark that reflects the company name. This Mercedes-Benz 814D carries a body built by the Autobus Classique company which has been purchased by Optare and now trades as subsidiary Autobus. *Steve Sanderson*

HOLLOWAYS

Holloways Coaches Ltd, Cottage Beck Road, Scunthorpe, North Lincolnshire, DN16 1TP

CWG681V	Leyland Atlantean AN68A/1R	Alexander AL	B45/29D	1979	South Yorkshire's Transport, 1991
CWG684V	Leyland Atlantean AN68A/1R	Alexander AL	B45/29D	1979	South Yorkshire's Transport, 1991
CWG699V	Leyland Atlantean AN68A/1R	Alexander AL	B45/29D	1979	South Yorkshire's Transport, 1991
CWG746V	Leyland Atlantean AN68A/1R	Roe	B45/29D	1979	Bygone Buses, Biddenden, 1994
CWG756V	Leyland Atlantean AN68A/1R	Roe	B45/29D	1979	Mainline, 1997
CWG773V	Leyland Atlantean AN68A/1R	Roe	B45/29D	1979	Mainline, 1999
PSV436	Leyland Tiger TRCTL11/2R	Plaxton Paramount 3200	C53F	1983	
B228XUB	Bedford YMP	Plaxton Paramount 3200	C35F	1985	Barron, Hull, 1997
E692UNE	Leyland Tiger TRCTL11/3RZ	Plaxton Paramount 3200 III	C53F	1988	Hague, Sheffield, 1995
F201HSO	Leyland Tiger TRCTL11/3ARZ	Plaxton Paramount 3200 III	C53F	1988	Park's of Hamilton, 1992
F774GNA	Leyland Tiger TRCL10/3ARZ	Plaxton Paramount 3200 III	C53F	1989	Hanson, Halifax, 1995
F597HYC	Dennis Javelin 8.5SDL1903	Plaxton Paramount 3200 III	C35F	1989	Southern National (Taylors), 1996
F92WFA	Dennis Javelin 12SDA1907	Plaxton Paramount 3200 III	C57F	1989	Robin Hood, Rudyard, 1994
H231FFE	Dennis Javelin 11SDA1906	Plaxton Paramount 3200 III	C53F	1991	
M162KAT	Dennis Javelin	Plaxton Premiére 320	C50FT	1995	Alpha, Anlaby, 1999
P306HWG	LDV Convoy	Onyx	M16	1997	
R667KFE	LDV Convoy	Onyx	M16	1997	

Previous Registrations:

F92WFA	9595RU		PSV436	A513LPP

Livery: Yellow and red (buses); white, blue and red (coaches)

Depots: Cottage Beck Road & Kettering Road, Scunthorpe

A network of services to the Freshney Place shopping centre in Grimsby is operated by Holloways. These routes serve many of the North Lincolnshire villages. School services are operated in Scunthorpe using Leyland Atlanteans. A Roe-bodied example is CWG746V, which is seen here. *Richard Belton*

HORNSBY TRAVEL

Hornsby Travel Services Ltd, 51 High Street, Ashby, Scunthorpe,
North Lincolnshire, DN15 6EN

Reg	Chassis	Body	Seating	Year	History
KUC179P	Daimler Fleetline CRL6	Park Royal	B44/28D	1976	London Transport, 1984
KUC181P	Daimler Fleetline CRL6	Park Royal	B44/27D	1976	London Transport, 1981
SUA141R	Leyland Atlantean AN68/1R	Roe	B43/33F	1977	Yorkshire Rider, 1994
THX173S	Leyland National 10351A/2R		B44F	1977	London Buses, 1992
THX542S	Daimler Fleetline FE30ALRSp	Park Royal	B44/27D	1977	London Buses, 1992
XFW983S	Leyland Atlantean AN68/1R	Roe	B43/33F	1978	
FBV492W	Leyland Atlantean AN68B/1R	Eastern Coach Works	B43/31F	1980	ITG, Anston, 1998
FBV500W	Leyland Atlantean AN68B/1R	Eastern Coach Works	B43/31F	1980	ITG, Anston, 1998
3730RH	Leyland Tiger TRCTL11/3R(Vo)	Plaxton Paramount 3500	C49FT	1984	
7455RH	Leyland Tiger TRCTL11/3RZ	Plaxton Paramount 3500 II	C49FT	1985	
RJI8583	Dennis Javelin 12SDA1908	Plaxton Paramount 3200 III	C57F	1988	Bakers, Weston-super-Mare, 1994
RJI8608	Dennis Javelin 12SDA1907	Plaxton Paramount 3200 III	C53F	1989	Bakers, Weston-super-Mare, 1994
WUK155	Renault PR100.2	Northern Counties	B47F	1989	Northern Counties, 1991
G276VML	Renault PR100.2	Northern Counties	B48F	1989	Parfitt's, Rhymney Bridge, 1994
G409NAK	Renault Master T35D	Coachcraft	M15	1990	
G365FOP	Mercedes-Benz 811D	Carlyle	B31F	1990	
6053RH	Dennis Javelin 12SDA1929	Plaxton Premiére 320(1995)	C53F	1990	
2732RH	Dennis Javelin 12SDA1929	Plaxton Paramount 3200 III	C53F	1991	
H220TCP	DAF SB220LC550	Ikarus	B50F	1991	Walls, Shartson, 1997
J718MFE	Toyota HiAce	Toyota	M8	1992	van, 1995
J693AWB	Toyota HiAce	Toyota	M8	1992	van, 1995
L591CJW	Renault Trafic	Jubilee	M12	1993	
L403VGP	Iveco Daily 49-10	Nuova	C19F	1994	Hotelink, Crawley, 1996
L804YTL	Mercedes-Benz 811D	Plaxton Beaver	B31F	1994	
971OHT	MAN 11.190	Caetano Algarve II	C35F	1994	
8227RH	Volvo B10M-62	Plaxton Excalibur	C49F	1994	
N661OFE	Iveco TurboDaily 59-12	Mellor	B27F	1996	
P772VVL	Iveco TurboDaily 59-12	Mellor	B25F	1996	
1642RH	Dennis Javelin 12SDA2155	Plaxton Premiére 320	C53F	1996	
8955RH	Dennis Javelin	Plaxton Excalibur	C53F	1998	
R189NFE	Dennis Dart SLF	Plaxton Pointer 2	N43F	1998	
R839WOH	Mercedes-Benz Vario O814	Plaxton Beaver 2	B31F	1998	
R841WOH	Mercedes-Benz Vario O814	Plaxton Beaver 2	B31F	1998	
R402RJV	Hyundai H100	Hyundai	M9	1998	
T142KBC	Renault Master LH35TD	Jubilee	M15	1999	
T208KJV	Dennis Javelin	Plaxton Premiére 320	C39FT	1999	

Previous Registrations:

1642RH	From new	7455RH	C248CKH	RJI8583	E503JWP
2732RH	H299GVL	8227RH	M21GAT	RJI8608	F908UPR
3730RH	From new	8955RH	R220GFU	WUK155	F100AKB
6053RH	G414YAY	971OHT	From new		

Livery: Blue and red

Opposite, top: **The curved front to the Plaxton body of 8227RH indicates that it is Plaxton's premium product, Excalibur, a type that has been specified by a number of operators for high quality coach work. This Volvo B10M is used by Hornsby Travel on the company's own holiday tour programme.** *Richard Belton*
Opposite, bottom: **The service between Scunthorpe and Brigg passing through Broughton is now operated solely by Hornsby Travel following the cessation of the Daisy Bus Service business. Seen at the Brigg terminus of this route is R189NFE a recently delivered Dennis Dart SLF which carries the Ogle redesigned Pointer 2 body so far only carried by the low floor variant of the Dart.** *Richard Belton*

HULLEYS

Henry Hulley & Sons Ltd, Derwent Garage, Calver Road, Baslow, Derbyshire, DE45 1RF

1	N847YHH	Mercedes-Benz 711D	Onyx	C24F	1996	Reay, Fletchertown, 1998
2	D850PWN	Mercedes-Benz 609D	Reeve Burgess	B20F	1987	Thomas Bros, Llandeilo, 1994
3	F24HGG	Volvo B10M-60	Plaxton Paramount 3500 III	C53F	1989	Stagecoach East London, 1995
4	E289MMM	Van Hool T815	Van Hool Alizée	C49FT	1988	Whites Coaches, Heathfield, 1995
5	A53HRE	Leyland Tiger TRCTL11/2R	Plaxton Paramount 3200 E	C53F	1984	Docherty's Midland, Auchterarder, 1993
6	R140XWF	Dennis Javelin	Plaxton Premiére 320	C53F	1998	
7	E753HJF	Bedford YNT	Duple 320	C53F	1988	Horton, Ripley, 1991
8	H179EJF	Dennis Javelin 12SDA1919	Caetano Algarve II	C53F	1991	Meadway, Birmingham, 1997
9	D451CNR	Bedford YNT	Duple 320	C53F	1987	Horton, Ripley, 1990
10	G945JPW	Volvo B10M-60	Plaxton Paramount 3500 III	C53F	1989	Express Travel, Perth, 1995
11	LRB214W	Leyland National 2 NL116L11/1R		BC50F	1981	City of Nottingham, 1996
12	RRA222X	Leyland National 2 NL116L11/1R		B50F	1981	City of Nottingham, 1996
14	Q364FVT	Leyland Leopard PSU3A/4RT	Willowbrook(1992)	B52F	1970	Border, Burnley, 1995
15	NLS985W	Leyland National 2 NL116L11/1R		B52F	1980	Stagecoach Midland Red, 1999
16	YPD112Y	Leyland Tiger TRCTL11/2R	Duple Dominant IV Express	C53F	1983	Whitelaw, Stonehouse, 1990
17	E71MVV	Mercedes-Benz 709D	Robin Hood	B25F	1988	MK Metro, 1998
18w	BVP814V	Leyland National 2 NL116L11/1R		B49F	1979	City of Nottingham, 1996
19	RRA218X	Leyland National 2 NL116AL11/1R		B52F	1981	City of Nottingham, 1996
20	SCH117X	Leyland Fleetline FE30ALR	Eastern Coach Works	B44/31F	1981	City of Nottingham, 1996
21	RAU804M	Leyland Atlantean AN68/1R	East Lancs Sprint (1994)	B45F	1974	City of Nottingham, 1999

Previous Registrations:
Q364FVT   LJX817H   RAU804M   OTO555M

Named vehicles: G945JPW *Lady Diana II*; F24HGG *Lady Catherine*; R140XWF *Lady Carole*. **Livery:** Blue and white

---

Route 170 is, in the main, a commercial operation run by Hulleys of Baslow, between Chesterfield and Bakewell in the heart of the Peak District. Seen on the service is Leyland National 2, NLS985W, one of four acquired from Nottingham City Transport. *Tony Wilson*

HUNT'S

F Hunt (Coach Hire) Ltd, 18 Market Place, Alford, Lincolnshire, LN13 9EB

HDL406N	Bristol VRT/SL2/6LX	Eastern Coach Works	B39/31F	1975	Southern Vectis, 1991
XFW951S	Bristol LH6L	Eastern Coach Works	B43F	1977	Derby Blue Bus, 1995
PJI5924	Leyland National 11351A/1R(Volvo)		B52F	1977	Paul Winson, Loughborough, 1998
GMS289S	Leyland Leopard PSU3D/4R	Alexander AY	B53F	1978	Tame Valley, Birmingham, 1993
XFP502S	Bedford YMT	Plaxton Supreme III	C53F	1978	Moor Dale, Newcastle, 1981
DVL940T	Bedford YMT	Plaxton Supreme IV Express	C53F	1978	
WFS139W	Leyland Leopard PSU3F/4R	Alexander AY	B53F	1980	Fife Scottish, 1998
PNW308W	Leyland Leopard PSU3F/4R	Plaxton Supreme IV	C53F	1981	Silverwing, Hedon, 1994
5611FH	Leyland Tiger TRCTL11/3R	Plaxton Paramount 3500	C53F	1983	The Londoners, Nunhead, 1986
TWJ340Y	Dennis Falcon SDA410	East Lancashire	B52F	1983	Ipswich, 1995
TWJ341Y	Dennis Falcon SDA410	East Lancashire	B52F	1983	Ipswich, 1995
TWJ342Y	Dennis Falcon SDA410	East Lancashire	B52F	1983	Ipswich, 1995
A29XFW	Leyland Tiger TRCTL11/3R	Plaxton Paramount	C53F	1983	Payne, Caistor, 1995
9882FH	Leyland Tiger TRCTL11/3R	Van Hool Alizée	C51F	1984	Travellers, Hounslow, 1988
B878WUU	Ford Transit 190	Ford	M14	1985	Private owner, 1992
3272FH	Volvo B10M-61	Van Hool Alizée	C53F	1986	Epsom Coaches, 1996
3613FH	Leyland Tiger TRCTL11/3RZ	Van Hool Alizée	C53F	1987	Travellers, Hounslow, 1990
3275FH	Volvo B10M-61	Van Hool Alizée	C53F	1987	Lochview, Gourock, 1993
E404EPE	Renault-Dodge S46	Northern Counties	B22F	1987	McConnachie, Port Glasgow, 1994
7683FH	Mercedes-Benz 609D	Whittaker Europa	C21F	1989	Stockdale, Selby, 1995
HDZ5416	Renault S75	Wright TS303 Citybus	B31F	1990	First CentreWest, 1998
HDZ5468	Renault S75	Wright TS303 Citybus	B31F	1990	First CentreWest, 1998

Previous Registrations:

3272FH	C529DND	7683FH		F569EWJ	HDZ5416		From new
3275FH	D559MVR	9882FH		A140RMJ	HDZ5468		From new
3613FH	D230HMT	A29XFW		A528LPP, 4066FH	PJI5924		VAR896S
5611FH	KGS492Y						

Livery: White, red and grey

Former Southern Vectis Bristol VRT HDL406N is the only double deck bus in the Hunt's fleet. It is employed on the main road service between Skegness Ingoldmells and Chapel St Leonards. This route passes several caravan sites and can be very busy in summer months. As a result, a number of operators compete for business on this route. This summer 1999 view shows the vehicle rounding the famous Skegness Clock Tower roundabout.
Tony Wilson

HYLTON & DAWSON

A E Hylton, 25 Chestnut Road, Glenfield, Leicester, LE3 8DB

HDZ101	Bedford YMT	Plaxton Supreme IV	C53F	1979	Garratt, Ashby, 1997
HDZ102	Bedford YMT	Plaxton Supreme IV	C53F	1980	Smith, Market Harborough, 1997
CAX14V	Bedford YMT	Duple Dominant II	C53F	1980	Bailey, Kirkby in Ashfield, 1988
HDZ205	Bedford YMT	Duple Dominant II	C53F	1979	Kirby, Bushey Heath, 1983
HD9923	Bedford YNT	Duple Laser	C53F	1984	
HD2122	Bedford YNT	Duple 320	C53F	1986	
HD8755	Dennis Javelin SDA1906	Duple 320	C53F	1990	
P10HDC	Dennis Javelin	Plaxton Premiére 320	C53FT	1997	

Previous Registrations:

HDZ101	YDO509T, GIL7965, GPV379T	HDZ205	HRO985V
HDZ102	MMJ475V	HD8755	G424YAY
HDZ122	C321UFP	HD9923	A705TEW

Livery: Cream and maroon

Depots: Chestnut Road, Glenfield and West Street, Glenfield

ISLE COACHES

J Bannister, 97 High Street, Owston Ferry,
North Lincolnshire, DN9 1RL

TET745S	Leyland Fleetline FE30AGR	Roe	B43/33F	1977	South Yorkshire's Transport, 1986
SHE557S	Leyland Fleetline FE30AGR	Alexander AL	B45/33F	1978	Astons, Kempsey, 1991
CWG696V	Leyland Fleetline FE30AGR	Alexander AL	B43/33F	1979	Mainline, 1994
FWA472V	Leyland National 2 NL106L11/1R		B44F	1980	South Yorkshire's Transport, 1990
FWA475V	Leyland National 2 NL106L11/1R		B44F	1980	South Yorkshire's Transport, 1991
KWA22W	Leyland National 2 NL116L11/1R		B52F	1980	Mainline, 1998
KWA24W	Leyland National 2 NL116L11/1R		B52F	1980	South Yorkshire's Transport, 1991
LMS153W	Leyland Fleetline FE30AGR	Alexander AL	B44/31F	1980	MTL Heysham, 1995
NKU144X	Dennis Dominator DDA133	Alexander RH	B46/32F	1981	Mainline, 1996
RRA220X	Leyland National 2 NL116AL11/1R		B50F	1981	City of Nottingham, 1997
GIJ9093	Volvo B10M-61	Van Hool Alizée	C49FT	1984	Daisy, Broughton, 1992
A101SUU	Volvo Ailsa B55-10	Alexander RV	B45/21D	1984	Black Prince, Morley, 1999
A102SUU	Volvo Ailsa B55-10	Alexander RV	B36/30F	1984	Black Prince, Morley, 1998
B152ALG	Leyland Tiger TRCTL11/2RH	Duple Laser 2	C49F	1984	Andy James, Sherston, 1993
B673EHL	Mercedes-Benz L307D	Reeve Burgess	M12	1985	
D500RWF	Leyland Tiger TRCTL11/3RZ	Plaxton Paramount 3200 II	C57F	1987	Wood's Coaches, Barnsley, 1992

Previous Registration:

GIJ9093	A195MNE

Livery: Cream and blue

Route 94, operating between Leicester and Glenfield, has for many years been served by Hylton and Dawson. Bedfords with coach bodies are now used on the service. HDZ205 carries a Duple Dominant II body. It is seen unloading in the centre of Leicester. It is of note that only one of the vehicles in the fleet does not carry HD in its registration mark. *Steve Sanderson*

Isle coaches operate bus services in the Isle of Axholme, an area between Scunthorpe and Doncaster. The blue and cream livery of the fleet is carried here by B152ALG, a Duple Laser-bodied Leyland Tiger that was new to Crosville. As well as operating bus and coach services, the proprietor also deals in second-hand buses and coaches and has had a number of former MoD Tigers on his premises in this capacity. *Steve Sanderson*

N L JOHNSON

Johnson's Coaches, Ashlea, Thornton Road, Goxhill, Barrow-upon-Humber,
North Lincolnshire, DN19 7HN

NNW119P	Leyland Leopard PSU3E/4R	Duple Dominant	C53F	1976	K W Beard, Cinderford, 1999
ARB527T	Bedford YMT	Plaxton Supreme III Express	C49F	1978	Barton, 1988
NLG909T	Leyland Leopard PSU5C/4R	Plaxton Supreme IV	C53F	1979	Meredith, Malpas, 1995
FYT335V	Leyland Leopard PSU3E/4R	Plaxton Supreme IV Express	C49F	1979	Titlesure, Bedlington, 1999
FYT336V	Leyland Leopard PSU3E/4R	Plaxton Supreme IV Express	C49F	1979	Titlesure, Bedlington, 1999
HAX6W	Bedford YMT	Duple Dominant II	C53F	1980	Carnell, Sutton Bridge, 1996
B496UNB	Leyland Tiger TRCTL11/3RZ	Plaxton Paramount 3500 II	C53F	1985	Shearings, 1992
D956WJH	Freight Rover Sherpa	Dormobile	B16F	1986	Hampshire Bus, 1993
XXI2489	Volvo B10M-61	Plaxton Paramount 3500 III	C53F	1988	Classic Tours, Paignton, 1999
G418RYJ	Iveco Daily 49-10	Phoenix	B23F	1990	Sussex Coastline, 1997

Previous Registrations:

FYT335V	JVF815V, 185CLT	NLG909T	EDF270T, MIB614, ARF930T, 469KNP
FYT336V	JVF816V, 205CLT	XXI2489	E317UUB

Livery: Cream

Johnsons of Goxhill operate a town service in the town of Barton upon Humber as well as shopping services to Brigg and Scunthorpe. The service to Scunthorpe terminates outside the RoadCar depot in Little John Street. HAX6W is a Bedford YMT that carries a Duple Dominant II body. The Dominant II was easily identified by the chrome moulding below the side windows and the deep windscreen, though many operators have now removed this during refurbishment. *Richard Belton*

JOHNSON BROS

C B & C A Johnson, Green Lane Garage, Green Acres, Green Lane, Hodthorpe,
Derbyshire, S80 4XR

	Reg	Chassis	Body	Type	Year	History
	OSF305G	Bristol VRT/SL/6LX	Eastern Coach Works	B43/31F	1969	Southern Vectis, 1986
	OSF307G	Bristol VRT/SL/6LX	Eastern Coach Works	B43/31F	1969	Southern Vectis, 1986
	NGM168G	Bristol VRT/SL/6LX	Eastern Coach Works	B43/31F	1969	Southern Vectis, 1986
	PKE810M	Bristol VRT/SL/6LX	Eastern Coach Works	B43/34F	1974	Maidstone & District, 1988
	HTU155N	Bristol VRT/SL2/6LX	Eastern Coach Works	B43/31F	1975	Crosville, 1989
	JWL993N	Bristol VRT/SL2/6LX	Eastern Coach Works	B43/34F	1975	Moffat & Williamson, Gauldry, 1994
	JWL997N	Bristol VRT/SL2/6LX	Eastern Coach Works	B43/34F	1975	Moffat & Williamson, Gauldry, 1994
	HWE826N	Bristol VRT/SL2/6LX	Eastern Coach Works	B43/34F	1975	Yorkshire Traction, 1993
	KKY833P	Bristol VRT/SL3/501	Eastern Coach Works	B43/34F	1976	Yorkshire Traction, 1993
	KKY835P	Bristol VRT/SL3/501	Eastern Coach Works	B43/34F	1976	RoadCar, 1994
	OWE854R	Bristol VRT/SL3/501	Eastern Coach Works	B43/31F	1977	Yorkshire Traction, 1993
	OWE857R	Bristol VRT/SL3/501	Eastern Coach Works	B43/31F	1977	Yorkshire Traction, 1993
	OWE858R	Bristol VRT/SL3/501	Eastern Coach Works	B43/31F	1977	Yorkshire Traction, 1993
w	RWA859R	Bristol VRT/SL3/501	Eastern Coach Works	B43/31F	1977	RoadCar, 1994
	RWT544R	Bristol VRT/SL3/6LX	Eastern Coach Works	B43/31F	1977	Moffat & Williamson, Gauldry, 1994
	RWT546R	Bristol VRT/SL3/6LX	Eastern Coach Works	B43/31F	1977	Moffat & Williamson, Gauldry, 1994
	PTT98R	Bristol VRT/SL3/6LXB	Eastern Coach Works	B43/31F	1977	Solent Blue Line, 1997
	ODL661R	Bristol VRT/SL3/6LXB	Eastern Coach Works	B43/31F	1977	Solent Blue Line, 1997
	ODL662R	Bristol VRT/SL3/6LXB	Eastern Coach Works	B43/31F	1977	Solent Blue Line, 1997
	ODL663R	Bristol VRT/SL3/6LXB	Eastern Coach Works	B43/31F	1977	Solent Blue Line, 1997
	ODL664R	Bristol VRT/SL3/6LXB	Eastern Coach Works	B43/31F	1977	Solent Blue Line, 1997
	TDT864S	Bristol VRT/SL3/501	Eastern Coach Works	B43/31F	1977	Yorkshire Traction, 1993
	UDL668S	Bristol VRT/SL3/6LXB	Eastern Coach Works	B43/31F	1978	Solent Blue Line, 1997
	MIW2422	Bristol VRT/SL3/501	Eastern Coach Works	B43/31F	1978	Clarkson, South Elmsall, 1994
w	KTL24V	Bristol VRT/SL3/6LXB	Eastern Coach Works	B43/31F	1979	RoadCar, 1997
	KTL27V	Bristol VRT/SL3/6LXB	Eastern Coach Works	B43/31F	1979	RoadCar, 1998
	RKH766T	Volvo B58-56	Plaxton Supreme V	C53F	1979	Thorne's, Bubwith, 1996
	LVL804V	Bristol VRT/SL3/6LXB	Eastern Coach Works	B43/31F	1980	RoadCar, 1997
	LVL809V	Bristol VRT/SL3/6LXB	Eastern Coach Works	B43/31F	1980	RoadCar, 1996
	PFE540V	Bristol VRT/SL3/6LXB	Eastern Coach Works	B43/31F	1980	RoadCar, 1998
	PFE544V	Bristol VRT/SL3/6LXB	Eastern Coach Works	B43/31F	1980	RoadCar, 1997
	SVL177W	Bristol VRT/SL3/6LXB	Eastern Coach Works	B43/31F	1981	RoadCar, 1996
	SVL178W	Bristol VRT/SL3/6LXB	Eastern Coach Works	B43/31F	1981	RoadCar, 1996
	SVL179W	Bristol VRT/SL3/6LXB	Eastern Coach Works	B43/31F	1981	RoadCar, 1996
	SVL180W	Bristol VRT/SL3/6LXB	Eastern Coach Works	B43/31F	1981	RoadCar, 1996
	LHE601W	Volvo B58-56	Plaxton Supreme IV	C53F	1981	
	B8JBT	Volvo B10M-61	Plaxton Paramount 3500	C53F	1984	
	E911EAY	Volvo B10M-61	Plaxton Paramount 3500 III	C57F	1989	
	YXI4381	Volvo B10M-61	Van Hool Alizée H	C53F	1989	Shearings, 1996
	JBT16S	Volvo B10M-61	Van Hool Alizée	C57F	1989	Sworder, Walkern, 1992
	JBT3S	Scania K113CRB	Van Hool Alizée SH	C49FT	1989	Top Deck, Horsell, 1992
	H4JBT	Scania K93CRB	Duple 320	C59F	1990	Snell, Newton Abbot, 1995
	H5JBT	Volvo B10M-60	Van Hool Alizée H	C53F	1991	Shearings, 1997
	J827EWS	Leyland Tiger TR2R62C2IZ5/8	Plaxton Paramount 3200 III	C44FT	1991	First Wessex, 1998
	J1JBT	Scania K113CRB	Van Hool Alizée H	C51FT	1991	
	J269NNC	Scania K93CRB	Plaxton Premiére 320	C53F	1992	Shearings, 1997
	848FXN	DAF SB3000DKV601	Caetano Algarve II 3.35	C49FT	1992	On seasonal hire for 1999
	K1JBT	Ford Transit VE6	Ford	M14	1993	Green, Woodlands, 1996
	K19FTG	Volvo B10M-60	Plaxton Excalibur	C49FT	1993	Flights, Birmingham, 1997
	L82YBB	Volvo B10M-62	Plaxton Expressliner 2	C44FT	1993	Stagecoach Busways, 1999
	L84YBB	Volvo B10M-62	Plaxton Expressliner 2	C44FT	1993	Stagecoach Busways, 1999
	L3JBT	Scania K113CRB	Van Hool Alizée HE	C49FT	1994	
	L991CRY	Toyota Coaster HZB50R	Caetano Optimo III	C18F	1994	Ralphs, Langley, 1999
	M711FFL	Ford Transit VE6	Ford	M8	1994	Maun Motors, Suttton in Ashfield, 1997
	M1JBT	Scania K113CRB	Irizar Century	C49FT	1995	Sun Fun Luxury, Earith, 1997
	N1JBT	Scania K113CRB	Van Hool Alizée HE	C46FT	1995	
	N2JBT	Scania K113CRB	Van Hool Alizée HE	C46FT	1996	
	N809NHS	Volvo B10M-62	Jonckheere	C53F	1996	Chambers, Moneymore, 1997
	P1JBT	Scania K113CRB	Irizar Century 12.35	C49FT	1997	
	P3JBT	Volvo B10M-62	Jonckheere	C51FT	1997	

The Traction Group companies have been a source of Bristol VRT double deck buses for the Johnson Brothers fleet for some time. RoadCar have provided a large number in recent times but an earlier addition from Yorkshire Traction was OWE853R. The company has run VR events for enthusiasts which have proved to be a showcase for this type which are used by the operator on school services. *Paul Hill*

R960RCH	Volvo B9M	Plaxton Premiere 320	C41F	1997	Ralphs, Langley, 1999
R1JBT	Scania K113CRB	Van Hool Alizée HE	C51FT	1997	
R2JBT	Toyota Coaster BB50R	Caetano Optimo IV	C21F	1998	
R414YWJ	Volvo B10M-62	Plaxton Excalibur	C53F	1998	
T3JBT	Neoplan N116/2	Neoplan Cityliner	C49FT	1999	
T4JBT	Volvo B10M-62	Plaxton Excalibur	C49FT	1999	

Previous Registrations:

848FXN	K486BCY	K1JBT	K841OBY
B8JBT	B833KRY	M1JBT	N699AHL
H4JBT	H79COD	MIW2422	VHB679S
H5JBT	H184DVM	RKH766T	FNW23T, SMV24
JBT3S	G39HKY	YXI4381	F737ENE
JBT16S	F238MVS		

Named vehicles: B8JBT *Euroliner I*; JBT16S *Eurotourer I*; YXI4381 *Eurotourer II*; E911EAY *Eurocruiser I*; JBT3S *Euromaster I*; H5JBT *Euroflyer I*; J1JBT *Euromaster II*; L3JBT *Eurostar I*; N1JBT *Eurostar II*; N2JBT, *Euroclass I*; T4JBT *Euro Eclipse*; R414YWJ *Euro Excalibur*.

Livery: Blue and gold

Opposite: **The Johnson Brothers blue and gold colour scheme has been dramatically departed from for two of the latest additions to the coaching stock. R414YWJ is a Plaxton Excalibur bodied Volvo B10M which carries a purple livery while T3JBT, a Neoplan Cityliner, is blue, yellow and purple. The graphic details have been achieved using advanced air brushing techniques which are becoming a feature on new coaches. Named *Euro Excalibur* and *Euro Eclipse*, in Johnson Brothers style, both coaches were posed for the camera at Skegness coach park in July 1999 .** *Steve Sanderson*

KETTLEWELL'S

Kettlewell (Retford) Ltd; Pegasus Coachways Ltd, Grove Street, Retford, DN22 6LA

	Registration	Chassis	Body	Seating	Year	Notes
	NEV678M	Leyland National 1151/1R/0402		B49F	1973	Constable, Long Melford, 1995
	GHV67N	Daimler Fleetline CRL6	Park Royal	B45/32F	1975	Cutting, Brockley, 1986
	JOV701P	Bristol VRT/SL2/6LX	MCW	B43/33F	1975	West Midlands, 1986
	JOV777P	Ailsa B55-10	Alexander AV	B44/35F	1976	London Buses, 1991
	JOV780P	Ailsa B55-10	Alexander AV	B44/35F	1976	London Buses, 1991
w	THX120S	Leyland National 10351A/2R		B40F	1978	London Buses, 1991
	THX196S	Leyland National 10351A/2R		B40F	1978	London Buses, 1991
	AYR315T	Leyland National 10351A/2R		B40F	1979	London Buses, 1991
w	HAL598V	Volvo B58-56	Irizar Urko	C53F	1980	
w	JRR359V	Ford R1014	Plaxton Supreme IV	C45F	1980	
	BFU909W	Volvo B58-56	Plaxton Supreme IV	C57F	1980	
	WXH612	Neoplan N216H	Neoplan Jetliner	C49FT	1983	
	JXI9144	Neoplan N216H	Neoplan Jetliner	C51F	1983	Wilson of Bonnybridge, 1999
	XFP1Y	DAF SB2005DHU585	Smit Euroliner	C53F	1983	
	XFP2Y	DAF SB2005DHU585	Smit Euroliner	C53F	1983	
	JIL7899	Volvo B10M-61	Jonckheere Jubilee P90	C49/9F	1983	
	KET6	Scania K112CRS	Ajokki Deltaplan	C49FT	1984	
	670PUO	Leyland Royal Tiger B50	Plaxton Paramount 3500	C49FT	1984	Hudson, Pilham, 1999
	C181KET	DAF SB2005DHU585	Smit Orion	C53F	1986	
	D538VRR	Renault-Dodge S56	East Lancashire	B29F	1987	
	HIL4619	Neoplan N122/3	Neoplan Skyliner	C57/20CT	1987	Bestall, Loxley, 1994
	E861URH	Mercedes-Benz 407D	Coachcraft	C15F	1988	
	G704HPW	Leyland Tiger TRCTL11/3ARZM	Plaxton Paramount 3500 III	C53F	1989	Rosemary, Terrington St Clement, 1993
	P6KET	Scania K113CRB	Van Hool Alizée HE	C51FT	1996	
	P66KET	Scania K113TRB	Irizar Century 12.37	C49FT	1997	
	P106GHE	Scania K113CRB	Van Hool Alizée HE	C53FT	1997	
	R66KET	Scania K113CRB	Irizar Century 12.35	C49FT	1997	
	R3KET	Scania L94IB	Irizar Century 12.35	C49FT	1998	
	S8KET	Scania L94IB	Irizar Century 12.35	C55F	1999	
	V335EAK	Scania N113DRB	East Lancashire Cityzen	B / F	1999	
		Scania L94IB	Irizar Century	C55F		Two on order March 2000

Previous Registrations:

670PUO	A321XHE	JIL7899	A147JTA	KET6	A60WVL
BFU909W	LVO47W, KET6	JXI9144	ELN82Y	WXH612	MUL60
HIL4619	D327NWG				

Livery: White, black and gold

Kettlewell's has so far operated three former London Buses Leyland Nationals. Based at Retford the vehicles are regularly used on stage services throughout north Nottinghamshire. AYR315T, the youngest of the trio, departs from Newark late one hot afternoon in June 1999. With door ajar to assist airflow, the bus is bound for its home town.
Tony Wilson

KIME'S

J R & SR Kime, The Garage, Sleaford Road, Folkingham, Sleaford,
Lincolnshire, NG34 0SB

SJI6568	Leyland Fleetline FE30AGR	Northern Counties	B43/31F	1978	Cleveland Transit, 1990
SJI6569	Bristol VRT/SL3/501(6LXB)	Eastern Coach Works	B43/31F	1978	Nottingham Omnibus, 1994
YAZ4142	Leyland National 2 NL116L11/1R		B52F	1980	Cityline (Wycombe Bus), 1999
YAZ4143	Leyland National 2 NL116L11/1R		B52F	1980	Cityline (Wycombe Bus), 1999
SJI6571	Bristol VRT/SL3/501	Eastern Coach Works	B43/31F	1980	Red and White, 1994
SJI6570	Leyland Atlantean AN68B/1R	Alexander AL	B45/29D	1981	Mainline, 1993
TAZ4061	Leyland Titan TNLXB2RR	Leyland	B44/28D	1981	Cityline, Oxford, 1998
TAZ4062	Leyland Titan TNLXB2RR	Leyland	B44/28D	1981	Cityline, Oxford, 1998
TAZ4063	Leyland Titan TNLXB2RR	Leyland	B44/28D	1982	Cityline, Oxford, 1998
TAZ4064	Leyland Titan TNLXB2RR	Leyland	B44/28D	1982	Cityline, Oxford, 1998
KYN519X	Leyland Titan TNLXB2RR	Leyland	B44/28D	1982	Cityline, Oxford, 1998
NUW66Y	Leyland Titan TNLXB2RR	Leyland	B44/28D	1982	Cityline, Oxford, 1998
WAZ8278	Leyland Titan TNLXB2RR	Leyland	B44/32F	1983	Cityline, Oxford, 1998
PAZ3185	Leyland Tiger TRCTL11/3R	Marshall	BC53F	1983	MoD, 1997 (20KB80)
PAZ7356	Bedford YNT	Plaxton Paramount 3200 E	C53F	1983	
PAZ9319	Bedford YNT	Plaxton Paramount 3200	C53F	1985	
PAZ9257	Bedford YNT	Plaxton Paramount 3200	C53F	1985	
PAZ3184	Bedford YNT	Plaxton Paramount 3200 II	C53F	1986	
PAZ9346	Leyland Tiger TRCTL11/3RZ	Marshall	BC51F	1986	MoD, 1997 (82KF07)
DAZ4300	Volvo B10M-61	Van Hool Alizée	C53F	1987	Cambridge Coach Services, 1993
DAZ4301	Volvo B10M-61	Plaxton Paramount 3200 III	C53F	1987	
DAZ4302	Dennis Javelin 12SDA1907	Plaxton Paramount 3200 III	C53F	1988	
DAZ1400	Volvo B10M-61	Van Hool Alizée	C52FT	1989	Fowler, Holbeach Drove, 1997

Previous Registrations:

DAZ1400	F56DAV, A10WHF	PAZ9257	B705GFE		TAZ4061	KYV328X
DAZ4300	D345KVE	PAZ9319	B193DVL		TAZ4062	KYV370X
DAZ4301	E686BTL	PAZ9346	D345YDO		TAZ4063	KYV457X
DAZ4302	E174FFW	SJI6568	YVN518T		TAZ4064	KYV516X
PAZ3184	C925WFO	SJI6569	LHG439T		WAZ8278	OHV711Y
PAZ3185	first civilian number	SJI6570	JKW299W		YAZ4142	JWV127W
PAZ7356	KVL442Y	SJI6571	GTX749W		YAZ4143	JWV128W

Livery: Green and cream

Former London vehicles are popular with provincial operators. The Leyland Titan, already a quality built vehicle, found ready and eager purchasers when they came up for sale. Here former London Buses T519 is one of seven of the type acquired from Cityline during 1998. Converted to single-door and re-registered, WAZ8278 heads out of Lincoln bus station having deposited passengers on a Friday-only service. *Tony Wilson*

KINCHBUS

Kinchbus Ltd, Mansfield Road, Heanor, Derbyshire, DE75 7BG

Part of the Wellglade group

EFN178L	Leyland National 1151/1R/2402		B44FL	1973	East Kent, 1989
STK132T	Leyland Atlantean AN68/1R	Roe	B43/31F	1979	Citybus, Plymouth, 1996
BAU674T	Leyland Atlantean AN68/1R	Northern Counties	B47/31D	1979	City of Nottingham, 1996
BAU675T	Leyland Atlantean AN68/1R	Northern Counties	B47/31D	1979	City of Nottingham, 1996
BRC677T	Leyland Atlantean AN68/1R	Northern Counties	B47/31D	1979	City of Nottingham, 1996
BRC678T	Leyland Atlantean AN68/1R	Northern Counties	B47/31D	1979	City of Nottingham, 1996
WYV51T	Leyland Titan TNLXB/2RRSp	Park Royal	B44/22D	1979	London Buses, 1994
WYV53T	Leyland Titan TNLXB/2RRSp	Park Royal	B44/22D	1979	London Buses, 1994
WYV62T	Leyland Titan TNLXB/2RRSp	Park Royal	B44/24D	1979	London Buses, 1994
CUL119V	Leyland Titan TNLXB/2RRSp	Park Royal	B44/31F	1980	City of Nottingham, 1995
RGS820V	Leyland National NL116L11/1R		B22FL	1980	Fife Scottish, 1996
FRA525V	Leyland National 11351A/1R		B52F	1980	Trent, 1998
FRA528V	Leyland National 11351A/1R		B52F	1980	Trent, 1998
FRA529V	Leyland National 11351A/1R		B52F	1980	Trent, 1998
FRA530V	Leyland National 11351A/1R		B52F	1980	Trent, 1998
FRA531V	Leyland National 11351A/1R		B52F	1980	Trent, 1998
RNU426X	Leyland Atlantean AN68C/1R	Northern Counties	B47/31D	1981	City of Nottingham, 1999
RNU432X	Leyland Atlantean AN68C/1R	Northern Counties	B47/31D	1981	City of Nottingham, 1999
RNU433X	Leyland Atlantean AN68C/1R	Northern Counties	B47/33D	1981	City of Nottingham, 1999
L807YBC	Mercedes-Benz 709D	Dormobile Routemaker	B27F	1993	
L814DJU	Mercedes-Benz 709D	Marshall C19	B27F	1994	
L401CJF	Dennis Dart 9.8SDL3035	Plaxton Pointer	B40F	1994	
L402CJF	Dennis Dart 9.8SDL3035	Plaxton Pointer	B40F	1994	
L403CJF	Dennis Dart 9.8SDL3035	Plaxton Pointer	B40F	1994	
L404CJF	Dennis Dart 9.8SDL3035	Plaxton Pointer	B40F	1994	
M405HFP	Dennis Dart 9.8SDL3035	Plaxton Pointer	B40F	1994	
M406HFP	Dennis Dart 9.8SDL3035	Plaxton Pointer	B40F	1994	
M815KJU	Mercedes-Benz 709D	Plaxton Beaver	B27F	1995	
N816PJU	Mercedes-Benz 709D	Plaxton Beaver	B27F	1995	
N817PJU	Mercedes-Benz 709D	Plaxton Beaver	B27F	1995	
N818RFP	Mercedes-Benz 709D	Plaxton Beaver	B27F	1996	
N819RFP	Mercedes-Benz 709D	Plaxton Beaver	B27F	1996	
N820RFP	Mercedes-Benz 709D	Plaxton Beaver	B27F	1996	
N821RFP	Mercedes-Benz 811D	Plaxton Beaver	B31F	1996	
P822BNR	Mercedes-Benz 711D	Plaxton Beaver	B27F	1996	
P407BNR	Dennis Dart SLF	Plaxton Pointer	N40F	1996	
P408BNR	Dennis Dart SLF	Plaxton Pointer	N40F	1996	
P409BNR	Dennis Dart SLF	Plaxton Pointer	N40F	1996	
P410BNR	Dennis Dart SLF	Plaxton Pointer	N40F	1996	
P411BNR	Dennis Dart SLF	Plaxton Pointer	N40F	1996	
P201BNR	Optare L1070	Optare Excel	N45F	1996	
P202BNR	Optare L1070	Optare Excel	N45F	1996	
P541BUT	Iveco TurboDaily 49-10	Leicester Carriage Builders	B7FL	1997	
R823MJU	Mercedes-Benz Vario O814	Plaxton Beaver 2	B31F	1997	
R824MJU	Mercedes-Benz Vario O814	Plaxton Beaver 2	B31F	1997	
R825MJU	Mercedes-Benz Vario O814	Plaxton Beaver 2	B31F	1997	
R826MJU	Mercedes-Benz Vario O814	Plaxton Beaver 2	B31F	1997	
R827WBC	Mercedes-Benz Vario O814	Plaxton Beaver 2	B31F	1998	
R828WBC	Mercedes-Benz Vario O814	Plaxton Beaver 2	B31F	1998	
S285UAL	Mercedes-Benz Vario O810	Plaxton Beaver 2	B31F	1998	

Livery: Two-tone blue and yellow; **Depot:** Sullivan Way, Loughborough. Outstations are at Leicester and Melton Mowbray.

Opposite: **Kinchbus is now part of the Wellglade group which owns Trent and Barton. The last Leyland National 2 operated by the group is RSG820V, and that was deployed on Access bus services on behalf of the local authority. Back-up for this bus is provided by EFN178L, a mark 1 Leyland National. A number of mark 1 versions are now employed in the Kinchbus fleet having been displaced from the Trent fleet. The lower picture shows P541BUT, an Iveco TurboDaily which carries a body constructed locally by Leicester Carriage Builders. The Kinchbus fleet now have fleet numbers allocated which correspond with the registration plate though the fleet is expected to be allocated numbers in the Wellglade series later in 1999.** *Steve Sanderson*

The East Midlands Bus Handbook

MACPHERSON

MacPherson Coaches Ltd, The Garage, Hill Street, Donisthorpe, Leicestershire, DE12 7PL

A330VHB	Ford R1115	Plaxton Paramount 3200	C53F	1984	Hoyhead, Willenhall, 1994
B921GUX	Ford R1115	Plaxton Paramount 3200	C53F	1985	Lakeside, Ellesmere, 1996
C58USS	Ford R1115	Plaxton Paramount 3200 II	C53F	1986	Mayne, Buckie, 1994
H177EJF	Toyota Coaster HB31R	Caetano Optimo	C21F	1991	Britannia, Oakengates, 1997
J213DYL	Mercedes-Benz OH1628L	Jonckheere Deauville	C49FT	1992	Redwing, Camberwell, 1996
J33MCL	Mercedes-Benz O303/15R	Plaxton Paramount 3500 III	C49FT	1992	
J55MCL	Mercedes-Benz O303/15R	Plaxton Paramount 3500 III	C49FT	1992	
K401STL	Setra S210HD	Setra Optimal	C35F	1993	Redwing, Camberwell, 1996
M22MCL	EOS E180Z	EOS 90	C49FT	1995	
M44MCL	EOS E180Z	EOS 90	C49FT	1995	
N66MCL	EOS E180Z	EOS 90	C49FT	1996	
N77MCL	EOS E180Z	EOS 90	C49FT	1996	
R42GNW	Mercedes-Benz Vario O814	Plaxton Beaver 2	B27F	1998	
R43GNW	Mercedes-Benz Vario O814	Plaxton Beaver 2	B27F	1998	
T156AUA	Mercedes-Benz Vario O814	Alexander ALX100	B27F	1999	

Previous Registrations:
C58USS   C643LKU, XXI8950

Named vehicles: J33MCL *Hauf Two*; J55MCL *Amy Jade*; R42GNW *Hector*; R43GNW *Finlay*.

Livery: Cream, black and red

MARRIOTT'S TRAVEL

D & S Marriott, 9 Retford Park Road, Retford, DN22 7GE

E623BVK	Renault-Dodge S56	Alexander AM	B25F	1987	Busways, 1996
E626BVK	Renault-Dodge S56	Alexander AM	B25F	1987	Busways, 1996

Livery: White, red and green

Depot: Beck Garage, Clayworth

A town service is provided by MacPherson in Ashby-de-la-Zouch. Two Mercedes-Benz Vario 0814 minibuses were purchased for this work in 1998. They carry Plaxton Beaver 2 bodies and are built to the shorter length, so only carry 27 seats. Seen in the town is R43GNW. This bus is named 'Hector' after one of the characters in the 'Oor Wullie' cartoon strip.
Tony Wilson

MARSHALLS

J A Marshall, 11 Main Street, Sutton-on-Trent, Newark, Nottinghamshire, NG23 6PF

B30	RAU624R	Bedford YLQ	Plaxton Supreme III	C45F	1976	Gash, Newark, 1988
DF34	A15DAF	DAF SB2300DHS585	Plaxton Paramount 3200	C53F	1984	Sykes, Appleton Roebuck, 1992
MR37	A3YRR	MCW MetroRider MF154/4	MCW	C26F	1989	Warrington, Ilam, 1993
VH38	YRR3	Van Hool T815H	Van Hool Alizée H	C49FT	1988	Tellings-Golden Miller, Cardiff, 1993
DD41	VRC480S	Leyland Fleetline FE30ALR	Northern Counties	B44/31F	1978	City of Nottingham, 1994
VL42	H3YRR	Volvo B10M-60	Plaxton Paramount 3500 III	C53F	1991	Westerham Coaches, 1995
DD43	BTV654T	Leyland Atlantean AN68A/1R	East Lancashire	B47/33D	1979	City of Nottingham, 1995
DD45	UNA787S	Leyland Atlantean AN68A/1R	Northern Counties	B43/32F	1977	GM Buses, 1996
L46	JKV441	Leyland Tiger TRCTL11/3RZ	Plaxton Paramount	C53F	1985	Pathfinder, Newark, 1996
MR47	E149KYW	MCW MetroRider MF150/38	MCW	B25F	1987	Londonlinks, 1997
DD48	NNN477W	Leyland Atlantean AN68A/1R	Roe	B46/34F	1981	City of Nottingham, 1997
L49	XAL494S	Leyland National 11351A/1R		B50F	1978	Trent, 1998
DS50	S3YRR	Dennis Javelin	Plaxton Premiére 320	C53F	1998	
DS51	S4YRR	Dennis Dart SLF	Plaxton Pointer 2	N39F	1998	
DD52	NNN471W	Leyland Atlantean AN68A/1R	Roe	B46/34F	1981	City of Nottingham, 1998

Special Event vehicles

1409	FW5696	Leyland Tiger TS7	Burlingham	B35F	1935	preservation, 1988
DD6	KNN959	Daimler CVD6	Roberts	H30/28R	1949	preservation, 1985
DD7	LNN353	Daimler CVD6	Duple	L27/26RD	1950	Gash, Newark, 1977
DD10	RAL795	Daimler CVG6	Massey	H33/28RD	1954	Gash, Newark, 1987

Previous Registrations:

FW5696	From new	A3YRR	G228FJX	JKV441	C808FMC
KNN959	From new	A15DAF	A462HJF	YRR3	E447MMM
LNN353	From new	H3YRR	H836AHS		
RAL795	From new				

Livery: Blue and cream

From their base at Sutton-on-Trent, north of Newark, Marshalls are best placed to offer services to the many villages in this part of north Nottinghamshire. Their operations include a number of school-time services, one being the 22 through Newark. Here DD48, NNN477W in June 1999, keeps alive the former Gash-company fleet numbering on this Roe bodied Leyland Atlantean, previously operated by Nottingham City Transport.
Tony Wilson

MAUN CRUSADER

Maun International Travel Consultants Ltd, 151 Outram Street, Sutton-in-Ashfield
Nottinghamshire, NG17 4FU
R A Read, Maun Classic Coaches, 126, Parkhall Road, Mansfield Woodhouse, NG18 5EZI

Reg	Chassis	Body	Seating	Year	History
SXF319	DAF MB200DKL600	Plaxton Supreme IV	C53F	1979	Copeland, Meir, 1996
FKM304V	Dennis Dominator	Willowbrook	B44/31F	1980	Maidstone & District, 1995
MNC513W	Leyland Atlantean AN68A/1R	Northern Counties	B43/32F	1980	Stagecoach Manchester, 1996
AFY180X	Leyland Atlantean AN68B/1R	Willowbrook	B45/33F	1981	South Manchester, Hyde, 1996
FGE440X	Dennis Dominator DD137B	Alexander RL	B45/34F	1982	Delta, Kirkby in Ashfield, 1996
A669HNB	Leyland Atlantean AN68D/1R	Northern Counties	B43/32F	1983	Stagecoach Manchester, 1997
A684HNB	Leyland Atlantean AN68D/1R	Northern Counties	B43/32F	1983	Stagecoach Manchester, 1997
A211EHN	Dennis Dominator DDA167	Northern Counties	B43/31F	1984	Stagecoach Transit, 1998
B214OAJ	Dennis Dominator DDA906	Northern Counties	B43/28F	1985	Stagecoach Transit, 1998
C113CAT	Dennis Dominator DDA1007	East Lancashire	BC43/28F	1986	Stagecoach Transit, 1998
278EPX	Hestair Duple SDK1503	Duple 425	C57F	1986	Riggott, Kingsley, 1997
899DXV	DAF MB230DKFL615	Duple 320	C52FT	1987	
470WYA	DAF MB230DKFL615	Duple 340	C53FT	1987	
MIL6214	Hestair Duple SDA1512	Duple 425	C49FT	1987	Moore, Davenport, 1996
E751JAY	Hestair Duple SDA1512	Duple 425	C53FT	1988	Silverdale, Ruddington, 1998
G870YDU	DAF MB230DKFL615	Caetano Algarve H-NDH	C49FT	1989	Supreme, Coventry, 1992
J82CRR	Hestair Duple SDA1517	Duple 425	C53FT	1991	Skills, Nottingham, 1996
J8WSB	Plaxton 425	Lorraine	C51FT	1992	Western Buses, 1997
K213CBD	MAN 16.290	Jonckheere Deauville	C51FT	1993	Andrew, Bermondsey, 1997
R398NRR	Dennis Javelin	Plaxton Premiére 320	C53FT	1998	
B3MAU	Mercedes-Benz 0817L	SC Coachbuilders	C29FT	1999	

Previous Registrations:

276EPX	C207HSD, VLT54, C391BOS	MIL6714	D525BBV, 112ETU, D660GBP
470WYA	E317EVH	SXF319	KVS174V
899DXV	E318EVH		

Livery: Ivory, red, green, yellow and orange.

Depot: Westfield Site, Bellamy Rd, Mansfield.

The Maun Crusader fleet now contains Leyland Atlanteans which were new to Greater Manchester, and Dennis Dominators that originated with Transit and Kingston upon Hull. One of the former Manchester Atlanteans, which carries a Northern Counties body, is MNC513W. It is seen in the multi-coloured Maun Crusader livery while parked in the company's yard.
Steve Sanderson

MOXON'S

C W Moxon Ltd, Maltby Road Garage, Oldcotes, Worksop, Nottinghamshire, S81 8JN

FRR194J	Leyland Leopard PSU3B/4R	Plaxton Panorama Elite	C51F	1971	
HIL3476	Bristol VRT/SL2/6G	MCW	B43/33F	1976	Roger Hill, Congleton, 1992
HIL3075	Bristol VRT/SL2/6G	MCW	B43/33F	1976	Roger Hill, Congleton, 1992
LUX536P	Bedford YLQ	Duple Dominant	C28DL	1976	Hughes, Ashford, 1984
RDT89R	AEC Reliance 6U2R	Plaxton Supreme III	C51F	1977	Hague, Sheffield, 1993
RWB801R	AEC Reliance 6U2R	Plaxton Supreme III	C51F	1977	Hague, Sheffield, 1993
DNG233T	Bristol VRT/SL3/6LXB	Eastern Coach Works	B43/31F	1979	MK CityBus, Milton Keynes, 1996
XAM130A	Leyland Leopard PSU3F/4R	Plaxton Supreme IV	C47F	1981	Soul, Olney, 1997
A755HPL	Bedford YNT	Plaxton Paramount 3200	C53F	1984	Mills, Harlington, 1997
B85DTH	Bedford YNT	Plaxton Paramount 3200 II	C53F	1985	Mullen, Cramlington, 1995
C696DVG	Bedford YMP	Plaxton Paramount 3200 II	C35F	1986	Mitchell, Birmingham, 1998
GIL4271	DAF SB2305DHS585	Van Hool Alizée H	C55F	1988	Lowland, 1996
JIL7889	DAF SB2305DHS585	Van Hool Alizée H	C53F	1989	London Coaches, 1994
7715KV	DAF SB2305DHTD585	Duple 340	C51FT	1989	
F212LTV	Renault Master	Holdsworth	M12	1989	Rhodes, Bestwood, 1996
5711MT	DAF SB3000DKV601	Van Hool Alizée	C51FT	1992	Wood, Barnsley, 1996
166YHK	DAF SB3000KS601	Van Hool Alizée	C51FT	1993	Hughes-DAF, Gomersal, 1997
L406VGP	Iveco Turbo Daily 49-10	Nuova	C19F	1994	Hotelink, Crawley, 1996
FIL7997	EOS E180Z	EOS 90	C53F	1994	Kenzies, Shepreth, 1999
M761RCP	DAF DE33WSSB3000	Van Hool Alizée HE	C51F	1995	MacLean, Buckie, 1998
P880PWW	DAF DE33WSSB3000	Van Hool Alizée HE	C53F	1996	Buddens, Romsey, 1998

Previous Registrations:

166YHK	K509RJX	C696DVG	C935GWL, OJI4758	HIL3476	GOG662N
5711MT	J813KND	FIL7997	L58TEW	JIL7889	F257RJX
7715KV	F860RJX	GIL4271	E606LVH	XAM130A	PWW334W
A755HPL	A122MAC, THU514	HIL3075	JOV699P		

Named vehicles: DNG233T *Barry*: JGA183N *Bill*; HIL3075 *Daniel*; HIL3476 *Lynsey Michelle*.

Livery: Cream and red

A recent addition to the Moxon's fleet is FIL7997. It is an EOS integral coach, a model latterly constructed by LAG until that company was acquired by Van Hool. The new owners have dropped the LAG name but still market the vehicle as a separate product from the more familiar Van Hool family of body styles.
Steve Sanderson

NOTTINGHAM CITY TRANSPORT

Nottingham City Transport - Nottingham City Coaches - South Notts - Pathfinder

Nottingham City Transport Ltd, Lower Parliament Street, Nottingham, NG1 1GG

2	M665JFP	Mercedes-Benz 709D	Alexander AM	B29F	1994	Pathfinder, 1997
3	L965VGE	Mercedes-Benz 709D	Dormobile Routemaker	B29F	1993	Pathfinder, 1997
4	L967VGE	Mercedes-Benz 709D	Dormobile Routemaker	B29F	1993	Pathfinder, 1997
5	M42DLN	Mercedes-Benz 709D	WS Wessex II	B29F	1995	Pathfinder, 1997
6	M424GUS	Mercedes-Benz 709D	WS Wessex II	B29F	1995	Pathfinder, 1997
7	M879DDS	Mercedes-Benz 709D	WS Wessex II	B29F	1994	Pathfinder, 1997
8	M882DDS	Mercedes-Benz 709D	WS Wessex II	B29F	1994	Pathfinder, 1997
9	N743LUS	Mercedes-Benz 709D	WS Wessex II	B29F	1995	Pathfinder, 1997
10	L256VSU	Mercedes-Benz 811D	Dormobile Routemaker	B33F	1993	Pathfinder, 1997
11	L964VGE	Mercedes-Benz 811D	Dormobile Routemaker	B33F	1993	Pathfinder, 1997
12	P493TGA	Mercedes-Benz 811D	UVG	B33F	1996	Pathfinder, 1997
15	L988AEA	Iveco Turbo Daily 59-12	Marshall C31	B29F	1993	Pathfinder, 1997
16	L865BEA	Iveco Turbo Daily 59-12	Marshall C31	B29F	1993	Pathfinder, 1997
17	N983XCT	Peugeot Boxer	TBP Freeway II	B25F	1996	Pathfinder, 1997
18	N984XCT	Peugeot Boxer	TBP Freeway II	B25F	1996	Pathfinder, 1997
19	N985XCT	Peugeot Boxer	TBP Freeway II	B25F	1996	Pathfinder, 1997
20	N991XCT	Peugeot Boxer	TBP Freeway II	B25F	1996	Pathfinder, 1997
21	N992XCT	Peugeot Boxer	TBP Freeway II	B25F	1996	Pathfinder, 1997
22	P106WJO	Peugeot Boxer	TBP Freeway II	B25F	1996	Pathfinder, 1997
23	P107WJO	Peugeot Boxer	TBP Freeway II	B25F	1996	Pathfinder, 1997
24	P108WJO	Peugeot Boxer	TBP Freeway II	B25F	1996	Pathfinder, 1997

Before Pathfinder of Newark was acquired by Nottingham City Transport, some of the newest vehicles purchased were a small number of Peugeot Boxer midibuses. Fitted with 25-seater TBP Freeway bodywork, these buses created an interesting sight with their unusual split-level appearance. Numbered 23 with Nottingham, P107WJO passes the entrance of the bus station in Newark bound for its terminus at the town's Northgate rail station in June 1999. *Tony Wilson*

25	R987VAU	Mercedes-Benz Vario O814	Plaxton Beaver 2	B33F	1997	Pathfinder, 1997			
26	R988VAU	Mercedes-Benz Vario O814	Plaxton Beaver 2	B33F	1997	Pathfinder, 1997			
27	R989VAU	Mercedes-Benz Vario O814	Plaxton Beaver 2	B33F	1997	Pathfinder, 1997			
28	R990VAU	Mercedes-Benz Vario O814	Plaxton Beaver 2	B33F	1997	Pathfinder, 1997			
29	M453LJF	Mercedes-Benz 709D	Alexander AM	B29F	1995	Pathfinder, 1997			
44	N744LUS	Mercedes-Benz 811D	WS Wessex II	B33F	1995	Pathfinder, 1997			
67	M667JFP	Mercedes-Benz 709D	Alexander AM	B29F	1995	Pathfinder, 1997			
83	M983CYS	Mercedes-Benz 811D	WS Wessex II	B33F	1994	Pathfinder, 1997			
96	M996CYS	Mercedes-Benz 811D	WS Wessex II	B33F	1994	Pathfinder, 1997			

101-110

Mercedes-Benz 811D — Plaxton Beaver — B30F — 1995

101	N101WRC	103	N103WRC	105	N105WRC	107	N107WRC	109	N109WRC
102	N102WRC	104	N104WRC	106	N106WRC	108	N108WRC	110	N110WRC

114	F114JTO	Renault-Dodge S56	Reeve Burgess Beaver	B25F	1989		
115	F115JTO	Renault-Dodge S56	Reeve Burgess Beaver	B25F	1989		
116	F116JTO	Renault-Dodge S56	Reeve Burgess Beaver	B25F	1989		
118	F118JTO	Renault-Dodge S56	Reeve Burgess Beaver	B25F	1989		
130	S130NRB	Mercedes-Benz Vario O814	Plaxton Beaver 2	B33F	1998		
131	S131NRB	Mercedes-Benz Vario O814	Plaxton Beaver 2	B33F	1998		
138	E138ATV	Renault-Dodge S56	Reeve Burgess Beaver	B25F	1987		
139	E139ATV	Renault-Dodge S56	Reeve Burgess Beaver	B25F	1987		
142	E142ERA	Renault-Dodge S56	Northern Counties	B25F	1988		
143	E143ERA	Renault-Dodge S56	Northern Counties	B25F	1988		
150	E70XKW	Mercedes-Benz 709D	Reeve Burgess Beaver	B25F	1988	Reeve Burgess demonstrator, 1988	
151	F151GVO	Mercedes-Benz 709D	Reeve Burgess Beaver	B29F	1988		
152	F152GVO	Mercedes-Benz 709D	Reeve Burgess Beaver	B29F	1988		
153	F153GVO	Mercedes-Benz 709D	Reeve Burgess Beaver	B29F	1988		

154-164

Renault-Dodge S56 — Reeve Burgess Beaver — B28F* — 1989-90   *154-57 are B25F

154	G154NRC	157	G157NRC	159	G159NRC	161	G161PVO	163	G163PVO
155	G155NRC	158	G158NRC	160	G160PTO	162	G162PVO	164	G164PVO
156	G156NRC								

165	G165RRA	Mercedes-Benz 709D	Reeve Burgess Beaver	B29F	1990
166	G166RRA	Mercedes-Benz 709D	Reeve Burgess Beaver	B29F	1990
167	H167ANU	Renault-Dodge S56	Reeve Burgess Beaver	B29F	1991

168-176

Mercedes-Benz 709D — Plaxton Beaver — B29F — 1991

168	J168CTO	170	J170CNU	172	J172CNU	174	J174CNU	176	J176CNU
169	J169CTO	171	J171CNU	173	J173CNU	175	J175CNU		

177-184

Mercedes-Benz 811D — Carlyle — B31F — 1990-91 177/8 Carlyle demonstrators, 1991

177	H727LOL	179	J179CRB	181	J181CRB	183	J183CTO	184	J184CTO
178	H732LOL	180	J180CRB	182	J182CTO				

185-193

Mercedes-Benz 811D — Dormobile Routemaker — B31F — 1993

185	K185HTV	187	K187HTV	189	L189MAU	191	L191MAU	193	L193OVO
186	K186HTV	188	K188HTV	190	L190MAU	192	L192MAU		

194	L194OVO	Mercedes-Benz 811D	Plaxton Beaver	B31F	1994
195	L195OVO	Mercedes-Benz 811D	Plaxton Beaver	B31F	1994
196	M196SRR	Mercedes-Benz 811D	Alexander AM	B31F	1995
197	M197SRR	Mercedes-Benz 811D	Alexander AM	B31F	1995
198	M198TNU	Mercedes-Benz 811D	Alexander AM	B31F	1995
199	P199ENN	Mercedes-Benz 811D	Plaxton Beaver	BC31F	1997

The East Midlands Bus Handbook

201-219

Optare MetroRider MR15 — Optare — B30F — 1994-95

201	L201ONU	205	L205ONU	209	L209ONU	213	M213STO	217	N217VVO
202	L202ONU	206	L206ONU	210	L210ONU	214	M214STO	218	N218VVO
203	L203ONU	207	L207ONU	211	L211ONU	215	M215TNU	219	N219VVO
204	L204ONU	208	L208ONU	212	M212STO	216	M216TNU		

220-233

Optare MetroRider MR15 — Optare — B31F — 1996-97

220	N220BAL	223	N223BAL	226	R226SCH	229	R229SCH	232	R232SCH
221	N221BAL	224	N224BAL	227	R227SCH	230	R230SCH	233	R233SCH
222	N222BAL	225	P225FRB	228	R228SCH	231	R231SCH		

282-299

Optare M920 — Optare Solo — N33F — 1998-99

282	S282NRB	286	S286NRB	290	S290NRB	294	T294BNN	297	T297BNN
283	S283NRB	287	S287NRB	291	S291NRB	295	T295BNN	298	T298BNN
284	S284NRB	288	S288NRB	292	T293BNN	296	T296BNN	299	T299BNN
285	S285NRB	289	S289NRB	293	T293BNN				

301-307

Volvo Citybus B10M-50 — East Lancashire — B51/35D — 1985

301	B301KVO	303	B303KVO	305	B305KVO	306	B306KVO	307	B307KVO
302	B302KVO	304	B304KVO						

308-314

Volvo Citybus B10M-50 — Northern Counties — B49/35D — 1985-86

308	C308NRC	310	C310NRC	312	C312NRC	313	C313NRC	314	C314NRC
309	C309NRC	311	C311NRC						

315-329

Volvo Citybus B10M-50 — East Lancashire — B47/38D — 1988

315	E315BVO	318	E318BVO	321	E321BVO	324	E324BVO	327	E327BVO
316	E316BVO	319	E319BVO	322	E322BVO	325	E325BVO	328	E328BVO
317	E317BVO	320	E320BVO	323	E323BVO	326	E326BVO	329	E329BVO

330	E825OMS	Volvo Citybus B10M-50	Alexander RV	B47/37F	1987	Volvo demonstrator, 1988
331	G331NRC	Volvo Citybus B10M-50	Alexander RV	B47/35F	1989	
332	G332NRC	Volvo Citybus B10M-50	Alexander RV	B47/35F	1989	
333	G333NRC	Volvo Citybus B10M-50	Alexander RV	B47/35F	1989	
334	G334NTV	Volvo Citybus B10M-50	Alexander RV	BC47/35F	1989	
335	G335PAL	Volvo Citybus B10M-50	Alexander RV	B47/37F	1989	Volvo demonstrator, 1989

336-340

Volvo Citybus B10M-50 — East Lancashire Pyoneer — BC47/35F — 1997

336	R336RRA	337	R337RRA	338	R338RRA	339	R339RRA	340	R340RRA

341-345

Volvo Citybus B10M-50 — East Lancashire Pyoneer — B49/35F — 1997

341	R341RRA	342	R342RRA	343	R343RRA	344	R344RRA	345	R345RRA

346	A398CRA	Volvo Citybus BD10-XB5	East Lancashire	B49/37D	1983
347	A399CRA	Volvo Citybus BD10-XB7	East Lancashire	B49/37D	1983

349-353

Scania N113DRB — East Lancashire — B49/35F — 1994

349	L349MRR	350	L350MRR	351	L351MRR	352	L352MRR	353	L353MRR

354-358

Scania N112DRB — Alexander RH — B47/31F — 1988 — Kentish Bus, 1992

354	E701GCU	355	OTO555M	356	F703JCN	357	F704JCN	358	F705JCN

Opposite top: **Launched at the 1997 Coach & Bus Exhibition, the Optare Solo was that company's first low-floor service midibus for the UK market. Early models were only supplied in the 8.5metre length, however, Nottingham City Transport was the first company to receive the longer 9.4 metre version. Here, 284, S284NRB negotiates the bottom side of the roundabout at the western end of Upper Parliament Street during April 1999.** *Tony Wilson*

Opposite bottom: **Five former Chester City Leyland Lion double-deckers were acquired towards the end of 1998. Nottingham City Transport has been one of the few purchasers of this model introduced by Leyland to compete with the double-deck Volvo B10M. With Alexander RH bodywork, the vehicles have joined other Lions sporting East Lancashire bodies. Numbered 395, E935CDS originated with the Clydeside 2000, but was one of three specially painted in a white, red and blue livery for a Chester Park & Ride operation. The bus is shown here turning from Market Street into Long Row in March 1999.** *Tony Wilson*

A batch of Volvo Olympians started to appear with Nottingham City Transport during late 1998, just in time for the Christmas rush. East Lancashire Pyoneer bodywork is carried on this batch, represented here by 456, S456ATV as it is pictured crossing the Huntingdon Street and Woodborough Road junction in April 1999. *Tony Wilson*

359	E307EVW	Scania N112DRB	Alexander RH	B47/31F	1988	Harris Bus, West Thurrock, 1991
360	G879TVS	Scania N113DRB	Alexander RH	B47/33F	1990	Scania demonstrator, 1991
361	E200WHS	Scania N112DRB	East Lancashire	B47/31F	1987	Brown, Dreghorn, (A1) 1990

362-379 Scania N113DRB   Alexander RH   B47/33F   1989-90

362	G362SRB	366	G366SRB	370	G370RTO	374	G374NRC	377	G377NRC
363	G363SRB	367	G367SRB	371	G371RTO	375	G375NRC	378	G378NRC
364	G364SRB	368	G368RTO	372	G372RTO	376	G376NRC	379	G379NRC
365	G365SRB	369	G369RTO	373	G373RTO				

380	F380JTV	Scania N113DRB	Alexander RH	B47/33F	1988	Scania demonstrator, 1989
381	E381ERB	Scania N112DRB	Alexander RH	B47/33F	1988	Scania demonstrator, 1989

382-391 Leyland-DAB Lion LDTL11/1R   East Lancashire   BC43/37F*   1988-89 *387-391 are B47/41F
*383 is BC43/33F, 384 is BC43/35F

382	F382GVO	384	F384GVO	386	F386GVO	388	F388GVO	390	F390GVO
383	F383GVO	385	F385GVO	387	F387GVO	389	F389GVO	391	F391GVO

392	D392TAU	Leyland Lion LDTL11/1R	Northern Counties	B47/38D	1986	
393	D393TAU	Leyland Lion LDTL11/1R	Northern Counties	B47/37D	1986	
394	D394TAU	Leyland Lion LDTL11/1R	Northern Counties	B47/38D	1986	

395-399 Leyland Lion LDTL11/1R   Alexander RH   B49/37F   1987   Chester, 1998

395	E935CDS	396	E941CDS	397	E925CDS	398	E938CDS	399	E899CDS

Nottingham City Transport has, in the past, created interest through their purchasing policy. Many former demonstration vehicles, have been acquired after the period of demonstration is over. Another arrival is 361, E200WHS, an East Lancashire-bodied Scania N112 that was acquired from the A1 Buses co-operative in 1990. It is illustrated here boarding passengers in Angel Row in March 1999, prior to heading out to the suburbs of the Strelley Estate. *Tony Wilson*

401	N401ARA	Dennis Arrow DDA3116	Northern Counties Palatine II	BC44/36F	1995
402	N402ARA	Dennis Arrow DDA3116	Northern Counties Palatine II	BC44/36F	1996
403	N403ARA	Dennis Arrow DDA3116	Northern Counties Palatine II	B49/37F	1996
404	N404ARA	Dennis Arrow DDA3116	Northern Counties Palatine II	B49/37F	1996

405-416

Dennis Trident — East Lancashire Lolyne — N53/35F — 1999

405	T405BNN	408	T408BNN	411	T411BNN	413	T413BNN	415	T415BNN
406	T406BNN	409	T409BNN	412	T412BNN	414	T414BNN	416	T416BNN
407	T407BNN	410	T410BNN						

417-436

Dennis Trident — East Lancashire Lolyne — N53/35F — 1999

417	T417LCU	421	T421LCU	425	V425	429	V429	433	V433
418	T418LCU	422	T422LCU	426	V426	430	V430	434	V434
419	T419LCU	423	V423	427	V427	431	V431	435	V435
420	T420LCU	424	V424	428	V428	432	V432	436	V436

436-445

Leyland Atlantean AN68C/1R — Northern Counties — B47/33D — 1981

| 436 | RTV436X | 439 | RTV439X | 443 | RTV443X | 444 | RTV444X | 445 | RTV445X |

450-465

Volvo Olympian — East Lancashire Pyoneer — B49/35F — 1998-99

450	S450ATV	454	S454ATV	457	S457ATV	460	S460ATV	463	S463ATV
451	S451ATV	455	S455ATV	458	S458ATV	461	S461ATV	464	S464ATV
452	S452ATV	456	S456ATV	459	S459ATV	462	S462ATV	465	S465ATV
453	S453ATV								

Having gathered a collection of Volvo B10B, including five formerly used as demonstration models with Alexander and Plaxton bodywork, six Plaxton Verde models were delivered to Nottingham City Transport during 1995. One of these, 609, M609UTV is seen circumnavigating the roundabout at the western end of Upper Parliament Street. *Tony Wilson*

466-480   Volvo Olympian   East Lancashire Pyoneer   B49/39F   1998

466	R466RRA	469	R469RRA	472	R472RRA	475	R475RRA	478	R478RRA
467	R467RRA	470	R470RRA	473	R473RRA	476	R476RRA	479	R479RRA
468	R468RRA	471	R471RRA	474	R474RRA	477	R477RRA	480	R480RRA

481	K481GNN	Leyland Olympian ON2R56C19Z5	East Lancashire	B49/35F	1992
482	K482GNN	Leyland Olympian ON2R56C19Z5	East Lancashire	B49/35F	1992
483	L483LNN	Volvo Olympian YN2RV18Z5	East Lancashire	B49/35F	1993
484	L484LNN	Volvo Olympian YN2RV18Z5	East Lancashire	B49/35F	1993

485-489   Volvo Olympian YN2RV18Z4   East Lancashire   B49/35F   1994

| 485 | L485NTO | 486 | L486NTO | 487 | L487NTO | 488 | L488NTO | 489 | L489NTO |

490	P490CVO	Volvo Olympian YN2RV18Z4	East Lancashire	B49/35F	1996
491	P491CVO	Volvo Olympian YN2RV18Z4	East Lancashire	B49/35F	1996
492	P492FRR	Volvo Olympian	East Lancashire	B49/35F	1997
493	P493FRR	Volvo Olympian	East Lancashire	B49/35F	1997

501-513   Volvo B6-9.9M   Alexander Dash*   B40F   1994-95
*511 East Lancashire Spryte (1997)

501	L501OAL	504	L504OAL	507	L507OAL	510	L510OAL	512	M512TRA
502	L502OAL	505	L505OAL	508	L508OAL	511	M511TRA	513	M513TRA
503	L503OAL	506	L506OAL	509	L509OAL				

| 514 | P514CVO | Dennis Dart SLF | East Lancashire Spryte | N44F | 1996 | |
| 520 | M113SLS | Scania L113CRL | Wright Access-ultralow | N47F | 1995 | Scania demonstrator, 1995 |

521-525

Scania L113CRL — Wright Access-ultralow — N47F — 1995-96

521	M521UTV	522	M522UTV	523	N523XRR	524	N524XRR	525	N525XRR

540-544

Optare Excel L1150 — Optare — N46F — 1996-97

540	P540CTO	541	P541CTO	542	P542GAU	543	P543GAU	544	P544GAU

600	M664KHP	Volvo B10B-58	Alexander Strider	B51F	1995	Volvo demonstrator, 1995
601	M601TTV	Volvo B10B-58	Alexander Strider	B51F	1995	
602	M602TTV	Volvo B10B-58	Alexander Strider	B51F	1995	
603	M603TTV	Volvo B10B-58	Alexander Strider	B51F	1995	
604	M604TTV	Volvo B10B-58	Alexander Strider	B51F	1995	

605-610

Volvo B10B-58 — Plaxton Verde — B51F — 1995

605	M605UTV	607	N607UTV	608	N608UTV	609	N609UTV	610	N610XRC
606	M606UTV								

611-615

Volvo B10B-58 — Alexander Strider — B51F — 1995-96

611	N611XVO	612	N612YRA	613	N613YRA	614	N614YRA	615	N615YRA

640	P640ENN	Scania L113CRL	East Lancashire Flyte	B53F	1996
641	P641ENN	Scania L113CRL	East Lancashire Flyte	B53F	1996
642	P642ENN	Scania L113CRL	East Lancashire Flyte	B53F	1996
666	ARC666T	Leyland Atlantean AN68A/1R	Northern Counties	B47/31D	1978

682-696

Leyland Atlantean AN68A/1R — Northern Counties — B47/31D — 1980

682	JRC682V	690	LRR690W	693	MNU693W	695	MNU695W	696	MNU696W
689	LRR689W	692	LRR692W	694	MNU694W				

698	F128KTV	Leyland Olympian ONCL10/2RZ	Northern Counties	B49/34F	1989	South Notts, 1991
699	G129NRC	Leyland Olympian ONCL10/2RZ	Northern Counties	B49/34F	1989	South Notts, 1991
711	GTO711V	Leyland National 2 NL116L11/1R		B50F	1980	
712	ETT319Y	Leyland National 2 NL116HLXB/1R (Leyland)		B50F	1983	Athelstan, Malmesbury, 1989

713-724

Leyland National 2 NL116TL11A/1R — B50F — 1985

713	B713LAL	716	B716LAL	719	B719LAL	721	C721MRC	723	C723MRC
714	B714LAL	717	B717LAL	720	C720MRC	722	C722MRC	724	C724MRC
715	B715LAL	718	B718LAL						

725-739

Leyland Lynx LX112L10ZR1 — Leyland Lynx — B49F* — 1988 — *725/7/32 are B51F, 729 is B48F

725	E725BVO	728	E728BVO	731	E731BVO	734	E734BVO	737	E737BVO
726	E726BVO	729	E729BVO	732	E732BVO	735	E735BVO	738	E738BVO
727	E727BVO	730	E730BVO	733	E733BVO	736	E736BVO	739	E739BVO

740-744

Leyland Lynx LX112L10ZR1R — Leyland Lynx — B49F — 1989

740	F740HRC	741	F741HRC	742	F742HRC	743	F743HRC	744	F744HRC

745-749

Leyland Lynx LX2R11C15Z4R — Leyland Lynx — B50F — 1989-90

745	G745PNN	746	G746PNN	747	G747PNN	748	G748PNN	749	G749PNN

750	H47NDU	Leyland Lynx LX2R11V18Z4R	Leyland Lynx 2	B50F	1991	Volvo Euro Show bus, 1991

751-758

Scania N113CRB — Alexander PS — BC51F — 1990

751	G751SRB	753	G753SRB	755	G755SRB	757	G757SRB	758	G758SRB
752	G752SRB	754	G754SRB	756	G756SRB				

759	J759DAU	Leyland Lynx LX2R11V18Z4S	Leyland Lynx 2	B50F	1991	
760	J760DAU	Leyland Lynx LX2R11V18Z4S	Leyland Lynx 2	B50F	1991	
761	K761JTV	Scania N113CRB	Plaxton Verde	B50F	1993	MIRA Test centre, 1993
762	L829HEF	Volvo B10B-58	Alexander Strider	B51F	1994	Volvo demonstrator, 1994
763	M763SVO	Scania L113CRL	Northern Counties Paladin	B51F	1994	
764	M919MRW	Volvo B10B-58	Alexander Strider	B51F	1995	Volvo demonstrator, 1996
765	N480DKH	Volvo B10B-58	Plaxton Verde	B51F	1995	Plaxton demonstrator, 1996
766	N779DRH	Volvo B10B-58	Plaxton Verde	B51F	1995	Plaxton demonstrator, 1996

767-771

Volvo B10M-55 — Alexander PS — B48F — 1995

767	N767WRC	768	N768WRC	769	N769WRC	770	N770WRC	771	N771WRC

781	T781LCH	Volvo B10M-62	Plaxton Premiére	C53F	1999	
782	T782LCH	Volvo B10M-62	Plaxton Premiére	C53F	1999	
783	T783LCH	Volvo B10M-62	Plaxton Premiére	C53F	1999	
784	B784JAU	Leyland Tiger TRCTL11/3R	Duple Caribbean 2	C53F	1985	
785	75RTO	Leyland Royal Tiger RTC	Leyland Doyen	C53F	1988	
786	83RTO	Leyland Royal Tiger RTC	Leyland Doyen	C53F	1988	
791	F791JTV	Leyland Tiger TRCTL11/3ARZ	Duple 320	C53F	1989	
792	F792JTV	Leyland Tiger TRCTL11/3ARZ	Duple 320	C53F	1989	
793	E113FNU	Leyland Tiger TRCTL11/3RZ	Plaxton Paramount 3200 III	C53F	1988	
796	65RTO	Leyland Tiger TRCL10/3ARZA	Plaxton Paramount 3200 III	C57F	1991	
797	77RTO	Bova FLC12-280	Bova Futura Club	C53F	1995	Bova demonstrator, 1996

918-927

Leyland Atlantean AN68C/1R — Northern Counties — B47/33D — 1981

918	MVO418W	923	MVO423W	924	MVO424W	925	MVO425W	926	MVO426W

Previous Registrations:

65RTO	J796CNN		E925CDS	E161YGB, FSU661
83RTO	E786BTV		E935CDS	E164YGB, VLT204
75RTO	E785BTV		E938CDS	E163YGB, WLT364
77RTO	M784RVY		E941CDS	E162YGB, 32CLT
E115FNU	E793BTV, 65RTO		L988AEA	L773YHA
E899CDS	E160YGB, VLT166		OTO555M	F702JCN

Liveries: Green and cream (buses); blue and cream (South Notts): cream, brown and orange (Nottingam City Coaches); white (Pathfinder). 401 and 666 carry special liveries.

Allocations:

Bulwell (Piccadilly)

Volvo Citybus	301	302	303	304	305	306	307	308
	309	310	311	312	313	314	315	316
	317	318	319	320	321	322	323	324
	325	326	327	328	329			
Atlantean	923	925	439	682	689	690		

Gotham (Leake Road)

Mercedes-Benz	44	67	83	168	169	170	171	172
	173	174	175	199				
MetroRider	201	202	203					

Newark (Brunel Drive) - Pathfinder

Mercedes-Benz	2	3	4	5	6	7	8	9
	10	11	12	25	26	27	28	29
	96	130	131					
Iveco	15	16						
Peugeot	17	18	19	20	21	22	23	24

Trent Bridge (Trinity Street, Nottingham)

Mercedes-Benz	101	102	103	104	105	106	107	108
	109	110	176	177	178	179	180	181
	182	183	183	185	186	187	188	189
	190	191	192	193	194	195	196	
	197	198						
Atlantean	692	693	694	695	696	698	699	
Volvo Olympian	462	463	464	465	466	467	468	469
	470	471	472	473	474	475	476	477
	478	479	480					

Nottingham (Lower Parliament Street)

Remainder

NOTTINGHAMSHIRE COMMUNITY BUSES

Nottinghamshire County Council, Planning and Transport, Trent Bridge House, Fox Road, West Bridgford, Nottingham, NG2 6BJ

H998VRR	Mercedes-Benz 811D	Phoenix	C16F	1991
P579DAU	Mercedes-Benz 609D	UVG CityStar	B16F	1996

Liveries: White or orange

Two community buses are provided for the more rural parts of Nottinghamshire. The minibuses are supplied and maintained by the County Council but the drivers are local volunteers who also manage the operation. P579DAU operates in the Farnsfield area to the west of Newark and this Mercedes-Benz minibus can be seen in Newark bus station on Wednesdays.
Paul Harvey

P C COACHES

P C and J Smith, 110 Rasen Lane, Lincoln, LN1 3KD

KBV144S	Bedford YMT	Duple Dominant II	C53F	1978	Arnold Shaw, 1995
JTM105V	Bedford YMT	Plaxton Supreme IV	C53F	1979	KM, Lundwood, 1991
FUJ949V	Bedford YMT	Plaxton Supreme IV	C53F	1979	Wings, Sleaford, 1991
CDN711V	Bedford YMT	Plaxton Supreme IV	C53F	1980	Kingston-upon-Hull, 1994
GRF703V	Bristol VRT/SL3/501	Eastern Coach Works	B43/31F	1980	PMT, 1994
EWF474V	MCW Metrobus DR102/13	MCW	B46/26D	1980	Arriva Fox County, 1998
EWF488V	MCW Metrobus DR102/13	MCW	B46/27D	1980	Arriva Fox County, 1998
JHE177W	MCW Metrobus DR104/6	MCW	B46/31F	1981	Arriva Fox County, 1998
CKS390X	MCW Metrobus DR102/24	Alexander RL	B45/33F	1981	Arriva Fox County, 1998
ULS615X	MCW Metrobus DR102/28	Alexander RL	B45/33F	1982	Arriva Fox County, 1998
MIB9246	DAF SB2300DHTD585	Plaxton Paramount 3200	C53F	1984	Dore, Leafield, 1992
A448EVO	Mercedes-Benz L608D	Devon Conversions	BC19F	1984	Mertrux, Leicester, 1986
LIL2512	DAF SB2300DHSD585	Plaxton Paramount 3200	C53F	1985	Bowers, Chapel-en-le-Frith, 1998
C516KMW	Bedford YNV	Plaxton Paramount 3200	C53F	1985	Hughes, Slough, 1997
C530UUT	Bedford YNV	Duple	C53F	1986	KM, Lundwood, 1999
D720PTU	Freight Rover Sherpa	Dormobile	B16F	1986	Hearn, Stibb Cross, 1997
D102SPP	Bedford YNT	Plaxton Paramount 3200 III	C53F	1987	Cedar, Bedford, 1996
D282XCX	DAF SB2305DHTD585	Plaxton Paramount 3200 III	C55F	1987	Burton, Haverhill, 1999
E219FLD	Scania N112DRB	Van Hool Alizée L	C47F	1987	Speedlink, 1997
E220FLD	Scania N112DRB	Van Hool Alizée L	C47F	1987	Speedlink, 1997
217MYB	Bedford YNT	Plaxton Paramount 3200 III	C53F	1988	Emmersons, Immingham, 1999
E450MSE	Bedford YNT	Plaxton Paramount 3200 III	C53F	1988	Burtons, Haverhill, 1999

The Irizar Century is now becoming a familiar sight on the roads of Britain but, when it was introduced, its dramatic style was considered extraordinary. PC Coaches have nine vehicles with this body which is currently only supplied in Britain on Scania chassis. All feature different illustrations on the white orange and red fleet livery. L8PCC was the first to arrive and, in common with all this type in the fleet, is often seen on the working holidays to other parts of Europe. *David Heath*

Local bus services from Lincoln to Saxilby are operated by PC coaches with minibuses while double deckers are provided on school contract runs. For local private hire and school contract work PC Coaches have a number of coaches which they brand as Landcruisers. *Landcruiser III* is C516KMW, a Bedford YNV that carries a Plaxton 3.2-metre high Paramount 3200 body. It is seen negotiating a roundabout on the Lincoln bypass. *Steve Sanderson*

E590BDB	Mercedes-Benz L307D	Mellor	M12	1988	Taylor, Childwall, 1992
F533EWJ	Mercedes-Benz 609D	Whittaker	BC25F	1989	
J1PCC	Mercedes-Benz 811D	Reeve Burgess Beaver	BC33F	1991	
J602KGB	Mercedes-Benz 709D	Dormobile	B29F	1991	Pathfinder, Newark, 1996
J175GGG	Ford Transit VE6	Made to Measure	M16	1991	Degnan, Spurstow, 1998
K813VNF	Ford Transit VE6	Ford	M14	1992	S J Carlton, Hellaby, 1996
RIL1018	Volvo B10M-60	Van Hool Alizée	C48FT	1993	Limebourne, Battersea, 1999
RIL1019	Volvo B10M-60	Van Hool Alizée	C48FT	1993	Limebourne, Battersea, 1999
L8PCC	Scania K113CRB	Irizar Century 12.35	C48FT	1994	
M694BLT	LDV 400	A Line	M16	1994	Degnan, Spurstow, 1998
M7PCC	Ford Transit VE6	Mellor	M14	1994	
M8PCC	Mercedes-Benz 609D	Autobus Classique	C23FL	1994	
M99PCC	Scania K113CRB	Irizar Century 12.35	C48FT	1995	
N10PCC	Scania K113CRB	Irizar Century 12.35	C49FT	1995	
N11PCC	Scania K113CRB	Irizar Century 12.35	C49FT	1996	
N12PCC	Scania K113CRB	Irizar Century 12.35	C49FT	1996	
P14PCC	Scania K113CRB	Irizar Century 12.35	C49FT	1997	
P15PCC	Scania K113CRB	Irizar Century 12.35	C49FT	1997	
R16PCC	Scania K124IB4	Irizar Century 12.35	C49FT	1998	
S17PCC	Scania L94IB	Irizar Century 12.35	C49FT	1998	
T7PCC	Mercedes-Benz Vario O814	Plaxton Beaver 2	B33F	1999	

Previous Registrations:

217MYB	E391KCW	LIL2512	B232RRU	RIL1018	K809HUM
C530UUT	C530UUT, ACH80A	MIB9246	A875PJX, 1576CD	RIL1019	K819HUM
KBV144S	FFR531S, 1302TJ				

Named Vehicles: MIB9246 *Landcruiser;* D102SPP *Landcruiser II;* C516KMW *Landcruiser III;* LIL2512 *Landcruiser IV;* 217MYB *Landcruiser V;* D282XCX *Landcruiser VI;* E450MSE *Landcruiser VII.*

Livery: White, orange and maroon; **Depot**: Crofton Road, Allenby Road Industrial Estate, Lincoln

PAUL JAMES

K S & PJ O'Brien, A Houlker & K Markham, 9 Church Lane,
Ratcliffe-on-the-Wreake, Leicestershire, LE7 8JF

AYA199	Leyland Leopard PSU5D/4R	Plaxton Supreme IV	C53F	1981	Friends of the Blind, Leeds, 1997
PTV601X	Bedford YNT	Plaxton Supreme IV Express	C53F	1981	Barton, 1987
VFA70X	Leyland Leopard PSU3F/4R	Willowbrook 003	C49F	1982	Reliance, Sutton-on-the-Forest, 1989
PJI7929	Bedford YNT	Plaxton Paramount 3200	C49F	1982	
PJI7930	Bova FLD12.250	Bova Futura	C49F	1984	Harnard, Brinsworth, 1988
PJI7931	Bova EL29/581	Bova Europa	C53F	1984	Tom Jackson, Chorley, 1989
B290YSL	Leyland Tiger TRCTL11/3RZ	Plaxton Paramount 3500 II	C57F	1985	Moffat & Williamson, Gauldry, 1997
C113AFX	Bedford YNV	Plaxton Paramount 3200 II	C49F	1986	Kevin Radley, Broughton, 1996
GSK664	Ford Transit VE6	Made-to-Measure	C20F	1991	Carreglefn Coaches, 1997
PJI7754	Dennis Javelin 12SDA1907	Plaxton Paramount 3200 III	C53F	1988	Kingston Coaches, Winterslow, 1991
J8PJC	Dennis Javelin 12SDA1929	Caetano Algarve II 3.35	C49FT	1992	Smithson, Spixworth, 1995
L66PJC	Dennis Javelin 12SDA2117	Plaxton Premiére 320	C53F	1993	Fowler, Holbeach Drove, 1999
L88PJC	Volvo B10M-60	Van Hool Alizée HE	C53F	1993	Park's of Hamilton, 1997
M8PJC	Scania K113CRB	Van Hool Alizée HE	C49FT	1995	Slattery, Kentish Town, 1996
3476PJ	Dennis Javelin	Neoplan Transliner	C50FT	1996	Jones, Eccles, 1998
S20PJC	Mercedes-Benz Vario O814D	Autobus Nouvelle 2	C29F	1999	

Previous Registrations:

3476PJ	N12JEJX	L88PJC	HSK643, L692ADS
AYA199	LPN354W	M8PJC	M327VET
B290YSL	B509UNB, BSK790	PJI7929	SMK146Y
GSK664	H547EVM	PJI7930	A145BET
J8PJC	J915OAY	PJI7931	A829RHG
L66PJC	L701MRA	PJI7754	E639NEL

Livery: Cream and red

Depot: London Road, Coalville and Ratcliffe Farm, Fosseway, Ratcliffe

C113AFX is seen leaving a school in Melton Mowbray and displays the obligatory school bus sign in the nearside windscreen of its Plaxton Paramount body. This Bedford YNV joined the Paul James fleet from Kevin Radley of Broughton near Scunthorpe. Paul James have recently been successful in securing a tendered service that runs between Melton Mowbray and Nottingham.
Steve Sanderson

PAUL S WINSON

Paul S Winson Ltd, The Coach Station, Royal Way, Belton Park, Loughborough, LE11 0DZ

24	C21PSW	Volvo B10M-61	Plaxton Paramount 3200 II	C57F	1985	Wings, Sleaford, 1990
25	2968PW	Bova FHD12.290	Bova Futura	C55F	1990	
28	H2PSW	DAF SB2305DHTD585	Plaxton Paramount 3200 III	C53F	1991	
32	FJU973	Volvo B10M-60	Plaxton Paramount 3500 III	C53F	1990	Horseshoe, Tottenham, 1991
33	H3PSW	Mercedes-Benz 609D	Made-to-Measure	C24F	1990	Burton, Finchley, 1992
39	F424RTL	DAF MB230LB615	Plaxton Paramount 3500 III	C53F	1989	Wings, Sleaford, 1993
40	J40PSW	DAF SB2305DHS585	Caetano Algarve II 3.35	C53F	1992	Brittain's, Northampton, 1994
43	N3PSW	DAF DE33WSSB3000	Van Hool Alizée HE	C53F	1995	
45	MNM31V	Leyland Leopard PSU3E/4R	Plaxton Supreme IV Express	C53F	1980	Andy James, Tetbury, 1996
46	BTV656T	Leyland Atlantean AN68A/1R	Northern Counties	B47/31D	1978	City of Nottingham, 1996
47	M300ARJ	Mercedes-Benz 709D	Autobus Classique 2	C25F	1994	
50	P50PSW	Bova FHD12.290	Bova Futura	C53F	1996	
51	L5PSW	Mercedes-Benz 609D	Onyx	C21F	1994	Skills, Nottingham, 1997
52	L6PSW	Mercedes-Benz 814D	Autobus Classique	C33F	1994	Sproat, Bouth, 1997
54	NNN479W	Leyland Atlantean AN68A/1R	Roe	B46/34F	1981	City of Nottingham, 1998
55	R5PSW	Dennis Javelin	Plaxton Première 320	C53F	1998	
56	R6PSW	Dennis Javelin	Plaxton Première 320	C53F	1998	
57	T7PSW	Bova FHD12.340	Bova Futura	C53F	1999	
58	T8PSW	Bova FHD12.340	Bova Futura	C53F	1999	
59	T9PSW	Mercedes-Benz Vario O814	Plaxton Beaver 2	B29F	1999	
60	NNN472W	Leyland Atlantean AN68A/1R	Roe	B46/34F	1981	City of Nottingham, 1998
61	NNN474W	Leyland Atlantean AN68A/1R	Roe	B46/34F	1981	City of Nottingham, 1998
62	HOD76	Neoplan N122/3	Neoplan Skyliner	C55/18CT	1988	Selwyns, Runcorn, 1999

Previous Registrations:

2968PW	G25YRY	HOD76	F615CWJ, SEL133
C21PSW	C799RJU, YNR778	J40PSW	J508LRY
F424RTL	F229RJX, VTL627, F424RTL, HOD76	L5PSW	L63ORC
FJU973	F896SMU	L6PSW	L968JFU
H2PSW	H28GFP	YNR778	MNU626P
H3PSW	H423DVM		

Livery: White, blue and red

The centre of Derby in July 1999 is the location for this picture of N3PSW, a Van Hool-bodied DAF SB3000 which was departing the city with a group of tourists. While the core business for the company is high quality coaching, a small number of midi and full sized buses are operated on tendered local bus services.
Tony Wilson

The village of Great Gonerby, to the north of Grantham, is the base for the Reliance company. A second Dennis Dart, a SLF type with Plaxton Pointer bodywork, was acquired for local services in the Grantham area. R439FTU is seen in Grantham bus station under grey snow-filled skies waiting time after arriving from Nottingham in April 1999. *Tony Wilson*

A T-junction between the Peak District villages of Litton and Tideswell in June 1999 provides us with an opportunity to view the Mellor bodywork applied to Mercedes Vario O814, S276LGA operated by Ringwood Coaches of Staveley, Chesterfield. During late 1998, the company was awarded a Derbyshire County Council contract to operate the long distance cross-Pennine X67 service, which links Chesterfield with Manchester. *Tony Wilson*

RELIANCE

W J Simmons (Coaches) Ltd, 47 High Street, Great Gonerby,
Grantham, Lincolnshire, NG31 8JR

YIA9006	Leyland Leopard PSU3D/4R	Duple Dominant (1986)	B55F	1976	National Travel (West), 1986
KBT343S	Volvo B58-56	East Lancashire (1993)	BC40/26F	1978	Skills, Nottingham, 1994
YTO996T	Leyland Leopard PSU3E/4R	Duple Dominant	B53F	1978	
SNS826W	Leyland National 2 NL116L11/1R		B52F	1980	Stagecoach Western, 1999
PNW306W	Leyland Leopard PSU3F/4R	Plaxton Supreme IV	C49F	1981	Wallace Arnold, 1986
B641JVO	Bova FHD12.280	Bova Futura	C49FT	1985	
D748XAU	MCW MetroRider MF150/12	MCW	B23F	1987	
F691PAY	Dennis Javelin 12SDA1907	Duple 320	C57F	1988	
F883SMU	Leyland Lynx LX112LXCTZR1S	Leyland	B51F	1989	
BAZ7049	Volvo B10M-60	Van Hool Alizée H	C53F	1990	Shearings, 1997
H790RWJ	Scania K113CRB	Van Hool Alizée DH	C55F	1990	
H845UUA	Optare MetroRider	Optare	B29F	1991	
M821RCP	Dennis Dart 9.8SDL3040	Plaxton Pointer	B40F	1994	
N272DWY	Mercedes-Benz 0405	Optare Prisma	B49F	1995	Optare demonstrator, 1996
N290DWY	MAN 11.190 HOCLR	Optare Vecta	B40F	1995	Optare demonstrator, 1996
F217RMR	EOS E180Z	EOS 90	C49FT	1997	Bernard Kavanagh, Urlingford, 1999
R439FTU	Dennis Dart SLF	Plaxton Pointer 2	N33F	1998	
S782FFW	Mercedes-Benz Vario O814	Plaxton Beaver 2	B27F	1998	

Previous Registrations:

BAZ7049	G849RNC	YIA9006	PWD841R
KBT343S	WUF155, BGG166S	F217RMR	F217RMR, 97-KK-3372

Livery: Red and ivory (buses); silver, blue and black (coaches).

RINGWOOD

D T Brockbank, Speedwell Garage, Crompton Road, Staveley, Derbyshire, S43 3PG

A737ADT	Bedford VAS5	Reeve Burgess	B26FL	1984	
E288KLD	Mercedes-Benz 609D	Pilcher Greene	M13L	1988	Convent of St Mary, Edgware, 1998
JAZ6794	DAF SB3000DKV601	Plaxton Paramount	C55F	1988	Palmer, Normanton 1998
F611GET	MCW Metrorider MF154/2	MCW	C28F	1989	Cliffs, High Wycombe, 1991
G690KNW	Mercedes-Benz 811D	Optare StarRider	C29FL	1989	
M881UMJ	LDV 400	Holloway	M16	1995	van, 1997
P591HMF	Mercedes-Benz 611D	Concept	M12L	1997	
S276LGA	Mercedes-Benz Vario O810	Mellor	B31F	1998	
S743RNE	Mercedes-Benz Vario O814	Plaxton Beaver 2	C14FL	1999	

Previous Registrations:

JAZ6794	F632OHD

Livery: White

ROADCAR

Lincolnshire Road Car Co Ltd, PO Box 15, St Mark Street, Lincoln, LN5 7BB

Part of The Traction group

23-36

							B23F	1987	Yorkshire Traction, 1992-7	

MCW MetroRider MF150/22 — MCW

23	D523SKY	29	D529SKY	31	D531SKY	34	D534SKY	36	D536SKY
27	D527SKY	30	D530SKY	32	D532SKY				

39	E539VKY	MCW MetroRider MF150/33	MCW	B23F	1987	Yorkshire Traction, 1995
66	D36NFU	Renault-Dodge S56	Alexander AM	B25F	1987	Chester, 1994
87	G327MUA	Renault-Dodge S56	Reeve Burgess Beaver	B23F	1990	Harrogate Independent, 1993
88	E318NSX	Renault-Dodge S56	Alexander AM	B25F	1988	Fife Scottish, 1994
89	E319NSX	Renault-Dodge S56	Alexander AM	B25F	1988	Fife Scottish, 1994
98w	E498HHN	Renault-Dodge S56	Alexander AM	B25F	1987	West Riding, 1995
103w	E512HHN	Renault-Dodge S56	Alexander AM	B25F	1987	West Riding, 1995
106	E506HHN	Renault-Dodge S56	Alexander AM	B25F	1987	Yorkshire Woollen, 1995
108	D308MHS	Renault-Dodge S56	Alexander AM	B21F	1986	Strathtay, 1995

126-133

Renault S75 — Reeve Burgess Beaver — B31F — 1990 — Yorkshire Traction, 1998*
*126-8 London Buses, 1994-95; 129 Strathtay, 1996

126	H126AML	128	H128AML	130	H130AML	132	H132AML	133	H133AML
127	H127AML	129	H129AML	131	H131AML				

134	J134HME	Renault S75	Plaxton Beaver	B31F	1991	Strathtay, 1996
137	H737THL	Renault S75	Whittaker-Europa	B29F	1990	Renault demonstrator, 1991
138	K378RFE	Renault S75	Wright TS303 Citybus	B31F	1992	
139	K379RFE	Renault S75	Wright TS303 Citybus	B31F	1992	
140	K380RFE	Renault S75	Wright TS303 Citybus	B31F	1992	
141	H191YMA	Renault S75	Wright TS303 Citybus	B31F	1990	The Wright Company, Wrexham, 1994

The RoadCar midibus fleet is primarily based on the Renault S75 but a number of MetroRiders are also operated. As well as vehicles purchased new from Optare, a number of MCW versions are also in the fleet most being obtained from Yorkshire Traction, though a pair of former London 30-seaters were acquired from South Lancs. The Great Northern Terrace depot in Lincoln is the setting for 346, E646KYW.
Steve Sanderson

The **Renault-Dodge S56** was the RoadCar choice for 23/25 seat minibuses with many being purchased from other operators. This type of vehicle is now being phased out and, by the end of 1999, it is envisaged that all will be sold. Number 87, G327MUA, is an example bodied by Reeve Burgess with the Beaver style body that is also carried by many of the larger S75 buses in the fleet. The vehicle is seen in Skegness having arrived on the town service 93 from Drake Road. *Steve Sanderson*

148	G448LKW	Renault S75	Reeve Burgess Beaver	B31F	1989	Harrogate & District, 1993
153	G293MWU	Renault S75	Reeve Burgess Beaver	BC31F	1990	Strathtay, 1999
154	G294MWU	Renault S75	Reeve Burgess Beaver	BC31F	1990	Harrogate & District, 1994
155	G295MWU	Renault S75	Reeve Burgess Beaver	BC31F	1990	Harrogate & District, 1994

162-168

		Renault S75		Reeve Burgess Beaver	B31F	1990	Yorkshire Traction, 1998-99

| 162 | H362TWJ | 164 | H364TWJ | 165 | H365TWJ | 166 | H366TWJ | 168 | H368TWJ |
| 163 | H363TWJ | | | | | | | | |

171-195

Renault S75 — Reeve Burgess Beaver — B31F* — 1990 — London Buses, 1994-95*
*171/93-5 are BC29F
*171-80 Yorkshire Traction, 1997-99; 193-5 Strathtay, 1996-99

171	G871WML	177	G877WML	182	G882WML	187	G887WML	191	G891WML
173	G873WML	178	G878WML	183	G883WML	188	G888WML	193	G893WML
174	G874WML	179	G879WML	184	G884WML	189	G889WML	194	G894WML
175	G875WML	180	G880WML	185	G885WML	190	G890WML	195	G895WML
176	G876WML	181	G881WML	186	G886WML				

201	EDT201V	Leyland National 2 NL116L11/1R		B52F	1980	Yorkshire Traction, 1995
204	EDT204V	Leyland National 2 NL116L11/1R		B52F	1980	Yorkshire Traction, 1995
207	LRB207W	Leyland National 2 NL116L11/1R		B50F	1980	City of Nottingham, 1997
208	LRB208W	Leyland National 2 NL116L11/1R		B50F	1980	City of Nottingham, 1997
213	LRB213W	Leyland National 2 NL116AL11/1R		B50F	1981	City of Nottingham, 1997
214	EDT214V	Leyland National 2 NL116L11/1R		B52F	1980	Yorkshire Traction, 1995
220	EDT220V	Leyland National 2 NL116L11/1R		B49F	1980	Yorkshire Traction, 1999
251	IIL2501	Leyland Atlantean AN68A/1R	East Lancs Sprint (1992)	B47F	1976	Andrews Sheffield Omnibus, 1997
252	XRF26S	Leyland Atlantean AN68A/1R	East Lancs Sprint (1993)	B47F	1978	Andrews Sheffield Omnibus, 1998
259	YBJ159X	Bristol B21	Alexander Q	B52F	1982	Ipswich, 1996
275	KHH375W	Leyland National 2 NL116L11/1R		BC52F	1980	Stagecoach Ribble, 1997
278	GTO708V	Leyland National 2 NL116L11/1R		B50F	1980	City of Nottingham, 1997
279	GTO709V	Leyland National 2 NL116L11/1R		B50F	1980	City of Nottingham, 1997
282	FUH32V	Leyland National 2 NL116L11/1R		B49F	1980	Stagecoach Burnley & Pendle, 1997

The East Midlands Bus Handbook

The RoadCar fleet has taken in Leyland Olympians cascaded from Trent and sister company Strathtay. Eastern Coach Works bodywork is fitted to the vehicles bought from both companies. Former Strathtay 625, TSO25X, is seen in the village of Cranwell, home of the RAF college. It is about to return to the market town of Sleaford on service 635. *Richard Belton*

284	EON824V	Leyland National 2 NL116L11/1R		B49F	1980	City of Nottingham, 1997
288	NLS988W	Leyland National 2 NL116L11/1R		BC52F	1980	Stagecoach Ribble, 1997
290	RFS590V	Leyland National 2 NL116L11/1R(6HLXB)		B52F	1980	Yorkshire Buses, 1993
291	NWY433V	Leyland National 2 NL116L11/1R		BC48F	1980	Catch-a-Bus, Hylton Castle, 1997
292	PNW605W	Leyland National 2 NL116L11/1R		B52F	1982	Keighley & District, 1995
293	UWY73X	Leyland National 2 NL116AL11/1R		B49F	1982	Harrogate & District, 1994
294	FUH34V	Leyland National 2 NL116L11/1R		B49F	1980	Stagecoach Burnley & Pendle, 1997
295	UWY65X	Leyland National 2 NL116AL11/1R		B49F	1981	Harrogate & District, 1994
296	UWY76X	Leyland National 2 NL116AL11/1R		B49F	1982	Keighley & District, 1995
297	UWY70X	Leyland National 2 NL116AL11/1R		B49F	1982	Harrogate & District, 1995
298	FAO927V	Leyland National 2 NL106L11/1R		B43F	1979	Catch-a-Bus, Hylton Castle, 1997
299	YSX929W	Leyland National 2 NL106L11/1R		B44F	1980	Fife Scottish, 1996
300	YSX930W	Leyland National 2 NL106L11/1R		B44F	1980	Fife Scottish, 1996

301-308

Dennis Dart 9.8SDL3035*   Wright HandyBus   B40F   1992-93 *301-3 are 9.8SDL3017

301	K301NJL	303	K303NJL	305	L305VFE	307	L307VFE	
302	K302NJL	304	L304VFE	306	L306VFE			308	L308VFE

321-328

Volvo B6-9.5M   East Lancashire EL2000   B44F   1995

321	N321JTL	323	N323JTL	325	N325JTL	327	N327JTL	
322	N322JTL	324	N324JTL	326	N326JTL			328	N328JTL

Opposite, top: **Two RoadCar open top buses run in Guide Friday livery on the Lincoln city tour. The other four Leyland Atlanteans that were converted to run without a roof are to be found in the seaside resort of Skegness. These buses are painted in a variation of the Hong Kong Citybus livery of yellow, red and blue and are branded *The Open Topper*. Number 1317, UBV87L, was new to Blackburn but the East Lancashire body was converted to open top when it was in the Lancaster fleet.** *Tony Wilson*
Opposite, bottom: **RoadCar purchased a number of buses from Ipswich including unique 259, YBJ159X. Built as a prototype National for Belfast Citybus, this was the only B21 built with a centre exit. This chassis variant was intended only for export, though the type was supplied to Belfast and Ipswich. The Belfast examples later went to Ipswich who sold this vehicle on to RoadCar in 1996. The middle door has now been removed.**

While the remaining RoadCar Bristol VRTs are confined to school duties, Leyland Atlanteans continue to be used in all day service. Skegness examples are busy in the resort throughout the year and carry large numbers of visitors. With this in mind, the Roe body of 1322, RDX12R, has been modified so that a luggage rack has replaced the middle door. *Steve Sanderson*

345	F815CWJ	MCW MetroRider MF158/10	MCW	B31F	1988	Rhondda, 1997
346	E646KYW	MCW MetroRider MF158/1	MCW	B30F	1988	South Lancs, 1997
348	E648KYW	MCW MetroRider MF158/1	MCW	B30F	1988	South Lancs, 1997
350	H793HEC	Optare MetroRider MR01	Optare	B33F	1990	ABC, Ainsdale, 1997

351-358		Optare MetroRider MR15	Optare	B31F	1994	

351	M351BFE	353	M353BFE	355	M355BFE	**357** M357BFE	**358**	M358BFE
352	M352BFE	354	M354BFE	356	M356BFE			

394	J394LJL	Mercedes-Benz 811D	Optare StarRider E	B31F	1991	
395	J395LJL	Mercedes-Benz 811D	Optare StarRider E	B31F	1991	
396	J396LJL	Mercedes-Benz 811D	Optare StarRider E	B31F	1991	
397	H397SYG	Mercedes-Benz 811D	Optare StarRider	B31F	1990	Optare demonstrator, 1991
401	N401LTL	Bova FLC 12.280	Bova Futura Club	C53F	1995	
411	WOI3001	Leyland Tiger TRCTL11/3R	Plaxton Supreme V	C51F	1980	Lincoln City, 1993
412	WOI3002	Leyland Tiger TRCTL11/3R	Duple Dominant IV	C53F	1983	Lincoln City, 1993
414	A159EPA	Leyland Tiger TRCTL11/3R	Plaxton Paramount 3200E	C51F	1984	Yorkshire Terrier, 1999
415	EAH891Y	Leyland Tiger TRCTL11/3R	Plaxton Paramount 3200E	C51F	1983	United, 1996
416	OIL2416	Leyland Tiger TRCTL11/3R	Plaxton Paramount 3200	C53F	1983	Yorkshire Traction, 1990
417	MSV927	Leyland Tiger TRCTL11/3R	Van Hool Alizeé	C51F	1981	Gash, Newark, 1989
418	HIL8418	Leyland Tiger TRCTL11/3R	Plaxton Paramount 3200	C51F	1983	Yorkshire Traction, 1991
419	HIL8419	Leyland Tiger TRCTL11/3R	*(Chassis currently awaiting rebodying)*		1983	Yorkshire Traction, 1992
420	HIL8420	Leyland Tiger TRCTL11/3R	Plaxton Paramount 3200	C53F	1983	Yorkshire Traction, 1992
421	KIB6620	Leyland Tiger TRCTL11/3R	Plaxton Paramount 3200	C51F	1983	Yorkshire Traction, 1992
422	MSV922	Leyland Tiger TRCTL11/3RH	Plaxton Paramount 3500 II	C46FT	1985	Yorkshire Traction, 1992
423	BLZ1423	Leyland Tiger TRCTL11/3R	Duple Laser	C51F	1984	Rhondda, 1995
424	BLZ1424	Leyland Tiger TRCTL11/3R	Duple Laser	C51F	1984	Rhondda, 1995
425	A185AHB	Leyland Tiger TRCTL11/3R	Duple Laser	C51F	1984	Rhondda, 1995
426	MSV926	Leyland Tiger TRCTL11/3R	Duple Laser	C51F	1984	Rhondda, 1995
427	KIB6527	Leyland Tiger TRCTL11/3R	Duple 340 (1987)	C51F	1982	Strathtay, 1993

The Lincoln to Skegness service has been featured in much of the press following the award of a substantial grant under the Government's Rural Challenge project. The frequency of the service has been doubled and extra early morning , evening and Sunday journeys added. Half the operation is resourced with Volvo Olympians fitted with East Lancashire Pyoneer bodies, with 688, R688MFE shown here. The livery of these vehicles includes branding as Connect6 hi-liners. *Steve Sanderson*

428-433

428	EWY28Y	Leyland Tiger TRCTL11/2R	Alexander TE		BC49F	1983	Tees & District, 1997	
428	EWY28Y	429	429SAR	430	EWY30Y	432	A31LWX	433	A32LWX

439	UJI2439	Leyland Tiger TRCTL11/3RZ	Plaxton Paramount 3200 II	C48FT	1986	Yorkshire Traction, 1995
440	IIL6440	Leyland Tiger TRCTL11/3RZ	Plaxton Paramount 3200 II	C50FT	1986	Yorkshire Traction, 1995
441	XPM41	Leyland Tiger TRCTL11/3RZ	Plaxton Paramount 3200 III	C53F	1988	Shearings, 1992
442	XPM42	Leyland Tiger TRCTL11/3RZ	Plaxton Paramount 3200 III	C53F	1988	Shearings, 1992
451	RFE482	Leyland Tiger TRCTL11/3R	East Lancs EL2000(1992)	BC57F	1983	Strathtay, 1992
452	TWO84	Leyland Tiger TRCTL11/3R	East Lancs EL2000(1992)	BC57F	1984	Rhondda, 1992
453	WVL515	Leyland Tiger TRCTL11/3R	East Lancs EL2000(1992)	BC57F	1984	Rhondda, 1992
454	IUI5454	Leyland Tiger TRCTL11/3R	East Lancs EL2000 (1993)	BC57F	1981	SMT, 1993
455	DAZ5455	Leyland Tiger TRCTL11/3R	East Lancs EL2000 (1994)	B72F	1983	Midland, Cannock, 1993
456	PIW4456	Leyland Tiger TRCTL11/3R	East Lancs EL2000 (1995)	BC57F	1983	Northern Bus, Anston, 1994
457	PIW4457	Leyland Tiger TRCTL11/3R	East Lancs EL2000 (1995)	BC57F	1982	Troika Travel,South Norwood, 1994
458	YDZ3458	Leyland Tiger TRCTL11/3R	East Lancs EL2000 (1995)	BC57F	1984	Rhondda, 1994
463	IUI3463	Leyland Tiger TRCTL11/2R	East Lancs EL2000 (1996)	BC53F	1982	Midland, Cannock, 1995
465	ESK965	Leyland Tiger TRCTL11/2R	Plaxton Paramount 3200E	C53F	1983	Yorkshire Traction, 1997
466	EWY26Y	Leyland Tiger TRCTL11/2R	Alexander TE	BC49F	1983	Tees & District, 1996
474	KIB6474	Scania K92CRB	Plaxton Paramount 3200 III	C55F	1988	Yorkshire Traction, 1996
476	F256CEW	Scania K93CRB	Plaxton Derwent II	B57F	1989	Fowler, Holbeach Drove, 1996
477	F257CEW	Scania K93CRB	Plaxton Derwent II	B57F	1989	Fowler, Holbeach Drove, 1996
478	F258CEW	Scania K93CRB	Plaxton Derwent II	B57F	1989	Fowler, Holbeach Drove, 1996
482	IUI5482	Volvo B10M-60	Plaxton Paramount 3200 III	C53F	1992	Strathtay, 1998

501-521

		Dennis Dart SLF		East Lancashire Spryte		N39F	1997-99		
501	R501JFE	506	R506MFE	510	S510BTL	514	T514SVL	518	V518XTL
502	R502JFE	507	S507BTL	511	S511BTL	515	V515XTL	519	V519XTL
503	R503JFE	508	S508BTL	512	S512BTL	516	V516XTL	520	V520XTL
504	R504JFE	509	S509BTL	513	T513SVL	517	V517XTL	521	V521XTL
505	R505MFE								

581-585

581-585		Dennis Dart MPD		Plaxton Pointer 2		N29F	1999		
581	V581XTL	**582**	V582XTL	**583**	V583XTL	**584**	V584XTL	**585**	V585XTL

601	B501FFW	Leyland Olympian ONLXB/1R	Eastern Coach Works	BC42/30F	1985	
602	B502FFW	Leyland Olympian ONLXB/1R	Eastern Coach Works	BC42/30F	1985	
603	B503FFW	Leyland Olympian ONLXB/1R	Eastern Coach Works	BC42/30F	1985	
613	B713HVO	Leyland Olympian ONLXB/1R	Eastern Coach Works	B45/30F	1985	Trent, 1997
618	TSO18X	Leyland Olympian ONLXB/1R	Eastern Coach Works	B45/32F	1982	Strathtay, 1998
621	C721NNN	Leyland Olympian ONLXB/1R	Eastern Coach Works	B45/30F	1985	Trent, 1997

622-628

622-628		Leyland Olympian ONLXB/1R		Eastern Coach Works		B45/32F	1982	Strathtay, 1998-99	
622	TSO22X	**625**	TSO25X	**626**	TSO26X	**627**	TSO27X	**628**	TSO28X

642	DFW42X	Leyland Olympian ONLXB/2R	East Lancashire	B49/35F	1982	Lincoln City, 1993
643	KTL43Y	Leyland Olympian ONLXB/2R	East Lancashire	B49/35F	1982	Lincoln City, 1993
644	KTL44Y	Leyland Olympian ONLXB/2R	East Lancashire	B49/35F	1982	Lincoln City, 1993
645	KTL45Y	Leyland Olympian ONLXB/2R	East Lancashire	B49/35F	1982	Lincoln City, 1993
646	C46KBE	Leyland Olympian ONLXCT/2R	East Lancashire	BC47/29F	1985	Lincoln City, 1993
647	C47KBE	Leyland Olympian ONLXCT/2R	East Lancashire	BC47/29F	1985	Lincoln City, 1993
648	C48KBE	Leyland Olympian ONLXCT/2R	East Lancashire	BC47/29F	1985	Lincoln City, 1993
649	A208DTO	Leyland Olympian ONLXB/1R	East Lancashire	B45/27F	1984	Lincoln City, 1993

681-686

681-686		Volvo Olympian VN2RV18Z4		East Lancashire		B51/37F	1996		
681	P681SVL	**683**	P683SVL	**684**	P684SVL	**685**	P685SVL	**686**	P686SVL
682	P682SVL								

687	R687MFE	Volvo Olympian	East Lancashire Pyoneer	BC47/33F	1998	
688	R688MFE	Volvo Olympian	East Lancashire Pyoneer	BC47/33F	1998	
701	KCK201W	Leyland Atlantean AN68C/2R	East Lancashire	B50/36F	1981	Barnsley & District, 1996
702	KCK202W	Leyland Atlantean AN68C/2R	East Lancashire	B50/36F	1981	Barnsley & District, 1996
703	KCK203W	Leyland Atlantean AN68C/2R	East Lancashire	B50/36F	1981	Barnsley & District, 1996
704	KCK204W	Leyland Atlantean AN68C/2R	East Lancashire	B50/36F	1981	Sheffield Omnibus, 1996
707	URN207V	Leyland Atlantean AN68A/2R	East Lancashire	B45/33F	1979	Barnsley & District, 1995
708	URN208V	Leyland Atlantean AN68A/2R	East Lancashire	B45/33F	1979	Barnsley & District, 1997
709	URN209V	Leyland Atlantean AN68A/2R	East Lancashire	B51/35F	1979	Barnsley & District, 1996
710	DHG210W	Leyland Atlantean AN68B/2R	East Lancashire	B45/33F	1980	Sheffield Omnibus, 1996
711	DHG211W	Leyland Atlantean AN68B/2R	East Lancashire	B45/33F	1980	Sheffield Omnibus, 1996
732	YJK932V	Leyland Atlantean AN68A/2R	East Lancashire	B47/35F	1979	Barnsley & District, 1996
734	YJK934V	Leyland Atlantean AN68A/2R	East Lancashire	B47/35F	1979	Eastbourne, 1996
735	YJK935V	Leyland Atlantean AN68A/2R	East Lancashire	B47/35F	1979	Eastbourne, 1996
740	VCX340X	Leyland Atlantean AN68D/2R	Northern Counties	B47/36F	1982	Sheffield Omnibus, 1996
746	UHG146V	Leyland Atlantean AN68A/2R	Alexander AL	B49/36F	1980	Preston Bus, 1995
750	SCN250S	Leyland Atlantean AN68A/2R	Alexander AL	B49/37F	1978	Circle Line, Gloucester, 1997
801	S801SJV	Scania L94UB	Wright Axcess Floline	N43F	1999	
802	S802SJV	Scania L94UB	Wright Axcess Floline	N43F	1999	
803	S803SJV	Scania L94UB	Wright Axcess Floline	N43F	1999	
1002w	PVL127V	Bedford YMT	Plaxton Supreme IV	C53F	1979	Pete's, Lincoln, 1997
1004w	BBB536V	Bedford YLQ	Plaxton Supreme IV	C45F	1980	Pete's, Lincoln, 1997
1304	LJA642P	Leyland Atlantean AN68A/1R	Northern Counties	O43/32F	1976	Greater Manchester, 1988
1306	LJA622P	Leyland Atlantean AN68A/1R	Northern Counties	O43/32F	1976	Greater Manchester, 1988
1309	UBV85L	Leyland Atlantean AN68/1R	East Lancashire	O45/31F	1972	Lancaster, 1989
1311	ETO911V	Leyland Atlantean AN68A/1R	Roe	B43/34F	1979	Gash, Newark, 1989
1314	UBV84L	Leyland Atlantean AN68/1R	East Lancashire	O45/31F	1972	Lancaster, 1993
1317w	UBV87L	Leyland Atlantean AN68/1R	East Lancashire	O45/31F	1972	Lancaster, 1993
1318	DBV198W	Leyland Atlantean AN68B/1R	East Lancashire	O45/33F	1980	Hyndburn, 1992
1319	MRT7P	Leyland Atlantean AN68/1R	Roe	B43/32F	1976	Ipswich, 1994
1320	HDX906N	Leyland Atlantean AN68/1R	Roe	B43/29F	1975	Ipswich, 1994

1321-1331

1321-1331		Leyland Atlantean AN68A/1R		Roe `		B43/32F*	1976-77 Ipswich, 1994-96		
							*1322/4/7 are B43/29F		
1322	RDX12R	**1324**	RDX14R	**1326**	RDX16R	**1328**	SDX28R	**1331**	SDX21R
1323	RDX13R	**1325**	RDX15R	**1327**	RDX17R	**1329**	SDX26R		

Alternate journeys on the Lincoln to Skegness service are provided with Scania single deck buses bodied by Wright with their Axcess Floline model. These buses provide wheelchair access onto the route. A feature of the new service is its connections, at various points, with a number of services. Through tickets are issued and buses are in contact by telephone to ensure connections are made. 802, S802SJV is one of the trio of Connect6 lo-liners pictured at Horncastle Market Place. *Steve Sanderson*

1334	LEO734Y	Leyland Atlantean AN68D/1R	Northern Counties	B43/32F	1983	Sheffield Omnibus, 1996
1335	LEO735Y	Leyland Atlantean AN68D/1R	Northern Counties	B43/32F	1983	Ribble, 1995
1341	ANA601Y	Leyland Atlantean AN68D/1R	Northern Counties	B43/32F	1982	Stagecoach Manchester, 1997
1342	ANA632Y	Leyland Atlantean AN68D/1R	Northern Counties	B43/32F	1983	Stagecoach Manchester, 1997
1346	ANA546Y	Leyland Atlantean AN68D/1R	Northern Counties	B43/32F	1982	Stagecoach Manchester, 1997

| *1367-1373* | | Leyland Atlantean AN68A/1R | Eastern Coach Works | B43/31F | 1979-80 | Sheffield Omnibus, 1995/6 |

| 1367 | TRN467V | **1369** | TRN479V | **1371** | TRN471V | **1372** | TRN472V | **1373** | TRN473V |
| 1368 | TRN468V | | | | | | | | |

| *1374-1383* | | Leyland Atlantean AN68C/1R | Eastern Coach Works | B43/31F | 1981 | Trent, 1995* |
| | | | | | | *1382 Sheffield Omnibus, 1995 |

| 1374 | LRB584W | **1378** | LRB578W | **1380** | LRB580W | **1382** | LRB582W | **1383** | LRB583W |
| 1377 | LRB577W | **1379** | LRB579W | **1381** | LRB581W | | | | |

1384	TRN484V	Leyland Atlantean AN68A/1R	Eastern Coach Works	B43/31F	1980	Ribble ,1995
1385	TRN485V	Leyland Atlantean AN68A/1R	Eastern Coach Works	B43/31F	1980	Ribble ,1995
1389	TRN469V	Leyland Atlantean AN68A/1R	Eastern Coach Works	B43/31F	1979	Ribble ,1995
1407	MDT337W	Leyland Leopard PSU5D/4R(TL11)	Plaxton Supreme IV	C48F	1981	Yorkshire Traction, 1998
1408	JHE98W	Leyland Leopard PSU5D/4R(TL11)	Plaxton Supreme IV	C48F	1981	Yorkshire Traction, 1998
1419	JFW915T	Leyland Leopard PSU3E/4R	Alexander AT	BC49F	1979	Strathtay, 1991
1421	ULS321T	Leyland Leopard PSU3E/4R	Alexander AYS	BC49F	1979	Strathtay, 1993
1422	ULS335T	Leyland Leopard PSU3E/4R	Alexander AYS(1981)	B53F	1979	Strathtay, 1994

| *1431-1442* | | Leyland Leopard PSU3D/4R* | Alexander AYS | B53F | 1977 | Strathtay, 1991-93 |
| | | | | | | *1431-32 are type PSU3E/4R |

| 1431 | XSG71R | **1433** | YSF73S | **1436** | YSF81S | **1440** | YSF80S | **1442** | YSF82S |
| 1432 | XSG72R | **1434** | YSF74S | **1439** | YSF89S | | | | |

| 1443 | TSJ73S | Leyland Leopard PSU3D/4R | Alexander AY | B53F | 1977 | Clydeside, 1995 |
| 1444 | TSJ58S | Leyland Leopard PSU3D/4R | Alexander AY | B53F | 1978 | Clydeside, 1995 |

1446	TSJ46S	Leyland Leopard PSU3D/4R	Alexander AY	B53F	1978	Clydeside, 1995
1447	GSO87V	Leyland Leopard PSU3E/4R	Alexander AYS	B53F	1980	Strathtay, 1994
1449	WFS149W	Leyland Leopard PSU3E/4R	Alexander AYS	B53F	1980	Fife Scottish, 1996
1456	AVL745X	Leyland Leopard PSU3G/4RT	Eastern Coach Works B51	BC53F	1982	
1475	UET1S	Leyland Leopard PSU3E/4R(DAF)	Plaxton Supreme IV	C49F	1978	Yorkshire Traction, 19987
1476	NPA223W	Leyland Leopard PSU3E/4R	Plaxton Supreme IV Express	C53F	1981	Gash, Newark, 1989
1477	NPA224W	Leyland Leopard PSU3E/4R	Plaxton Supreme IV Express	C53F	1981	Gash, Newark, 1989
1478	FTL992X	Leyland Leopard PSU3F/4R	Duple Dominant IV	C49F	1981	Yorkshire Traction, 1990
1479	FTL993X	Leyland Leopard PSU3F/4R	Duple Dominant IV	C49F	1981	Yorkshire Traction, 1990
1483	NWB163X	Leyland Leopard PSU3F/4R	Duple Dominant IV Express	C49F	1981	Yorkshire Traction, 1994
1952	LVL807V	Bristol VRT/SL3/6LXB	Eastern Coach Works	B43/31F	1980	
1957	PFE541V	Bristol VRT/SL3/6LXB	Eastern Coach Works	B43/31F	1980	
1958	PFE542V	Bristol VRT/SL3/6LXB	Eastern Coach Works	B43/31F	1980	
1972	HWJ922W	Bristol VRT/SL3/6LXB	Eastern Coach Works	B43/31F	1980	Yorkshire Traction, 1991
1973	HWJ923W	Bristol VRT/SL3/6LXB	Eastern Coach Works	BC39/31F	1980	Yorkshire Traction, 1991
1975	HWJ925W	Bristol VRT/SL3/6LXB	Eastern Coach Works	BC39/31F	1980	Yorkshire Traction, 1991
1990	MWG940X	Bristol VRT/SL3/6LXB	Eastern Coach Works	BC41/31F	1981	Yorkshire Traction, 1991
2310	SPC270R	Leyland National 10351A/1R		B41F	1977	South Riding, 1995
2312	THX212S	Leyland National 10351A/2R		B44F	1978	Stanley Gath, Dewsbury, 1992
2313	TRN803V	Leyland National 10351B/1R		B44F	1979	Cumberland, 1993
2315	CHH215T	Leyland National 10351B/1R		B44F	1979	Cumberland, 1993
2316	CHH212T	Leyland National 10351B/1R		B44F	1979	Cumberland, 1993
2317	AHH207T	Leyland National 10351B/1R		B44F	1979	Cumberland, 1993
2802	MBZ7142	Leyland National 11351/1R		B49F	1976	Globe, Barnsley, 1995
2831	UHG756R	Leyland National 11351A/1R		B49F	1977	Cumberland, 1993
2832	UHG752R	Leyland National 11351A/1R		B49F	1977	Cumberland, 1993
2845w	SWE439S	Leyland National 11351A/1R		B52F	1977	Yorkshire Traction, 1991
2849	UFG53S	Leyland National 11351A/2R		B52F	1977	Barnard, Kirton-in-Lindsey, 1992

2866-2879

		Leyland National 11351A/1R		B49F*	1978-79	Yorkshire Traction, 1991
						*2877 is B52F

2866w	YWG466T	**2870**	YWG470T	**2872**	DET472V	**2877**	DET477V	**2879**	DET479V

2883	XKA883T	Leyland National 11351A/1R		B49F	1978	Yorkshire Terrier, 1996

Special event vehicles:

DD1	KAL578	Daimler CVD6	Massey(1962)	B33/28RD	1948	Gash, Newark, 1989
2494	NVL165	Bristol SC4LK	Eastern Coach Works	B35F	1961	Majestic, Barnsley, 1989

Ancilliary vehicles:

3037	GLS277W	Leyland Leopard PSU3/3R	Alexander AY	TV	1974	Vanguard, Bedworth, 1989
3041	RDX11R	Leyland Atlantean AN68A/1R	Roe	TV	1976	Ipswich, 1994
3095	OEM785S	Leyland Atlantean AN68/1R	MCW	TV	1978	Nottingham Omnibuses, 1995

Previous Registrations:

429SAR	EWY27Y	KIB6620	VET55Y, 2408HE, MSV922
A185AHB	A228VWO, AKG231A	MBZ7142	MEL552P
BLZ1423	A230VWO, AKG265A	MDT337W	JHE99W, UHE373, 1975HE
BLZ1424	A232VWO, AKG282A	MSV922	B63EWE, 1533HE, KIB6474
DAZ5455	RCY121Y, MKH48A, SWN820Y	MSV926	A233VWO, AKG293A, A186AHB
ESK965	YAL511Y, MSV926, 1533HE	MSV927	FRN816W, MSV927, BFW233W
FTL992X	NAK5X, 3880HE	NVL165	RFE482, OWJ339A
FTL993X	NAK6X, 2316HE	NWY433V	CCY818V, BBT380V
H793HEC	H4ABC	OIL2416	UWJ53Y, 928GTA, ESK965
HIL8418	A57WDT, VHE890, 3141HE, MSV922	PIW4456	BDF204Y
HIL8419	A56WDT, YTC856	PIW4457	VSS6X, WLT759, KSP329X, IIL6440
HIL8420	VET54Y, 1619HE	PVL127V	429SAR
IIL2501	LJA645P	RFE482	A508HVT, 929GTA
IIL6440	C419VDO, 1737HE	TWO84	A254VWO
IUI3463	TDC853X	UJI2439	C418VDO, YTC49, MSV922
IUI5454	BSG550W, MSV926	WOI3001	FRN801W
IUI5482	J401KSR	WOI3002	PYE838Y
JFW915T	CRS66T ,565BNX	WVL515	A258VWO, AAX399A
JHE98W	JHE98W, 1901HE	XPM41	E679UNE
KAL578	From new	XPM42	E693UNE
KIB6474	E51WWF, HE8054, E797AHL	YBJ159X	WOI607
KIB6527	VSS5X, WLT921, MSL185X	YDZ3458	A226VWO, AKG213A

Livery: Green, yellow and white;yellow, blue and red (Superbuzz) 501-21/81-5.

Allocations

Gainsborough

Dart	301	302	303	304	305	306	307	308
Tiger	415	430	451	453	455	466		
National	275	293	295	296	297			
Olympian	602							

Grantham

Mercedes-Banz	394	395	396	397			
Renault	130	133	137	163			
Leopard	1421	1483					
Tiger	412	414	433	463			
National	207	208	213	278	284	2310	2312
Bristol VR	1952	1973	1975	1990			

Grimsby

Renault	126	132	155	171	175	177	179
Leopard	1419	1440	1444	1449	1456		
Tiger	423	424	425	432			
National	299	300					
Scania	476	477	478				

Lincoln

MetroRider	346	350						
Renault	129	131	134	162	164	165	166	168
	174	176	178	180	181	182	183	184
	185	186	187	188	190	191	194	195
Dart	509	510	511	512				
Volvo B6	321	322	323	324	325	326	327	328
Leopard	1434	1447						
National	201	204	214	279	290	292	2313	2315
	2316	2317	2802	2831	2849	2877	2883	
Bristol B21	259							
Tiger	416	422	427	442				
Bova	401							
Scania	474							
Bristol VR	1957	1958						

The RoadCar coach fleet contains a solitary Scania K92CRB. Registered E797AHL, 474 now carries the more appropriate number KIB6474. This coach carries the latest white, lime green and yellow *Lincolnshire Coachlink* livery on its Plaxton Paramount 3200 body. It was pictured in Newark bus station while on private hire duties. *Steve Sanderson*

Atlantean	701	704	708	746	750	1309	1318	1319
	1325	1326	1328	1329	1335	1341	1342	1346
	1377	1378	1379					
Olympian	603	625	627	628	642	643	644	645
	647	649	685	686	687	688		

(Lincoln City Transport vehicles: 181/2, 214/59/90, 327/8, 509-12, 642-5, 1335/41/6, 2316/7)

Louth

Dodge	66	106						
Leopard	1422	1433	1439					
National	2832							
Tiger	426	428	465					
Atlantean	702	703	709	740	1323	1368	1371	
Olympian	648	681	682	683	684			

Newark

Renault-Dodge	127	128	138	139	140	141	148	154
	173	189						
Dart	505	506	507	508				
Leopard	1475	1476	1477					
National	220	294	2872	2879				
Tiger	420							
Atlantean	707	735	1331	1381	1383	1384		
Olympian	618	622	626					

Scunthorpe

MetroRider	23	27	29	30	31	32	34	36
	39	345	348	351	352	353	354	355
	356	357	358					
Leopard	1407	1408						
National	282	288	291					
Tiger	421	441	456	457	458			
Volvo coach	482							
Atlantean s/d	251	252						
Atlantean	710	711	1372	1373	1374	1380	1382	
Olympian	601	613	621					

Skegness

Renault-Dodge	87	88	89	153	193			
Dart	501	502	503	504	513	514		
National	298							
Tiger	417	429	452					
Scania	801	802	803					
Atlantean	732	734	1304	1306	1311	1314	1320	1322
	1324	1327	1334					
Olympian	646							

Unallocated

Renault-Dodge	98	103	108					
Dart	515	516	517	518	519	520	521	581
	582	583	584	585				
Bedford	1002	1004						
Leopard	1431	1432	1436	1443	1446	1447	1479	
National	2845	2866						
Tiger	411	418	419	428	439	440		
Bristol VR	1972							
Atlantean	1317	1367	1369	1385	1389			

ROBINSON'S

M S Robinson, 4 Abbots Green Burbage, Leicestershire, LE10 2QZ

PAZ2532	Leyland Tiger TRCTL11/3RZ	Plaxton Paramount	C50F	1985	Smith Marple, 1996
B418CMC	Leyland Tiger TRCTL11/3RZ	Plaxton Paramount	C50F	1985	Kirkham Oswaldtwistle, 1998
S949RBE	Mercedes-Benz Vario O814	Autobus Nouvelle 2	C33F	1999	

Previous Registrations:

B418CMC	B418CMC, HCK947	PAZ2532	B404CMC, DUI672, B189XBU

Livery: White and Blue

Depot: Deepdale Farm, Lutterworth Road, Burbage

SCUTT

H A Scutt, 57 High Street, Owston Ferry, North Lincolnshire, DN9 1RH

	JVY676S	Bedford YMT	Plaxton Supreme III	C53F	1978	York Pullman, 1991
	JSV365	Leyland Tiger TRCTL11/3R	Plaxton Supreme V	C53F	1982	Armchair, Brentford, 1991
	BUA711X	Leyland Tiger TRCTL11/3R	Plaxton Viewmaster IV	C51F	1982	Wray, Harrogate, 1993
	A530LPP	Leyland Tiger TRCTL11/3R	Plaxton Paramount 3200	C57F	1983	WHM, Hutton, 1991
w	D965PJA	Renault-Dodge S56	Northern Counties	B20F	1987	Little Red Bus, Smethwick, 1997

Previous Registrations:

JSV365	XPP296X	BUA711X	TRN91X, HSV126

Livery: Red and white

Michael Robinson is a newcomer to the Leicestershire tendered bus service scene. He operates route 731 from Broughton Astley to Hinckley, the location of this view of S949RBE, a Mercedes-Benz Vario O814 bought new in 1999. It was bodied at the Autobus plant at Hellaby, near Rotherham, a company now part of the Optare group.
Steve Sanderson

SILVERDALE

Silverdale Tours (Nottingham) Ltd, 9 Westfield Way, Wilford, Nottingham, NG11 7ET
Croxmead Ltd, 3 Radford Estate, Old Oak Common Lane, North Acton, NW10

RRC489R	Leyland Leopard PSU3C/4R	Plaxton Supreme III Express	C53F	1976	Euroline, Radford, 1996
NNN473W	Leyland Atlantean AN68C/1R	Roe	B46/34F	1981	City of Nottingham, 1998
LHB50X	Leyland Tiger TRCTL11/3R	Plaxton Supreme V	C57F	1981	Cresswell, Moira, 1997
SND501X	Leyland Atlantean AN68B/1R	Northern Counties	B43/32F	1982	GM Buses South, 1997
SND518X	Leyland Atlantean AN68B/1R	Northern Counties	B43/32F	1982	GM Buses South, 1997
ATU200Y	Leyland Tiger TRCTL11/2R	Duple Dominant IV Express	C49F	1983	The Delaine, Bourne, 1996
TPD109Y	Leyland Tiger TRCTL11/2R	Duple Dominant IV Express	C53F	1983	The Delaine, Bourne, 1996
753BHT	Volvo B10M-61	Jonckheere Jubilee P90	C49/9FT	1984	Euroline, Radford, 1996
MCT812	Volvo B10M-61	Van Hool Astron	C49/11FT	1984	Euroline, Radford, 1996
LBZ6890	Neoplan N122/3	Neoplan Skyliner	C57/20CT	1986	Impact, Scotby, 1997
LBZ6891	Neoplan N122/3	Neoplan Skyliner	C57/20CT	1986	Impact, Scotby, 1997
J724CWT	Volvo B10M-60	Plaxton Premiere 350	C48FT	1992	Wallace Arnold, 1997
K590ABV	Scania K113TRB	Berkhof Excellence 3000 HD	C55/18CT	1992	Holmeswood Coaches, 1999
L911NWW	Volvo B10M-60	Van Hool Alizèe	C48FT	1994	Thorpe, Ossett, 1997
M939JJU	Volvo B10M-62	Plaxton Premiere 350	C53F	1995	Kime, Folkingham, 1996
M941JJU	Volvo B10M-62	Plaxton Premiere 350	C53F	1995	
M942JJU	Volvo B10M-62	Plaxton Premiere 350	C53F	1995	
IIB847	Toyota Coaster HZB50R	Caetano Optimo III	C21F	1996	Collins, Sandal, 1996
N125RJF	Volvo B10M-62	Plaxton Premiere 350	C53F	1996	
N126RJF	Volvo B10M-62	Plaxton Premiere 350	C53F	1996	
N127RJF	Volvo B10M-62	Plaxton Premiere 350	C53F	1996	
N164AHP	Volvo B10M-62	Plaxton Premiere 350	C53F	1996	
P394MDT	Volvo B10M-62	Plaxton Premiere 350	C53F	1997	
P395MDT	Volvo B10M-62	Plaxton Premiere 350	C53F	1997	
P350FRB	Dennis Javelin 12SDA2159	Plaxton Premiere 350	C53F	1997	
R964RCH	Volvo B10M-62	Plaxton Premiere 350	C53F	1998	
R965RCH	Volvo B10M-62	Plaxton Premiere 350	C53F	1998	
R498UFP	Volvo B10M-62	Caetano Enigma	C53F	1998	
R499UFP	Volvo B10M-62	Caetano Algarve II 3.5	C53F	1998	
R378AWP	MercedesBenz O1220L	Eurocoach	C33F	1998	
R830FWW	MercedesBenz O1220L	Ferqui-Optare Solera	C33F	1999	
R841FWW	MercedesBenz O1220L	Ferqui-Optare Solera	C33F	1999	
T361AJF	Volvo B10M-62	Caetano Enigma	C49FT	1999	
T362AJF	Volvo B10M-62	Caetano Enigma	C49FT	1999	
T363AJF	Volvo B10M-62	Caetano Enigma	C49FT	1999	
T364AJF	Volvo B10M-62	Caetano Enigma	C53F	1999	
T365AJF	Dennis Javelin	Caetano Enigma	C53F	1999	
T366AJF	Volvo B10M-62	Caetano Enigma	C53F	1999	
T180AUA	DAF DE33WSSB3000	Plaxton Premiere 350	C53F	1999	

Previous registrations:

753BHT	A119SNH	LBZ6841	D322NWL
IIB847	J489PJF	MCT812	A624UGD
LBZ6890	D321NWL		

Livery: White and red

Depots: Brookside Road, Ruddington; Chettles Industrial Estate, Radford; Old Oak Common Lane, North Acton.

SLACKS COACHES

K V & G L Slack, The Travel Centre, Lumsdale, Chesterfield Road, Matlock, Derbyshire, DE4 5LB

JRR566N	Ford R1114	Plaxton Panorama Elite III	C53F	1975	
XRR831S	Ford R1114	Plaxton Supreme III	C53F	1978	
DAZ8290	Leyland Leopard PSU3F/4R	Alexander AT	BC49F	1980	Shuttle Buses, Kilwinning, 1999
ORA452W	Leyland Atlantean AN68C/1R	East Lancashire	B47/31D	1981	City of Nottingham, 1998
PSV503	Volvo B10M-61	Van Hool Alizée H	C53FT	1994	Excelsior, Bournemouth, 1992
PSV259	DAF SB3000DKV601	Van Hool Alizée	C49FT	1990	Central, West Midlands, 1992
K112TCP	DAF SB3000DKVF601	Van Hool Alizée	C53F	1993	
K113TCP	DAF SB3000DKVF601	Van Hool Alizée	C53F	1993	
PSV562	Ford Transit VE6	Ford	M14	1993	Ford, Warley, 1994
M641RCP	DAF SB3000WS601	Van Hool Alizée HE	C51FT	1995	
M642RCP	DAF SB3000WS601	Van Hool Alizée HE	C51FT	1995	
N75FWU	DAF SB3000WS601	Van Hool Alizée HE	C51FT	1996	
P830ADO	Mercedes-Benz Vario O814	Autobus Classique	C29F	1997	
P25NKW	Dennis Javelin	Plaxton Premiére 320	C53F	1997	
R410YWJ	Dennis Javelin	Plaxton Premiére 320	C53F	1998	
R411YWJ	Dennis Javelin	Plaxton Premiére 320	C53F	1998	
S602ACT	Mercedes-Benz Vario 614D	Autobus Nouvelle 2	C24F	1999	
T859JBC	Iveco EuroRider 391.12.35	Beulas Stergo E	C49FT	1999	
T366JWA	Scania L94IB	Van Hool Alizée 2	C53F	1999	

Special event vehicles

774DNU	Commer Avenger III	Duple	C41F	1957	
878YTE	Commer Avenger IV	Plaxton	C41F	1962	Fairclough, Lostock, 1966

Previous Registrations:

774DNU	From new	DAZ8290	PGA829V		PSV503	E300OPR	
878YTE	From new	PSV259	G979KJX		PSV562	L446LVX	

Livery: Cream, green and red

Slack's main work is high-quality short break and long-term holidays. However, a small amount of local school work is also undertaken using a variety of vehicles. Prior to being replaced H831RWJ was seen on a day trip to Scarborough. This Scania K93CRB with Plaxton Paramount 3200 bodywork was on the seafront with imposing buildings and cliff lifts behind it.
Tony Wilson

SKILLS

**Skill's Motor Coaches Ltd; Skills Leisure Ltd; C G Littlewood Ltd;
1 St Peter's Street, Radford, Nottingham, NG7 3EL**

2	M150PKM	Volkswagen Caravelle	Volkswagen	M8	1995	private uowner, 1998
3	UIW9748	Mercedes-Benz 609D	Reeve Burgess	BC16F	1988	NCP, Paisley, 1998
4	R412DGU	Mercedes-Benz 412D	Crest	M15	1997	
5	R501BUA	Mercedes-Benz 412D	Crest	M15	1997	
7	CAZ2045	Kässbohrer Setra S210H	Kässbohrer	C35F	1994	Scancoaches, Battersea, 1998
8	CAZ2046	Kässbohrer Setra S210H	Kässbohrer	C35F	1994	Scancoaches, Battersea, 1998
9	L125XBD	Volkswagen Caravelle	Volkswagen	M8	1994	private owner, 1999
10	P210FRC	Kässbohrer Setra S215H	Kässbohrer	C48FT	1997	
11	P211FRC	Kässbohrer Setra S215H	Kässbohrer	C48FT	1997	
12	R612AAU	Setra S250 Special	Setra	C48F	1998	
14	R614AAU	Setra S250 Special	Setra	C48F	1998	
15	R615AAU	Setra S250 Special	Setra	C48F	1998	
16	R616AAU	Setra S250 Special	Setra	C48F	1998	
17	T	Setra S315 GT-HD	Setra	C44FT	1999	
18	N300TCC	Setra S250 Special	Setra	C57F	1996	Stort Valley-Travellers, Stansted, 1998
19	N400TCC	Setra S250 Special	Setra	C57F	1996	Stort Valley-Travellers, Stansted, 1998
21	N21ARC	DAF DE33WSSB3000	Plaxton Premiére 350	C49FT	1996	
22	T322KNN	Bova FHD12.340	Bova Futura	C49FT	1999	
30	S930ATO	Dennis Javelin	Plaxton Premiére 350	C49FT	1998	
31	M31TRR	Volvo B10M-62	Plaxton Premiére 350	C49FT	1995	
32	M32TRR	Volvo B10M-62	Plaxton Premiére 350	C49FT	1995	
33	M133TRR	Volvo B10M-62	Plaxton Premiére 350	C49FT	1995	
34	T	Setra S315 GT-HD	Setra	C44FT	1999	
35	T	Setra S315 GT-HD	Setra	C44FT	1999	
36	T	Setra S315 GT-HD	Setra	C44FT	1999	

39-44		Volvo B10M-62	Plaxton Premiére 350	C49FT	1996	

39	N39ARC	**42**	N746BAU	**43**	N43ARC	**44**	N144ARC	**45** N45ARC
40	N140ARC							

46	F46LCH	Volvo B10M-60	Plaxton Paramount 3200 III	C53F	1989	
53	G553RRR	Volvo B10M-60	Plaxton Paramount 3200 III	C53DL	1990	
54	YXI7380	Volvo B10M-61	Van Hool Alizée H	C53F	1989	Shearings, 1996
56	YXI9256	Volvo B10M-61	Van Hool Alizée H	C53F	1989	Shearings, 1996
57	YXI5503	Volvo B10M-61	Van Hool Alizée H	C53F	1989	Shearings, 1996
58	YXI9258	Volvo B10M-61	Van Hool Alizée H	C53F	1989	Shearings, 1996
61	M736RCP	DAF SB3000WS601	Van Hool Alizée HE	C53F	1995	London Coaches, Kent, 1999
62	M737RCP	DAF SB3000WS601	Van Hool Alizée HE	C53F	1995	London Coaches, Kent, 1999
63	M738RCP	DAF SB3000WS601	Van Hool Alizée HE	C53F	1995	London Coaches, Kent, 1999
64	M739RCP	DAF SB3000WS601	Van Hool Alizée HE	C53F	1995	London Coaches, Kent, 1999
66	YXI7906	Volvo B10M-61	Van Hool Alizée H	C53F	1989	Shearings, 1996
67	YXI5860	Volvo B10M-61	Van Hool Alizée H	C53F	1989	Shearings, 1996
68	YXI8421	Volvo B10M-61	Van Hool Alizée H	C53F	1989	Shearings, 1996
69	YXI9243	Volvo B10M-61	Van Hool Alizée H	C53F	1989	Shearings, 1996
70	K770JRA	Toyota Coaster HDB30R	Caetano Optimo II	C21F	1993	
72	BAZ7360	Volvo B10M-60	Van Hool Alizée H	C53F	1989	Shearings, 1997
74	IIL7074	Leyland Tiger TRCTL11/3ARZ	Duple 340	C53F	1989	Shearings, 1993

75-81		Volvo B10M-60	Van Hool Alizée H	C53F	1989	Shearings, 1997		

75	BAZ7059	**77**	BAZ7056	**79**	BAZ7057	**80**	BAZ7058	**81** BAZ7912
76	BAZ7918	**78**	BAZ7914					

85	UIW2285	Volvo B10M-60	Van Hool Alizée H	C52F	1989	Ralph's, Langley, 1996

These two views of Skills Setra coaches give the opportunity to compare two different models that have been built by the German manufacturer which is now part of Evobus, a division of Mercedes-Benz. R614AAU is a 12 metre S250 Special model built for the company in 1998. The S250 Special continued in production mostly for the right-hand drive market while the main deliveries in left-hand drive form had progressed to the new 300 series model. This high-floor coach includes some of the new features such as 'praying mantis' mirrors. CAZ2045 is an S210H model which is shorter and lower. New in 1994, this 35 seater was last operated by Scancoaches in 1998. Both carry the Skills livery produced by the well-known designer Ray Stenning. *David Heath*

There are a small number of minicoaches in the Skills fleet. They are used for small party hire and as feeder coaches for the company's extensive tour programme. UIW9748 is a Mercedes-Benz 609D converted by Reeve Burgess and displayed at Showbus in 1998, the principal bus rally held at RAF Duxford each September. *Steve Sanderson*

B40-90

B40-90		Volvo B10M-62		Plaxton Premiére 350	C49FT	1996	Speedlink, 1997
B40	N40SLK	**B60**	N60SLK	**B70**	N70SLK	**B80**	N80SLK	**B90**	N90SLK
B50	N50SLK						

B93	J693LGA	Volvo B10M-60		Van Hool Alizée H	C49FT	1992	Park's of Hamilton, 1996

Special event vehicle

1	6EBH	Bedford SB3		Duple Embassy	C37F	1958	Soul, Olney, 1992
	EJC1	Bedford SB3		Duple Embassy	C37F	1957	Clarke, Newthorpe, 1997

Previous Registrations:

6EBH	From new	CAZ2045	From new	YXI5860	F740ENE
BAZ7360	G860RNC	CAZ2046	From new	YXI7380	F742ENE
BAZ7059	G859RNC	EJC1	From new	YXI7906	F744ENE
BAZ7918	G863RNC	IIL7074	F786GNA	YXI8421	F745ENE
BAZ7056	G856RNC	J693LGA	J464HDS, LSK504	YXI9243	F748ENE
BAZ7914	G864RNC	N746BAU	N1SMC	YXI9258	F751ENE
BAZ7057	G857RNC	UIW2285	F812TMD	YXI9256	F750ENE
BAZ7058	G858RNC	UIW9748	E627FLD		
BAZ7912	G862RNC	YXI5503	F739ENE		

Named vehicles; 33 *Spirit of Lancing;* B40 *Spirit of Peacehaven*

Livery: Green, blue, black, and yellow; white ,blue and grey (Coachstyle Holidays) 55-57 ,61-4/6/8/9, 76-8, 80-2; white and red (Eurolines) 22; white (National Express Shuttle) - B30/40/50/60/70/80/90; white and blue (Leger Travel) 21; (Derby university) 67, multi-colour (Seaside shuttle) 54, 85; white B93.

Allocations: Brighton (New England Street) B30/40/50/60/70/80/90/3; Nottingham(Radford) remainder.

SKINNER

T A & T J Skinner, Main Street, Saltby, Melton Mowbray, Leicestershire, LE14 4QW

A141BTV	Bedford YNT	Plaxton Paramount 3200	C53F	1983	Leah, Huthwaite, 1988
A837EAY	Bedford YNT	Plaxton Paramount 3200	C53F	1983	Lester, Long Whatton, 1985
E752HJF	Dennis Javelin 12SDA1907	Duple 320	C57F	1988	Lewis, Pailton, 1990
E131PLJ	Dennis Javelin 12SDA1907	Plaxton Paramount 3200 III	C53F	1988	Winterbourne Pioneer, 1993
G324BHN	Dennis Javelin 12SDA1916	Plaxton Paramount 3200 III	C53F	1989	Winn Bros, Brompton, 1995
G453PGO	Dennis Javelin 12SDA1907	Plaxton Paramount 3200 III	C53F	1990	Bluebird of Neath, 1998
G48HDW	Dennis Javelin 12SDA1907	Duple 320	C57F	1990	Bebb, Llantwit Fardre, 1992
K813LMY	Toyota Coaster HB31R	Caetano Optimo	C21F	199?	Empress, Bethnal Green, 1999

Previous registration

G453PGO	G453PGO, RJI8603		K813LMY	K813VBC, PIW2635

Livery: Blue and white

The latest addition to the Skinner fleet is their first small vehicle to be purchased for some time. K813LMY is a Toyota Coaster HB31R which seats twenty-one passengers. This Japanese-chassied vehicle is imported into Britain by Salvador Caetano, a Portuguese coachbuilder, who holds the only such licence to construct such vehicles for the UK market. At Skinner's base in June 1999, the coach has just been washed down after operating Leicestershire school contract No S492. *Steve Sanderson*

SLEAFORDIAN

Sleaford Taxi Co Ltd, 49 Westgate, Sleaford, Lincolnshire, NG34 7GU

K953CJN	Ford Transit VE6	Ford	M12	1992	Ford, Swaythling, 1996
KTL982	Mercedes-Benz 811D	Reeve Burgess Beaver	C33F	199-	Red Arrow, Huddersfield, 1999
NTL939	Volvo B10M-60	Plaxton Première 320	C53F	1993	Supreme, Coventry, 1996
YCT463	Volvo B10M-62	Plaxton Première 320	C49FT	1995	Excelsior, Bournemouth, 1997
KVL261	Volvo B10M-62	Plaxton Première 320	C49FT	199x	Excelsior, Bournemouth, 1998
M691MRU	Volvo B10M-62	Plaxton Excalibur	C49FT	199-	Excelsior, Bournemouth, 1999
P887RHK	Ford Transit VE6	Ford	M12	1997	private owner, 1998

Previous Registrations:

KTL982	6499KX	NTL939	K887BRW
KVL261	A12EXC, N227THO	YCT463	A10EXC, M514NCG
M691MRU	A1XEL		

Livery: White and Yellow

Sleafordian operate a bus service into the company's home town of Sleaford from a number of villages to the south and east. A recent purchase for this work is 6499HX. This Mercedes-Benz 811D was last operated by Red Arrow of Huddersfield and when seen in Sleaford in July 1999 still carried the Red Arrow livery which is not dissimilar to Sleafordian colours. It has since been re-registered with cherished local mark, KTL982, originally issued by Kesteven. *Steve Sanderson*

STAGECOACH EAST MIDLAND

East Midland Motor Services Ltd, Grimsby Cleethorpes Transport Ltd, Chesterfield Transport Ltd, New Street, Chesterfield, Derbyshire, S40 2LQ

1-9   Dennis Lance 11SDA3106*   East Lancashire EL2000   B45F   1993   1-7 ex Grimsby Cleethorpes, 1993
*5-9 are type 11SDA3111

| 1 | K701NDO | 3 | K703NDO | 5 | L705HFU | 7 | L707HFU | 9 | L709HFU |
| 2 | K702NDO | 4 | K704NDO | 6 | L706HFU | 8 | L708HFU | | |

12-19   Mercedes-Benz 811D   Alexander Sprint   B31F   1992   Chesterfield, 1995

| 12 | J213AET | 15 | J215AET | 17 | J217AET | 18 | J218AET | 19 | J219AET |
| 14 | J214AET | 16 | J216AET | | | | | | |

21	EKY21V	Leyland National 2 NL116L11/1R		B52F	1980	Chesterfield, 1995
22	EKY22V	Leyland National 2 NL116L11/1R		B52F	1980	Chesterfield, 1995
23	EKY23V	Leyland National 2 NL116L11/1R		B52F	1981	Chesterfield, 1995

24-29   Leyland National 2 NL106L11/1R   B44F   1980   Chesterfield, 1995

| 24 | EKY24V | 25 | EKY25V | 27 | EKY27V | 28 | EKY28V | 29 | EKY29V |

30-34   Leyland National 2 NL116AL11/1R   B52F   1981   Chesterfield, 1995

| 30 | OWB30X | 31 | OWB31X | 32 | OWB32X | 33 | OWB33X | 34 | OWB34X |

35	SKY31Y	Leyland Tiger TRCTL11/3R	Eastern Coach Works B51	C51F	1983
36	SKY32Y	Leyland Tiger TRCTL11/3R	Eastern Coach Works B51	C51F	1983
37	PJI4316	Leyland Tiger TRCTL11/2R	Duple Dominant IV	C47F	1983
39	A39XHE	Leyland Tiger TRCTL11/2R	Alexander TE	BC45F	1983
41	A41XHE	Leyland Tiger TRCTL11/2R	Alexander TE	BC45F	1984
42	A42XHE	Leyland Tiger TRCTL11/2R	Alexander TE	BC49F	1984
44	A44XHE	Leyland Tiger TRCTL11/2R	Alexander TE	BC45F	1984
48	B54DWJ	Leyland Tiger TRCTL11/2RH	Alexander TE	BC49F	1985

50-55   Leyland National 2 NL116HLXCT/1R   B52F   1984   Chesterfield, 1995

| 50 | B150DHL | 52 | B152DHL | 53 | B153DHL | 54 | B154DHL | 55 | B155DHL |
| 51 | B151DHL | | | | | | | | |

59	B52DWE	Leyland Tiger TRCTL11/2RH	Alexander TE	BC49F	1984	
60	B53DWJ	Leyland Tiger TRCTL11/2RH	Alexander TE	BC49F	1985	
64	E60WDT	Leyland Lynx LX112TL11ZR1	Leyland Lynx	BC49F	1988	Chesterfield, 1995
65	E61WDT	Leyland Lynx LX112TL11ZR1	Leyland Lynx	BC49F	1988	Chesterfield, 1995
71	A71GEE	Leyland Olympian ONTL11/1R	Eastern Coach Works	B45/31F	1983	Grimsby Cleethorpes, 1993
72	A72GEE	Leyland Olympian ONTL11/1R	Eastern Coach Works	B45/31F	1983	Grimsby Cleethorpes, 1993
73	A73GEE	Leyland Olympian ONTL11/1R	Eastern Coach Works	B47/28D	1983	Grimsby Cleethorpes, 1993
74	A74GEE	Leyland Olympian ONTL11/1R	Eastern Coach Works	B47/28D	1983	Grimsby Cleethorpes, 1993
75	F75TFU	Dennis Dominator DDA1021	Alexander RH	B45/33F	1989	Grimsby Cleethorpes, 1993
76	F76TFU	Dennis Dominator DDA1021	Alexander RH	B45/33F	1989	Grimsby Cleethorpes, 1993
77	F77TFU	Dennis Dominator DDA1021	Alexander RH	B45/33F	1989	Grimsby Cleethorpes, 1993
78	F78TFU	Dennis Dominator DDA1022	Alexander RH	B45/33F	1989	Grimsby Cleethorpes, 1993
79	G79VFW	Dennis Dominator DDA1028	Alexander RH	B45/33F	1990	Grimsby Cleethorpes, 1993
80	G80VFW	Dennis Dominator DDA1028	Alexander RH	B45/33F	1990	Grimsby Cleethorpes, 1993
81	G81VFW	Dennis Dominator DDA1029	Alexander RH	B45/33F	1990	Grimsby Cleethorpes, 1993

82-89   Dennis Dominator DDA1034*   East Lancashire   B45/33F   1991-92 Grimsby Cleethorpes, 1993
*86-9 are DDA1036

| 82 | H482BEE | 84 | H484BEE | 86 | J91DJV | 88 | J93DJV | 89 | J94DJV |
| 83 | H483BEE | 85 | H485BEE | 87 | J92DJV | | | | |

90-98   Mercedes-Benz 709D   Alexander Sprint   B25F*   1988   Chesterfield, 1995
*97/8 are DP25F

| 90 | E90YWB | 92 | E92YWB | 94 | E94YWB | 96 | E96YWB | 98 | E98YWB |
| 91 | E91YWB | 93 | E93YWB | 95 | E95YWB | 97 | E97YWB | | |

| 99 | H257THL | Mercedes-Benz 709D | Reeve Burgess Beaver | B25F | 1991 | Chesterfield, 1995 |

101-109   Volvo Olympian YN2RV18Z4   Northern Counties Palatine   B47/29F   1993

| 101 | K101JWJ | 103 | K103JWJ | 105 | K105JWJ | 107 | K107JWJ | 109 | L109LHL |
| 102 | K102JWJ | 104 | K104JWJ | 106 | K106JWJ | 108 | L108LHL | | |

| 113 | MBE613R | Leyland Fleetline FE30AGR | Roe | O45/29D | 1976 | Grimsby Cleethorpes, 1993 |
| 114 | BJV103L | Daimler Fleetline CRG6LX | Roe | O45/29D | 1973 | Grimsby Cleethorpes, 1993 |

130-144   Volvo Olympian YN2RV18Z4   Alexander RL   B47/32F   1995

130	N130AET	133	N133AET	136	N136AET	139	N139AET	142	N142AET
131	N131AET	134	N134AET	137	N137AET	140	N140AET	143	N143AET
132	N132AET	135	N135AET	138	N138AET	141	N141AET	144	N144AET

145-160   Volvo Olympian   Alexander RL   B51/35F   1996-97

145	P145KWJ	149	P149KWJ	152	P152KWJ	156	P156KWJ	159	P159KAK
146	P146KWJ	150	P150KWJ	153	P153KWJ	157	P157KWJ	160	P160KAK
148	P148KWJ	151	P151KWJ	154	P154KWJ	158	P158KWJ		

161-169   Volvo Olympian   Alexander RL   B51/36F   1998

| 161 | S161RET | 163 | S163RET | 165 | S165RET | 167 | S167RET | 169 | S169RET |
| 162 | S162RET | 164 | S164RET | 166 | S166RET | 168 | S168RET | | |

172	XGS736S	Leyland Leopard PSU3E/4R	Plaxton Supreme III	C53F	1978	Grimsby Cleethorpes, 1993
173	BHO441V	Leyland Leopard PSU5C/4R	Duple Dominant II	C55F	1980	Grimsby Cleethorpes, 1993
174	MRJ270W	Leyland Leopard PSU5C/4R	Plaxton Supreme IV	C41DL	1980	Grimsby Cleethorpes, 1993
175	EFU935Y	Leyland Leopard PSU5C/4R	Duple Dominant I	C53F	1983	Grimsby Cleethorpes, 1993
176	OJL823Y	Leyland Leopard PSU5C/4R	Duple Dominant III	C53F	1983	Grimsby Cleethorpes, 1993
183	PJI4314	Leyland Tiger TRCTL11/2R	Plaxton Paramount 3200 E	C47F	1983	
187	PYE841Y	Leyland Tiger TRCTL11/3R	Duple Laser	C53F	1983	Grimsby Cleethorpes, 1993
188	PYE842Y	Leyland Tiger TRCTL11/3R	Duple Laser	C53F	1983	Grimsby Cleethorpes, 1993
190	PSU443	Leyland Tiger TRCTL11/3R	Duple Laser	C53F	1983	Grimsby Cleethorpes, 1993
191	A243YGF	Leyland Tiger TRCTL11/3RH	Duple Laser	C57F	1984	Grimsby Cleethorpes, 1993
192	PS2743	Leyland Tiger TRCTL11/3RH	Duple Laser	C57F	1984	Grimsby Cleethorpes, 1993

209-224   Bristol VRT/SL3/6LXB*   Eastern Coach Works   B43/31F   1980-81 *218 is type 6LXC

| 209 | EWE203V | 211 | JAK211W | 218 | KWA218W | 223 | KWA223W | 224 | KWA224W |
| 210 | EWE206V | 214 | KWA214W | 221 | KWA221W | | | | |

231	EJV31Y	Dennis Falcon H SDA411	Wadham Stringer Vanguard	B42F	1983	Grimsby Cleethorpes, 1993
232	EJV32Y	Dennis Falcon H SDA411	Wadham Stringer Vanguard	B42F	1983	Grimsby Cleethorpes, 1993
233	EJV33Y	Dennis Falcon H SDA411	Wadham Stringer Vanguard	B42F	1983	Grimsby Cleethorpes, 1993
234	EJV34Y	Dennis Falcon H SDA411	Wadham Stringer Vanguard	B42F	1983	Grimsby Cleethorpes, 1993
259	BFW136W	Ford R1114	Plaxton Supreme IV	C53F	1981	Grimsby Cleethorpes, 1993
260	UWA150S	Leyland Fleetline FE30AGR	Roe	B42/29D	1978	Chesterfield, 1995
261	UWA151S	Leyland Fleetline FE30AGR	Roe	B42/29D	1978	Chesterfield, 1995
262	OCU819R	Leyland Fleetline FE30AGR	Alexander AL	B44/30F	1977	Stagecoach Busways, 1998
263	OCU822R	Leyland Fleetline FE30AGR	Alexander AL	B44/30F	1977	Stagecoach Busways, 1998
299	TWF201Y	Leyland Olympian ONLXB/1R	Roe	B47/29F	1982	Chesterfield, 1995
300	TWF202Y	Leyland Olympian ONLXB/1R	Roe	B47/29F	1982	Chesterfield, 1995

301-325   Leyland Olympian ONLXB/1R   Eastern Coach Works   B45/32F   1981-84

301	NHL301X	306	SHE306Y	311	SHE311Y	316	A316XWG	321	A321YWJ
302	NHL302X	307	SHE307Y	312	UDT312Y	317	A317XWG	322	A322AKU
303	NHL303X	308	SHE308Y	313	UDT313Y	318	A318XWG	323	A323AKU
304	NHL304X	309	SHE309Y	314	A314XWG	319	A319YWJ	324	A324AKU
305	NHL305X	310	SHE310Y	315	A315XWG	320	A320YWJ	325	A325AKU

Having been made surplus to requirements from operating in Grimsby during 1998, this Dennis Falcon was transferred inland to Worksop and thence to the Stonegravels base of Stagecoach East Midlands at Chesterfield. Nicknamed 'The Fish Fryer', the vehicle has since provided sterling service on local services, predominantly the 38/39 routes linking the estates of Holme Hall and Grangewood Farm on either side of the town. East Midland 231, EJV31Y with Wadham Stringer body pulls away from the Town Hall. *Tony Wilson*

326-330

Leyland Olympian ONLXB/1R   Eastern Coach Works   BC40/32F   1985

326	C326HWJ	327	C327HWJ	328	C328HWJ	329	C329HWJ	330	C330HWJ

331-336

Leyland Olympian ONLXB/1R   Eastern Coach Works   B45/32F   1986

331	C331HWJ	333	C333HWJ	334	C334HWJ	335	C335HWJ	336	C336HWJ
332	C332HWJ								

337	GSO8V	Leyland Olympian ONLXB/1RV	Alexander RL	B45/32F	1987	Stagecoach United Counties, 1992

339-343

Leyland Olympian ON6LXB/2RZ   Alexander RL   BC51/31F   1989

339	G339KKW	340	G340KKW	341	G341KKW	342	G342KKW	343	G343KKW

344-353

Leyland Olympian ON2R56G13Z4 Alexander RL   BC51/31F*   1990-91 *349-353 are BC47/27F

344	H344SWA	346	H346SWA	348	H348SWA	350	J350XET	352	J352XET
345	H345SWA	347	H347SWA	349	J349XET	351	J351XET	353	J353XET

354-358

Leyland Olympian ON2R50G13Z4 Northern Counties Palatine   B47/29F   1992

354	K354DWJ	355	K355DWJ	356	K356DWJ	357	K357DWJ	358	K358DWJ

359-363

Leyland Olympian ON2R50G13Z4   Alexander RL   BC43/27F   1992

359	K359DWJ	360	K360DWJ	361	K361DWJ	362	K362DWJ	363	K363DWJ

370-386

Dennis Trident   Alexander ALX400   N--/--F   1999

370	T370FWG	374	T374FWG	378	T378FWG	381	T381FWG	384	T384FWG
371	T371FWG	375	T375FWG	379	T379FWG	382	T382FWG	385	T385FWG
372	T372FWG	376	T376FWG	380	T380FWG	383	T383FWG	386	T386FWG
373	T373FWG	377	T377FWG						

No.	Reg	Chassis	Body	Seating	Year	Notes
401	S401SDT	Dennis Dart SLF	Alexander ALX200	N37F	1998	
402	S402SDT	Dennis Dart SLF	Alexander ALX200	N37F	1998	
403	S403SDT	Dennis Dart SLF	Alexander ALX200	N37F	1998	
412	DWF22V	Leyland Leopard PSU3E/4R	Duple Dominant(1985)	B55F	1979	
413	DWF23V	Leyland Leopard PSU3E/4R	Duple Dominant(1985)	B51F	1979	
414	DWF24V	Leyland Leopard PSU3E/4R	Alexander P(1985)	B52F	1979	
416	DWF26V	Leyland Leopard PSU3E/4R	Duple Dominant(1985)	B55F	1980	
418	P418KWF	Dennis Dart	Alexander Dash	B41F	1996	
419	P419KWF	Dennis Dart	Alexander Dash	B41F	1996	
420	P420KWF	Dennis Dart	Alexander Dash	B41F	1996	
421	E927PBE	Leyland Tiger TRBLXCT/2RH	Alexander P	B51F	1987	Grimsby Cleethorpes, 1993
422	E928PBE	Leyland Tiger TRBLXCT/2RH	Alexander P	BC51F	1987	Grimsby Cleethorpes, 1993
423	E929PBE	Leyland Tiger TRBLXCT/2RH	Alexander P	BC51F	1987	Grimsby Cleethorpes, 1993
424	E930PBE	Leyland Tiger TRBLXCT/2RH	Alexander P	BC51F	1987	Grimsby Cleethorpes, 1993

425-433

Leyland Tiger TRCTL11/2RH — Alexander P — B52F — 1985

425	B625DWF	427	B627DWF	429	B629DWF	431	B631DWF	433	B633DWF
426	B626DWF	428	B628DWF	430	B630DWF	432	B632DWF		

435-453

Volvo B6-9.9M — Alexander Dash — B40F — 1993

435	L435LWA	439	L439LWA	443	L443LWA	448	L448LWA	451	L451LWA
436	L436LWA	440	L440LWA	445	L445LWA	449	L449LWA	452	L452LWA
437	L437LWA	441	L441LWA	446	L446LWA	450	L450LWA	453	L453LHL
438	L438LWA	442	L442LWA	447	L447LWA				

591-600

Volvo B10M-55 — Alexander PS — BC48F — 1994 — Stagecoach Ribble, 1995

591	L341KCK	593	L343KCK	595	L339KCK	597	M411RRN	599	M413RRN
592	L342KCK	594	L344KCK	596	L340KCK	598	M412RRN	600	M414RRN

601-609

Volvo B10M-55 — Alexander PS — BC48F — 1995

601	M601VHE	603	M603VHE	605	M605VHE	607	M607VHE	609	M609WET
602	M602VHE	604	M604VHE	606	M606VHE	608	M608WET		

No.	Reg	Chassis	Seating	Year	Notes
614	EKW614V	Leyland National 2 NL106L11/1R	B44F	1980	
615	EKW615V	Leyland National 2 NL106L11/1R	B44F	1980	
616	EKW616V	Leyland National 2 NL106L11/1R	B44F	1980	
617	GWE617V	Leyland National 2 NL116L11/1R	B49F	1980	
618	GWE618V	Leyland National 2 NL116L11/1R	B49F	1980	
619	GWE619V	Leyland National 2 NL116L11/1R	B49F	1980	
620	GWE620V	Leyland National 2 NL116L11/1R	B49F	1980	
622	MWG622X	Leyland National 2 NL116AL11/1R	B49F	1981	
623	MWG623X	Leyland National 2 NL116AL11/1R	B49F	1981	
624	MWG624X	Leyland National 2 NL116AL11/1R	B49F	1981	
625	LAG188V	Leyland National 2 NL116L11/1R	B49F	1980	East Yorkshire, 1988
626	LAG189V	Leyland National 2 NL116L11/1R	B49F	1980	East Yorkshire, 1988
627	NRP580V	Leyland National 2 NL116L11/1R	B49F	1980	Stagecoach United Counties, 1992
628	SVV586W	Leyland National 2 NL116L11/1R	B49F	1981	Stagecoach United Counties, 1992
634	VWA34Y	Leyland National 2 NL116HLXB/1R	BC47F	1983	
635	VWA35Y	Leyland National 2 NL116HLXB/1R	BC47F	1983	
636	VWA36Y	Leyland National 2 NL116HLXB/1R	BC47F	1983	

637-643

Volvo B10M-62 — Plaxton Premiére Interurban — BC51F — 1993

637	L637LDT	639	L639LDT	641	L641LDT	642	L642LDT	643	L643LDT
638	L638LDT	640	L640LDT						

Opposite, top: **Fourteen double-deck buses were added to the Chesterfield based fleet in 1996-97. With long wheelbases, these Volvo Olympians carried Alexander RL bodywork, a product that has now ceased production in favour of the ALX400. New Beetwell Street in Chesterfield finds one of the batch, 149, P149KWJ, on the long 747 service from Sheffield to Nottingham, a service that links three counties. As we go to press the first of the Dennis Tridents for the fleet are being delivered. These will displace Dennis Dominators at Grimsby.** *Tony Wilson*

Opposite, bottom: **Four recent arrivals with East Midlands fleet are Jonckheere Modulo-bodied Volvo B10M single-deckers. These are mostly used on the longer limited stop services. Seen descending Mansfield road in Nottingham as it approaches the Victoria terminus of the long 747 service is 670, S670RWJ.Some vehicles on Stagecoach Express route 757 are provided under franchise by Trent, whose vehicles used for the work carry Stagecoach livery.** *Tony Wilson*

The East Midlands Bus Handbook

The vagaries of vehicle requirements necessitate some fleets to have a pool of buses in reserve. Thus Stagecoach East Midland were the recipients of a couple of former Busways Daimler Fleetlines. Now numbered 262, OCU819R casts a long shadow as it leaves Chesterfield on the 17:25 departure bound for Matlock. The nearside lower window arrangement identifies the unusual position for the staircase, a layout unique to Tyne & Wear. *Tony Wilson*

644	J430HDS	Volvo B10M-60	Plaxton Premiére 350	C49FT	1992	Stagecoach United Counties, 1998	
645	J439HDS	Volvo B10M-60	Plaxton Premiére 350	C49FT	1992	Stagecoach United Counties, 1998	
646	J450HDS	Volvo B10M-60	Plaxton Premiére 350	C49FT	1992	Stagecoach United Counties, 1998	
656	M942TSX	Volvo B10M-60	Plaxton Premiére Interurban	BC51F	1994	Fife Scottish, 1997	
657	M943TSX	Volvo B10M-60	Plaxton Premiére Interurban	BC51F	1994	Fife Scottish, 1997	
658	K575DFS	Volvo B10M-60	Plaxton Premiére Interurban	BC51F	1993	Western Buses, 1997	
662	M808JTY	Volvo B10M-62	Plaxton Expressliner 2	C44FT	1995	Stagecoach Busways, 1997	
663	R663TKU	Volvo B10M-62	Plaxton Expressliner 2	C44FT	1997		
664	R664TKU	Volvo B10M-62	Plaxton Expressliner 2	C44FT	1997		
665	S665SDT	Volvo B10M-62	Jonckheere Mistral 50	C44FT	1998		
670	S670SDT	Volvo B10M-62	Jonckheere Modulo	BC51F	1998		
671	S671SDT	Volvo B10M-62	Jonckheere Modulo	BC51F	1998		
672	S672SDT	Volvo B10M-62	Jonckheere Modulo	BC51F	1998		
673	S673SDT	Volvo B10M-62	Jonckheere Modulo	BC51F	1998		

720-727   Mercedes-Benz 811D   Reeve Burgess Beaver   B31F   1989-90

720	G820KWF	722	G822KWF	724	G824KWF	726	G826KWF	727	G827KWF
721	G821KWF	723	G823KWF	725	G825KWF				

728	E721BVO	Mercedes-Benz 811D	Optare StarRider	B33F	1988	Maun, Mansfield, 1990
729	E880DRA	Mercedes-Benz 811D	Optare StarRider	B33F	1988	Maun, Mansfield, 1990

731-751   Mercedes-Benz 709D   Alexander Sprint   B25F   1993

731	L731LWA	735	L735LWA	739	L739LWA	743	L743LWA	748	L748LWA
732	L732LWA	736	L736LWA	740	L740LWA	744	L744LWA	749	L749LWA
733	L733LWA	737	L737LWA	741	L741LWA	745	L745LWA	750	L750LWA
734	L734LWA	738	L738LWA	742	L742LWA	746	L746LWA	751	L751LHL

752-776

		Mercedes-Benz 709D		Alexander Sprint		B25F*	1995-96 *752-61 are B23F

752	N752CKU	757	N757CKU	762	N762EWG	767	N767EWG	772	N772EWG
753	N753CKU	758	N758CKU	763	N763EWG	768	N768EWG	773	N773EWG
754	N754CKU	759	N759CKU	764	N764EWG	769	N769EWG	774	N774EWG
755	N755CKU	760	N760CKU	765	N765EWG	770	N770EWG	775	N775EWG
756	N756CKU	761	N761CKU	766	N766EWG	771	N771EWG	776	N776EWG

801	T801OHL	Dennis Dart SLF	Plaxton Pointer 2	BC38F	1999	
802	T802OHL	Dennis Dart SLF	Plaxton Pointer 2	BC38F	1999	
803	T803OHL	Dennis Dart SLF	Plaxton Pointer 2	BC38F	1999	
902	E47HFE	MCW MetroRider MF150/94	MCW	B23F	1988	Grimsby Cleethorpes, 1993
903	E48HFE	MCW MetroRider MF150/94	MCW	B23F	1988	Grimsby Cleethorpes, 1993
904	E49HFE	MCW MetroRider MF150/94	MCW	B23F	1988	Grimsby Cleethorpes, 1993
905	E50HFE	MCW MetroRider MF150/94	MCW	B23F	1988	Grimsby Cleethorpes, 1993
909	E58HFE	MCW MetroRider MF150/94	MCW	BC23F	1988	Grimsby Cleethorpes, 1993

Ancilliary vehicles:-

T1	LPT872T	Bedford YMT	Plaxton Supreme IV Express	TV	1978	Rainworth Travel, 1991
T2	YVL599X	Ford R1114	Duple Dominant III	TV	1981	Grimsby Cleethorpes, 1993
T3	FTO550V	Bedford YMT	Plaxton Supreme IV Express	TV	1979	Chesterfield, 1994
177	OJL822Y	Leyland Leopard PSU5C/4R	Duple Dominant III	TV	1983	Grimsby Cleethorpes, 1993
1023	D933TWE	Dodge Command G13	Wadham Stringer Vanguard	TV	1986	MoD, 1998 (81KF14)
1024	D932TWE	Dodge Command G13	Wadham Stringer Vanguard	TV	1987	MoD, 1998 (93KF03)
1025	E250AKW	Dodge Command G13	Wadham Stringer Vanguard	TV	1987	MoD, 1998 (93KF53)
1026	D935TWE	Dodge Command G13	Wadham Stringer Vanguard	TV	1986	MoD, 1998 (80KF53)

Previous Registrations:

A243YGF	A601HVT, PS2045	PJI4316	UHE37Y
GSO8V	D378XRS	PS2743	A602HVT
OJL822Y	SSG321Y, PS2945	PSU443	A844SYR
OJL823Y	EJV419Y, PS2743	PSU764	PYE843Y
PJI4314	UWJ33Y		

Allocations:-

Chesterfield (Stonegravels)

Mercedes-Benz	15	16	17	18	19	92	93	94
	95	96	97	99	720	721	722	723
	725	726	727	728	729	744	745	746
	749	750	751	752	753	754	755	756
	757	758	759	760	761	762	763	764
	765	766						
Coaches	644	645	646					
Dart	418	419	420	801	802	803		
Falcon	231							
National 2	29	30	31	32	33	34	54	614
	616	617	618	619	620	622	623	624
	625							
Tiger	39	44	183	425	426	427	428	429
	430	431	432	433				
Volvo PS	591	592	593	594	595	596	597	598
	640	641	672	673				
Bristol VR	260	261	262	263				
Olympian	145	146	148	149	150	151	152	153
	154	156	157	158	159	160	299	300
	304	305	306	307	310	312	316	317
	318	327	329	334	339	341	342	347
	348	349	350					

Calver (Flinthouse Garage)

Mercedes-Benz	12	14					
National 2	21	22	23	24	25	27	28	50
	51						
Lynx	64	65					

Grimsby (Victoria Street) - Grimsby-Cleethorpes

Mercedes-Benz	767	768	769	770	771	772	773
Dennis Lance	1	2	3	4	5	6	7	8
	9						
Dennis Falcon	232	233	234				
Dennis Dart	401	402	403				
Leopard	172	173	174	175	176		
Ford	259						
Tiger	35	37	59	60	187	188	190	191
	192	421	422	423	424		
Interurban	638	643	670	671			
Dominator	75	76	77	78	79	80	81	82
	83	84	85	86	87	88	89	
Fleetline Open-top	113	114					
Olympian	71	72	73	74	130	131	132	133
	134	135	136	137	138	139	140	141
	142	143	144	303			

Mansfield (Sutton Road)

MetroRider	902	904	909				
Mercedes-Benz	90	91	748	774	775	776	
Interurban	637	642	656	657			
Volvo B10M Coach	662	663	664	665			
National 2	615	626	627				
Tiger	42						
Volvo B6	435	436	437	438	439	440	441	442
	443	445	446	447	448	449	450	451
	452	453					
Volvo PS	601	602	603	604	605	606	607	608
	609						
Bristol VR	210	211	214	221	224		
Olympian	101	102	103	104	105	106	107	108
	109	308	309	311	314	315	322	
	324	325	331	332	335	336	337	340
	343	344	345	346	351	352	353	354
	355	356	357	358			

Worksop (Hardy Street)

Mercedes-Benz	98	724	731	732	733	734	735	736
	737	738	739	740	741	742	743	
Interurban	658						
Volvo PS	599	600	639				
T iger	36	41	48				
National 2	52	53	55	628	634	635	636	
Leopard	412	413	414	416			
Olympian	161	162	163	164	165	166	167	168
	169	301	319	320	321	323	326	328
	330	333	359	360	361	362	363	

Unallocated and stored

MetroRider	903	905	
Tiger	189		
Bristol VR	209	218	223
Olympian	313		
Dennis Trident	As we go to press these are starting to arrive and are expected to displace Dennis Dominators at Grimsby.		

SWEYNE

JE, JJ & M Holt, Longshores, Reedness Road, Swinefleet, North Lincolnshire, DN14 8EL

CSU935	Leyland Leopard PSU4E/2R	Plaxton P'mount 3200 (1987)	C45F	1977	Wallace Arnold, 1990
HSC104T	Leyland National 11351A/1R (DAF)		B49F	1978	Fife Scottish, 1992
PIL2482	Leyland Leopard PSU3F/4R	Plaxton Supreme IV	C46F	1980	King, Kirkcowan, 1987
APT118W	Leyland National 2 NL116AL11/1R		B49F	1980	Arriva North East (DC), 1999
PFR257X	Leyland Leopard PSU5C/4R	Duple Dominant II	C57F	1981	KM, Lundwood, 1998
JJI1533	DAF MB200DKTL600	Plaxton Supreme IV	C50F	1981	Harris Coaches, West Thurrock, 1990
VIW3785	Volvo B10M-61	Plaxton Paramount 3200 II	C53F	1985	Dodge, Bermondsey, 199x
TIB2875	Bova EL28/581	Duple Calypso	C53F	1984	Woods, Wigston 1995
WJI5167	DAF SB2305DHS500	Van Hool Alizée H	C53F	1986	Galloway, Mendlesham, 1998
D123OWG	Renault-Dodge S56	Reeve Burgess	B25F	1987	RoadCar, 1999
F121YVP	MCW MetroRider MF158/16	MCW	B28F	1988	Stagecoach East London, 1999
JJI1904	DAF SB2305DHTD585	Plaxton Paramount 3200 III	C57F	1988	
JJI1400	DAF SB2305DHTD585	Van Hool Alizée H	C49FT	1992	Marchwood Motorways, 1996
J77OLT	DAF SB2305DHS585	Van Hool Alizée H	C53FT	1991	

Previous Registrations:

CSU935	SWW125R	PIL2482	LUA278V
JJI1400	J852KHD	TIB2875	B554KRY
JJI1533	UHK202W, 104JEH	VIW3785	B785MLN
JJI1904	F659OHD	WJI5167	D862EFS, ESU370, 87KK1313, ESU370, D344ONW, ??, D391ONW

Livery: Turquoise, grey and white

Depot: Shrubland Farm, Swinefleet

Sweyne of Swinefleet provide the service between the inland port of Goole and the steelworks town of Scunthorpe, in addition to its coach work. New to Sweyne in 1991 was Van Hool Alizeé J77OLT, which carries the company colours of turquoise, grey and white. The chassis was manufactured by DAF and is imported from the Netherlands by Arriva Bus & Coach, the dealership formerly known as Hughes-DAF. *Richard Belton*

A relatively new addition to the public transport scene is TM Travel, based in Staveley, Chesterfield. A mixed fleet of nearly thirty vehicles is now operated on a variety of services types from private hire to schools and college work. Bristol VR BUH232V was photographed in King Street, Alfreton on a Swanwick Hall School swimming run. Also undertaking education is former Clydeside Alexander-bodied Daimler Fleetline WDS112V, pictured while parked in the grounds of the High Peak College at Buxton. *Tony Wilson*

TM TRAVEL

J M & T J Watts, 4 Cooke Close, Old Tupton, Derbyshire, S42 6JE

	NEV675M	Leyland National 1151/1R/0402		B49F	1973	Yorkshire Terrier, 1997
w	KRE276P	Leyland National 11351/1R		B52F	1976	Yorkshire Terrier, 1997
	UWA154S	Leyland Fleetline FE30AGR	Roe	B45/29D	1977	Stagecoach East Midland, 1997
	UWA159S	Leyland Fleetline FE30AGR	Roe	B45/29D	1977	Stagecoach East Midland, 1997
	ABA21T	Leyland National 11351A/1R		B49F	1979	Emmerson's, Immingham, 1999
	AYJ93T	Leyland National 11351A/1R		B52F	1979	Turner, Maidstone, 1998
	BKE849T	Bristol VRT/SL3/6LXB	Eastern Coach Works	B43/31F	1979	Stagecoach East Kent, 1998
	BUH232V	Bristol VRT/SL3/6LXB	Eastern Coach Works	B43/31F	1980	Stagecoach Red & White, 1998
	WDS112V	Leyland Fleetline FE30AGR	Alexander AL	B44/31F	1980	Clydeside, 1996
	FFL138V	Bedford YLQ	Duple Dominant II	C45F	1980	Canham, Broughton, 1997
	JWV255W	Bristol VRT/SL3/6LXB	Eastern Coach Works	B43/31F	1981	Stagecoach South, 1998
	URP943W	Bristol VRT/SL3/6LXB	Eastern Coach Works	B43/31F	1981	Stagecoach Cambus, 1999
	PWK2W	Leyland Leopard PSU5D/5R	Plaxton Supreme IV	C57F	1981	Brent, Brimington, 1998
	YPD130Y	Leyland Tiger TRCTL11/2R	Duple Dominant IV Express	C53F	1983	Felix, Stanley, 1996
	B160WRN	Leyland Tiger TRCTL11/3R	Duple Laser 2	C53F	1985	First Leicester, 1998
	F925YWY	Mercedes-Benz 811D	Optare StarRider	B26F	1988	London Central, 1999
	F269UDX	DAF SB2300DHTD585	Plaxton Paramount 3200 III	C53F	1989	Galloway, Mendlesham, 1998
	F513RTL	Dennis Javelin	Plaxton Paramount 3200 IV	C49FT	1989	Basset, Tittensor, 1997
	1294RU	Leyland Tiger TRCL10/3ARZM	Plaxton Paramount 3500 IV	C53F	1989	Lovering, Combe Martin, 1996
	G969KTX	Volvo B10M-60	Plaxton Paramount 3500 III	C46FT	1990	Wilson, Carnwath, 1998
	JIL3966	Leyland Tiger TRCL10/3ARZM	Plaxton Paramount 3500 III	C50F	1990	Armchair, Brentford, 1998
	VIB7471	Mercedes-Benz 811D	Optare StarRider	C29F	1990	Clay Lake Travel, Harlesden, 1998
	G53RGG	Volvo B10M-60	Plaxton Paramount 3500 III	C53F	1990	Johnson Bros, Hodthorpe, 1999
	H24JMJ	Leyland Tiger TRCL10/3ARZA	Plaxton Paramount 3500 III	C49FT	1991	Brents, Watford, 1997
	H706EOD	Leyland Tiger TRCL10/3RZM	Plaxton Paramount 3500 III	C53F	1991	Lovering, Combe Martin, 1999
	H157UUA	Optare MetroRider MR03	Optare	BC31F	1990	London Central, 1999
	J46SNY	Leyland Tiger TRCL10/3ARZM	Plaxton 321	C53F	1991	Essex Buses (Thamesway), 1998
	J48SNY	Leyland Tiger TRCL10/3ARZM	Plaxton 321	C53F	1991	Essex Buses (Thamesway), 1998
	J717EUA	Volvo B10M-60	Plaxton Première 350	C48FT	1992	Yorkshire Coachline, Masborough, 1998
	L4TCC	Volvo B10M-62	Plaxton Première 320	C49FT	1994	Minmar, East Boldon, 1998

Previous Registrations:

1294RU	F679JFU	JIL3966	G610XMD, G408XMK
F269UDX	F764RRT, 1482PP	NIB9313	UKW555S,310CCH,BUR63S
FFL138V	DLJ520V, WSU485	VIB7471	G839LWR, WLT792, G118CLO
F513RTL	F638UBE, PSU443	WDS112V	HSD73V, 705DYE
J717EUA	J721CWT, WA3399		

Named vehicle: L4TCC *Lady Catherine*

Livery: Cream and red; white and orange (National Holidays) E706EOD

TRANSLINC

Willoughby (121) Ltd, Jarvis House, 157 Sadler Road, Lincoln, LN6 3RS

JAU892V	Ford R1114	Plaxton Supreme IV	C53F	1980	Moxon, Oldcotes, 1993
SFH477W	Ford R1114	Plaxton Supreme IV	C53F	1981	Graham's Bristol, 1992
HYD266Y	Ford R1114	Duple Dominant III	C53F	1983	Gardners, Upton, 1994
C414DML	Bedford YMP	Plaxton Paramount 3200	C35F	1985	Forest Coaches, East Ham, 1992
E749HJF	Bedford YNV	Duple 320	C57F	1988	Wide Horizon, Burbage, 1992
BSK887	Dennis Javelin 12SDA1907	Duple 320	C53F	1988	Emmerson, Immingham, 1994
F906MPH	Dennis Javelin 12SDA1907	Duple 320	C57F	1988	Lever, East Knoyle, 1996
G281BEL	Dennis Javelin 12SDA1907	Caetano Algarve II 3.35	C53F	1989	Hill, Hersham, 1997
G427VAY	Dennis Javelin 12SDA1907	Duple 320	C53F	1990	Metrobus, Orpington, 1998
G429VAY	Dennis Javelin 12SDA1907	Duple 320	C57F	1990	Metrobus, Orpington, 1998
G529MNT	Dennis Javelin 12SDA1907	Caetano Algarve II 3.35	C57F	1990	Smith, Liss, 1994
H749UTV	Dennis Javelin 12SDA1906	Duple 320	C51FT	1990	Dunn Line, Nottingham, 1994
H393CJF	Dennis Javelin 12SDA1919	Caetano Algarve II 3.35	C53FL	1990	Harrington, Silvertown, 1996
H188EJF	Dennis Javelin 12SDA1919	Caetano Algarve II 3.35	C53F	1991	Steel, Skipton, 1998
J627HFW	Leyland-DAF 400	Cunliffe	B20FL	1991	
J628HFW	Leyland-DAF 400	Cunliffe	B20FL	1992	
J834KTL	Leyland-DAF 400	Cunliffe	M16L	1992	
J509LRY	Dennis Javelin 12SDA1919	Caetano Algarve II 3.35	C53F	1992	Tate, Markyate, 1996
J834KVH	Dennis Javelin 11SDL1905	Duple 320	C57F	1992	Pilling, Sowerby Bridge, 1997
J194NFE	Leyland-DAF 400	Cunliffe	B20FL	1992	
J201NFE	Leyland-DAF 400	Cunliffe	B18F	1992	
K983OFW	Leyland-DAF 400	Cunliffe	M16L	1992	
K393PVL	Leyland-DAF 400	Cunliffe	M16L	1992	
K394PVL	Leyland-DAF 400	Cunliffe	M16L	1992	
K420RFE	Leyland-DAF 400	Bedwas	M16L	1993	
L105VFE	Iveco Daily 49-10	Iveco	M16L	1993	

Opposite: **The transport arm of Lincolnshire County Council was privatised in 1998 though a management buyout. The company is also involved in vehicle leasing together with the maintenance of other vehicles including the County's fire appliances. A number of secondhand coaches are used on school contract and private hire work. H393CJF was pictured in Skegness in July 1999. It is a Dennis Javelin bodied by Caetano in Portugal.** *Tony Wilson*

Registration	Chassis	Body	Type	Year	
L715VVL	Leyland-DAF 400	Leyland-DAF	M16	1993	
L599YVL	Ford Transit VE6	Cunliffe	M15L	1994	
L601YVL	Ford Transit VE6	Cunliffe	M15L	1994	
M83CVL	Iveco Daily 49-10	Cunliffe	M16	1994	
M85CVL	Ford Transit VE6	Cunliffe	M16L	1994	
M744CVL	Mercedes-Benz 814D	Cunliffe	B32FL	1994	
M750CVL	Leyland-DAF 400	Leyland-DAF	M16	1994	
M751CVL	Leyland-DAF 400	Leyland-DAF	M16	1994	

	Iveco Daily 49-10	Cunliffe	M16L*	1994-95

* M752/3CVL, M966FFE are M16; M961/2FFE & M659GVL are B20FL

M752CVL	M235EFE	M429EVL	M963FFE	M407FTL
M753CVL	M236EFE	M961FFE	M966FFE	M659GVL
M234EFE	M425EVL	M962FFE		

Registration	Chassis	Body	Type	Year
M417EVL	Leyland-DAF 400	Leyland-DAF	M16	1994
M418EVL	Leyland-DAF 400	Leyland-DAF	M16	1994
M410FTL	Mercedes-Benz 814D	Cunliffe	B30FL	1995
M665GVL	Mercedes-Benz 814D	Plaxton Beaver	B33F	1995
M306XUA	Leyland-DAF 400	Cunliffe	M16L	1995
M471HFE	Leyland-DAF 400	Leyland-DAF	M16	1995

	Iveco Daily 49-10	Cunliffe	M16L*	1995-96

* N448KTL is B20FL; N455/6KTL, N462KTL are M16

N448KTL	N458KTL	N461KTL	N463KTL	N465KTL
N455KTL	N459KTL	N462KTL	N464KTL	N466KTL
N456KTL				

Registration	Chassis	Body	Type	Year
N456MFE	Iveco Daily 49-10	Cunliffe	M16L	1996

	Iveco Daily 49-10	TransLinc	M16*	1996	* N457/8MFE are M16L

N457MFE	N460MFE	N466MFE	N469MFE	N471MFE
N458MFE	N461MFE	N468MFE	N470MFE	N472MFE
N459MFE	N464MFE			

Registration	Chassis	Body	Type	Year
N467MFE	Iveco Daily 49-10	Frank Guy	M16	1996
N473MFE	Iveco Daily 49-10	Cunliffe	M16	1996

	Iveco Daily 49-10	Cunliffe	B20F	1996

N474MFE	N475MFE	N801OFW	N802OFW	N803OFW

Registration	Chassis	Body	Type	Year
N667MEW	Citroen Relay	Citroen	M12	1995
N899JFE	Ford Transit VE6	Ford	M14	1995

Minibuses of the type seen here operate throughout the country on local authority special transport work. Many are fitted with wheelchair lifts. M744CVL is a Mercedes-Benz 814D. The body was constructed by Cunliffe, a manufacturer that specialises in building buses for the social services market.
Steve Sanderson

Reg	Chassis	Body	Type	Year	Notes
	Iveco Daily 49-10	Cunliffe	M16L*	1995	*N909JFE is M16
N909JFE	N910JFE	N911JFE	N912JFE	N913JFE	
P502RFW	Iveco Daily 49-10	TransLinc	M16	1996	
P503RFW	Iveco Daily 49-10	TransLinc	M16	1996	
	Iveco Daily 49-10	Frank Guy	M16	1996	
P505RFW	P507RFW	P509RFW	P511RFW	P513RFW	
P506RFW	P508RFW	P510RFW	P512RFW	P514RFW	
P78SVL	LDV Convoy	Frank Guy	M16	1996	
P929TFE	Iveco Daily 49-10	TransLinc	M16	1996	
P932TFE	Mercedes-Benz 814D	Cunliffe	B33F	1996	
P940TFE	Mercedes-Benz 814D	Cunliffe	B33F	1997	
P946TFE	Iveco Daily 49-10	TransLinc	M16	1996	
P947TFE	Iveco Daily 49-10	Cunliffe	M16	1996	
P948TFE	Iveco Daily 49-10	TransLinc	M16	1996	
	LDV Convoy	LDV	M16	1996-97	
P298UFW	P306UFW	P82WFE	P876WFW	P877WFW	
P878WFW	Fiat Scudo	Fiat	M7	1997	
R951ETL	Iveco Daily 49-10	Iveco	M13	1997	
R952ETL	Iveco Daily 49-10	Iveco	M16	1997	
R954ETL	LDV Convoy	LDV	M16	1997	
R962ETL	Iveco Daily 49-10	Iveco	M16	1998	
R963ETL	Iveco Daily 49-10	Iveco	M16	1998	
R981LFE	Mercedes-Benz 814D	Mercedes-Benz	C32FL	1998	
R987LFE	LDV Convoy	LDV	M16L	1998	
R988LFE	LDV Convoy	LDV	M16L	1998	
S562AVE	Citroen Relay 1000	Citroen	M7	1998	
S564AVE	Citroen Relay 1000	Citroen	M7	1998	
S565AVE	Citroen Relay 1000	Citroen	M7	1998	
S259AVL	Iveco Daily 40-10	Oughtred & Harrison	M15L	1998	
S260AVL	Iveco Daily 40-10	Oughtred & Harrison	M15L	1998	
S261AVL	Iveco Daily 40-10	Oughtred & Harrison	M15L	1998	
S262AVL	Iveco Daily 40-10	Oughtred & Harrison	M15L	1998	
S263AVL	Iveco Daily 40-10	Oughtred & Harrison	M15L	1998	
S264AVL	Iveco Daily 40-10	Oughtred & Harrison	M16L	1998	
S264AVL	Iveco Daily 49-10	Oughtred & Harrison	M15L	1998	
S266AVL	LDV Convoy	LDV	M13	1998	
S267AVL	LDV Convoy	LDV	M16	1998	
S533BTL	LDV Convoy	LDV	M16	1998	
S535BTL	LDV Convoy	LDV	M16	1998	
S536BTL	LDV Convoy	LDV	M16	1998	
S537BTL	LDV Convoy	LDV	M16	1998	
S538BTL	LDV Convoy	LDV	M16	1998	
S32FFW	Toyota Coaster BB50R	Caetano Optimo IV	C26F	1999	
S34FFW	Iveco Daily 49-10	Oughtred & Harrison	B15FL	1999	
S35FFW	Iveco Daily 49-10	Oughtred & Harrison	B15FL	1999	
S36FFW	Iveco Daily 49-10	Oughtred & Harrison	B15FL	1999	
S382FVL	Iveco Daily 49-10	Oughtred & Harrison	B15FL	1999	
	Iveco Daily 49-10	Oughtred & Harrison	M16F	1999	
S37FFW	S41FFW	T383RFW	T183SFW	T185SFW	
S38FFW	T381RFW	T384RFW	T184SFW	T187SFW	
S39FFW					

Previous Registrations:

BSK887	E332PWO	SFH477W	KHB28W, GSB76	

Livery: Yellow and White

Depots: Allan House, Boston; Sadler Road, Lincoln; Warwick Road, Louth; Key Garage, Skegness: Eastgate Centre, Sleaford; Kings Garage, Stickney; Ryhall Road, Stamford. **Outstations:** Bardney, Bassingham, Bourne, Chapel St Leonards, Gainsborough, Grantham, Holbeach, Horncastle, Ludford, Market Deeping, Market Rasen, Marton, Pode Hole, Ropsley, Saxilby, Spalding, Spilsby, Theddlethorpe St Helens, Wood Enderby, Wragby.

TRAVEL WRIGHT

T D & M Wright, Lincoln Road Garage, Newark, Nottinghamshire, NG24 2DR

Reg	Chassis	Body	Config	Year	Notes
SNN747R	Bedford YLQ	Plaxton Supreme III	C41F	1977	
ANJ306T	Leyland Leopard PSU3E/4RT	Plaxton Supreme III Express	C53F	1979	Brighton & Hove, 1986
CAL845T	Bedford YMT	Plaxton Supreme IV	C53F	1979	
HAL242V	Bedford YMT	Duple Dominant II	C53F	1980	
JRB416V	Volvo B58-56	Duple Dominant II	C53F	1980	
NAU292W	Volvo B58-61	Duple Dominant II	C57F	1981	
ORR904W	Bedford YNT	Plaxton Supreme III	C53F	1981	
LAK985W	Bristol VRT/SL3/6LXB	Eastern Coach Works	B43/31F	1981	RoadCar, 1995
TNN696X	Volvo B10M-61	Plaxton Supreme V	C51F	1981	
SNU461X	Leyland Atlantean AN68C/1R	East Lancashire	B47/33D	1982	City of Nottingham, 1997
YTO861Y	Volvo B10M-61	Plaxton Paramount 3200	C53F	1983	
7179TW	Van Hool T815H	Van Hool Alicron	C53FT	1985	
C35VJF	Bova FLD12.250	Bova Futura	C57F	1986	
E434YHL	Mercedes-Benz 709D	Reeve Burgess Beaver	B25F	1988	Smith, Alcester, 1991
PJI3042	Volvo B10M-46	Caetano Algarve R-NDH	C41F	1988	Greenway Cs, Nottingham, 1992
PJI3043	Scania K113CRB	Van Hool Alizée DH	C55F	1988	Smith, Marple, 1992
F692PAY	Dennis Javelin 8.5SDL1903	Plaxton Paramount 3200 III	C35F	1989	
G865VAY	Mercedes-Benz 609D	Reeve Burgess Beaver	C23F	1989	
G430YAY	Dennis Javelin 12SDA1916	Plaxton Paramount 3200 III	C53FT	1990	
H160DJU	Dennis Javelin 12SDA1907	Plaxton Paramount 3200 III	C57F	1990	
K118KUA	Mercedes-Benz 609D	Autobus Classique	BC23F	1993	
LIL9842	Van Hool T815	Van Hool Alizée	C49F	1993	White & Urquhart, Newmachar, 1996
TIW5645	Van Hool T815	Van Hool Alizée	C49F	1994	White & Urquhart, Newmachar, 1998

The biscuit, brown and red colours of Travel Wright are carried by YTO861Y, shown here. This Plaxton Paramount-bodied Volvo B10M is used on a variety of work and is seen in Skegness having offloaded a party visiting the east coast resort. *Steve Sanderson*

Nottinghamshire County Council provides funding for a number of routes around Newark. Travel Wright gained a number of contracts in 1998 and has purchased Mercedes-Benz Varios with the shapely Plaxton Beaver II body to run the routes. Displaying its route branding, S577FFE was photographed as it left Newark bound for Harby in June 1999. *Tony Wilson*

	L29CAY	Dennis Javelin 12SDA2136	Caetano Algarve II 3.35	C53F	1994	
	M553SSA	EOS E180Z	EOS 90	C49FT	1995	White & Urquhart, Newmachar, 1996
	N240NNR	MAN 11-190	Caetano Algarve II	C35F	1995	
	P179ANR	Dennis Javelin 12SDA2134	Caetano Algarve II 3.35	C53F	1996	
	T707SUT	Volvo B10M-62	Caetano Enigma	C49FT	1999	
SL1	H34DGD	Mercedes-Benz 811D	Dormobile Routemaker	B33F	1991	Pathfinder, Newark, 1993
SL2	J914HGD	Mercedes-Benz 814D	Dormobile Routemaker	BC33F	1991	Pathfinder, Newark, 1994
SL3	N795PDS	Mercedes-Benz 709D	Marshall	B29F	1996	
SL4	R726EGD	Mercedes-Benz Vario O810	Plaxton Beaver 2	B31F	1997	
SL5	S577FFE	Mercedes-Benz Vario O814	Plaxton Beaver 2	B31F	1998	
SL6	T32JBA	Mercedes-Benz Vario O814	Plaxton Beaver 2	B31F	1999	

Previous Registrations:

7179TW	B925OFP	PJI3042	E998KJF	TIW5645	L958NRS
LIL9842	K546GSS	PJI3043	F99CWG		

Named vehicles: H160DJU *Paula Jane*; LIL9842 *Shannon Jade*; M553SSA *Catherine Megan*; P179ANR *Claudia Josephine*; T707SUT *Naomi Louise* .

Livery: Biscuit, red and brown; turquoise & white (TravelLink) R726EGD

TRENT

Barton - Blue Apple - Trent

Barton Buses Ltd; Notts & Derby Traction Co Ltd;Trent Motor Traction Co Ltd,
Mansfield Road, Heanor, Derbyshire, DE75 7BG

1-8 Volvo B10M-60 Plaxton Expressliner 2 C49FT 1993

1	L801MRA	3	L803MRA	5	L805MRA	7	L807MRA	8	L808MRA
2	L802MRA	4	L804MRA	6	L806MRA				

39	L809CJF	Mercedes-Benz 709D	Marshall C19	B27F	1994	Kinch, 1998
40	L810CJF	Mercedes-Benz 709D	Marshall C19	B27F	1994	Kinch, 1998
41	L811CJF	Mercedes-Benz 709D	Marshall C19	B27F	1994	Kinch, 1999
42	L812CJF	Mercedes-Benz 709D	Marshall C19	B27F	1994	Kinch, 1999
43	L813DJU	Mercedes-Benz 709D	Marshall C19	B27F	1994	Kinch, 1999
47	R47LNU	Mercedes-Benz Vario O810	Plaxton Beaver 2	B27F	1997	
49	R49SCH	Mercedes-Benz 711D	Plaxton Beaver	B27F	1997	

51-55 Volvo B10M-60 Alexander Q BC51F 1994

51	M51PRA	52	M52PRA	53	M53PRA	54	M54PRA	55	M455TCH

56-63 Volvo B10M-60 Plaxton Premiére Interurban C51F 1997

56	P56ETO	58	P58ETO	60	R960RAU	62	R62RAU	63	R63RAU
57	P57ETO	59	R59RAU	61	R61RAU				

101-128 Volvo B10B-58 Northern Counties Paladin B49F 1993-94

101	L101LRA	107	L107LRA	113	L113LRA	119	L119LRA	124	L124LRA
102	L102LRA	108	L108LRA	114	L114LRA	120	L120LRA	125	L125LRA
103	L103LRA	109	L109LRA	115	L115LRA	121	L121LRA	126	L126LRA
104	L104LRA	110	L110LRA	116	L116LRA	122	L122LRA	127	L127LRA
105	L105LRA	111	L911LRA	117	L117LRA	123	L123LRA	128	L128LRA
106	L106LRA	112	L112LRA	118	L118LRA				

129-138 Volvo B10B-58 Northern Counties Paladin B49F 1994

129	M129PRA	131	M131PRA	133	M133PRA	135	M135PRA	137	M137PRA
130	M130PRA	132	M132PRA	134	M134PRA	136	M136PRA	138	M138PRA

151	P151CTV	Optare L1150	Optare Excel	N43F	1996
152	P152CTV	Optare L1150	Optare Excel	N43F	1996
153	P153CTV	Optare L1150	Optare Excel	N43F	1996

154-172 Optare L1150 Optare Excel N45F 1998

154	S154UAL	158	S158UAL	162	S162UAL	166	S166UAL	170	S170UAL
155	S955PRA	159	S159UAL	163	S163UAL	167	S167UAL	171	S171UAL
156	S156UAL	160	S160UAL	164	S164UAL	168	S168UAL	172	S172UAL
157	S157UAL	161	S161UAL	165	S165UAL	169	S169UAL		

173-186 Optare L1150 Optare Excel N45F 1999

173	T173LCH	176	T976LCH	179	T179LCH	182	T182LCH	185	T185LCH
174	T174LCH	177	T977LCH	180	T180LCH	183	T183LCH	186	T186LCH
175	T975LCH	178	T178LCH	181	T181LCH	184	T184LCH		

187-200 Optare L1150 Optare Excel N45F On order

187	T787XVO	190	T790XVO	193	T793XVO	196	T796XVO	199	T799XVO
188	T788XVO	191	T791XVO	194	T794XVO	197	T797XVO	200	
189	T789XVO	192	T792XVO	195	T795XVO	198	T798XVO		

New route 555, which links Heanor with Beeston in the western suburbs of Nottingham, along with a number of other network changes, was introduced at the beginning of July 1999. A terminal point was created in the grounds of the recently opened Tesco superstore at Heanor where 299, T299LCH was pictured as it pulls away from the stand. The company policy on route branding is evident here on a standard red and cream livery but in many cases, such as TransPeak (white & green) or Rainbow (purple & cream) a different colour scheme is applied to all the buses allocated to a route. *Tony Wilson*

201-241

| | | | | | | | | | | Optare Metrorider MR15 | | Optare | | B31F | | 1995-96 |

201	M201URC	210	N210VRC	218	N218VRC	226	N226VRC	234	P234CTV
201	M201URC	210	N210VRC	218	N218VRC	226	N226VRC	234	P234CTV
202	M202URC	211	N211VRC	219	N219VRC	227	P227CTV	235	P235CTV
203	N203VRC	212	N212VRC	220	N220VRC	228	P228CTV	236	P236CTV
204	N204VRC	213	N213VRC	221	N221VRC	229	P229CTV	237	P237CTV
205	N205VRC	214	N214VRC	222	N322WCH	230	P230CTV	238	P238CTV
206	N206VRC	215	N215VRC	223	N223VRC	231	P231CTV	239	P239CTV
207	N207VRC	216	N216VRC	224	N224VRC	232	P232CTV	240	P240CTV
208	N208VRC	217	N217VRC	225	N225VRC	233	P233CTV	241	P241CTV
209	N209VRC								

271	M271URC	Mercedes-Benz 811D	Wright Nim-bus	B31F	1995
271	M271URC	Mercedes-Benz 811D	Wright Nim-bus	B31F	1995
272	M272URC	Mercedes-Benz 811D	Wright Nim-bus	B31F	1995
273	M273URC	Mercedes-Benz 811D	Wright Nim-bus	B31F	1995
274	M274URC	Mercedes-Benz 811D	Wright Nim-bus	B31F	1995

275-296

| | | | | | | | | | | Mercedes-Benz Vario O814 | | Plaxton Beaver 2 | | B31F | | 1997-98 |

275	R275RAU	280	R280RAU	284	R284RAU	289	S289UAL	293	S293UAL
275	R275RAU	280	R280RAU	284	R284RAU	289	S289UAL	293	S293UAL
276	R276RAU	281	R281RAU	286	S286UAL	290	S290UAL	294	S294UAL
277	R277RAU	282	R282RAU	287	S287UAL	291	S291UAL	295	S295UAL
278	R278RAU	283	R283RAU	288	S288UAL	292	S292UAL	296	S296UAL
279	R279RAU								

Opposite: **Northern Counties Paladin bodywork is carried by Volvo B10B 121, L121LRA, one of 38 operated by Trent. It is seen in Nottingham as it heads for the terminus of Rainbow route R10 at the Victoria shopping centre. Recent deliveries for Trent have included a batch of Optare Excels. Having sampled and subsequently purchased a small number for a Park & Ride operation in Nottingham, further vehicles were acquired for normal service. With quality service and customer care high on the company's profile, route branding is used. These particular buses are used on the high frequency route R1 between Alfreton, Ripley and Nottingham. Midway through the route at Eastwood, 186, T186LCH, is seen in a blue and cream livery that echoes the Midland General colours seen on this route prior to that company merging with Trent.** *TW*

The Nottinghamshire & Derbyshire Traction company is a low cost operation within the Wellglade Group, that also includes Barton, Kinch and Trent Motor Traction. This operation commenced by supplying buses for the Derby University network of services marketed as the *Blue Apple*, using Leyland Nationals and Eastern Coach Works-bodied Olympians in a green and blue livery. Illustrated here is 519, FRA519V, operating on a service in the Nottingham area in April 1999. *Tony Wilson*

297	T297LCH	Mercedes-Benz Vario O814	Plaxton Beaver 2	B31F	1999	
298	T298LCH	Mercedes-Benz Vario O814	Plaxton Beaver 2	B31F	1999	
299	T299LCH	Mercedes-Benz Vario O814	Plaxton Beaver 2	B31F	1999	
300	G600NRC	DAF SB220LC550	Optare Delta	B49F	1990	DAF demonstrator, 1992

301-325

			DAF SB220LC550		Optare Delta		B49F	1991-92	
301	J201BVO	306	J306BVO	311	J311BVO	316	J316BVO	321	J321BVO
302	J302BVO	307	J307BVO	312	J312BVO	317	J317BVO	322	J322BVO
303	J303BVO	308	J308BVO	313	J313BVO	318	J318BVO	323	J323BVO
304	J304BVO	309	J309BVO	314	J314BVO	319	J319BVO	324	J324BVO
305	J305BVO	310	J310BVO	315	J315BVO	320	J320BVO	325	J325BVO

326-353

			DAF SB220LC550		Optare Delta		B48F	1992-93	
326	K326FAL	332	K332FAL	338	K338FAL	344	K344FAL	349	K349FAL
327	K327FAL	333	K633FAU	339	K339FAL	345	K645FAU	350	K350FAL
328	K328FAL	334	K334FAL	340	K640FAU	346	K346FAL	351	K651FAU
329	K329FAL	335	K335FAL	341	K341FAL	347	K347FAL	352	K352FAL
330	K330FAL	336	K336FAL	342	K342FAL	348	K348FAL	353	K353FAL
331	K331FAL	337	K337FAL	343	K343FAL				

| 355 | M355PRA | Dennis Lance 11SDA3115 | Optare Sigma | B46F | 1994 |

356-370

			Dennis Lance 11SDA3113		Optare Sigma		B46F	1995	
356	N356VRC	359	N359VRC	362	N362VRC	365	N365VRC	368	N368VRC
357	N357VRC	360	N360VRC	363	N363VRC	366	N366VRC	369	N369VRC
358	N358VRC	361	N361VRC	364	N364VRC	367	N367VRC	370	N370VRC

During the latter half of 1998, revisions to the route structure introduced a new service. Marketed under the *Pegasus* name, the route complements *The Trans Peak* service that serves North and South Derbyshire. While the latter uses Volvo-based urban buses, the new service is run with high-back seated Mercedes-Benz Vario minibuses in a blue-based livery. Derby Bus Station is the location for 285, S285UAL. *Tony Wilson*

430	JHW103P	Leyland National 11351/1R						B52F	1975	Cheltenham & Gloucester 1995		
442	PRR442R	Leyland National 11351A/2R						B50F	1976			
450	PRR450R	Leyland National 11351A/2R						B50F	1976			
451	PRR451R	Leyland National 11351A/1R						B49F	1976			
453	PRR451R	Leyland National 11351A/1R						B49F	1976			
454	PRR451R	Leyland National 11351A/1R						B49F	1976			
458	PRR451R	Leyland National 11351A/1R						B49F	1976			

461-479

		Leyland National 11351A/2R						B50F*	1977	*463/7/8 are B52F		
461	RTO461R	464	RTO464R	467	RTO467R	471	URB471S	479	VCH479S			
463	RTO463R	466	RTO466R	468	URB468S							

480	WGY578S	Leyland National 11351A/2R						B50F	1976	Delta, Kirkby-in-Ashfield, 1996		

481-503

		Leyland National 11351A/2R						B50F*	1977-78	*501/2 have DAF engines		
										*481//93,500-2 are B52F		
481	XAL481S	491	XAL491S	495	XAL495S	498	XAL498S	501	YRR501T			
484	XAL484S	493	XAL493S	496	XAL496S	500	XAL500S	502	YRR502T			

504-535

		Leyland National 11351A/1R*						B52F	1978-80	*504 has a DAF engine		
										* 526/7/33-5 have Volvo engines		
504	ACH504T	509	ACH509T	514	ACH514T	519	FRA519V	526	FRA526V			
505	ACH505T	510	ACH510T	515	FRA515V	520	FRA520V	527	FRA527V			
506	ACH506T	511	ACH511T	516	FRA516V	522	FRA522V	533	FRA533V			
507	ACH507T	512	ACH512T	517	FRA517V	523	FRA523V	534	FRA534V			
508	ACH508T	513w	ACH513T	518	FRA518V	524	FRA524V	535	FRA535V			

536	CWX656T	Leyland National 11351A/1R						B49F	1978	West Riding, 1989		
538	CWX659T	Leyland National 11351A/1R						B49F	1978	West Riding, 1989		

The double-decker is becoming rare in the Trent fleet with one batch of Volvo Citybuses and eight Olympians now remaining. The Volvos are represented here by Citybus B10M 618, G618OTV, with Alexander RV bodywork. It is seen as it glides up the short incline of Friar Lane, Nottingham. The double-deck B10M is occasionally referred to as the D10M and the B10MD in various publications and brochures. However, Trent are now making this type available for sale. *Tony Wilson*

541	JBR684T	Leyland National 11351A/1R (DAF)	B49F	1978	Tees & District, 1992
542	LUP894T	Leyland National 11351A/1R (DAF)	B49F	1979	Tees & District, 1992
543	EPT879S	Leyland National 11351A/1R (DAF)	B49F	1978	Tees & District, 1992
544	VKE565S	Leyland National 11351A/1R (DAF)	B49F	1977	Stagecoach South 1992
545	UFX849S	Leyland National 11351A/1R (DAF)	B49F	1977	Solent Blue Line, 1993
546	UFX852S	Leyland National 11351A/1R	B49F	1977	Solent Blue Line, 1994
547	VFX985S	Leyland National 11351A/1R (DAF)	B49F	1978	Solent Blue Line, 1994
548	WPR150S	Leyland National 11351A/1R (DAF)	B49F	1978	Solent Blue Line, 1994
549	OHW492R	Leyland National 11351A/1R	B52F	1977	MTL Manchester, 1995
550	FBV525S	Leyland National 11351A/1R	B49F	1978	MTL Manchester, 1995
551	FPR65V	Leyland National 11351A/1R (DAF)	B49F	1980	Solent Blue Line, 1995

552-567			Leyland National 11351A/1R			B52F	1976-79 Cheltenham & Gloucester 1995

*552/3 have DAF engines

552	PHW987S	**555**	VEU229T	**558**	TTC532T	**561**	NOE555R	**565**	SAE751S
553	TAE638S	**556**	VEU232T	**559**	UHW101T	**562**	NOE584R	**566**	SAE755S
554	VEU228T	**557**	VEU230T	**560**	NFB602R	**564**	PHW986S	**567**	TAE643S

568	DAR120T	Leyland National 11351A/1R	B49F	1979	Thamesway, 1996
569	JHJ139V	Leyland National 11351A/1R	B49F	1979	Thamesway, 1996
570	JHJ146V	Leyland National 11351A/1R	B49F	1979	Thamesway, 1996

600-623			Volvo Citybus B10M-50		Alexander RV		B47/37F	1988-90

600	F600GVO	**604**	F604GVO	**608**	F608GVO	**612**	G612OTV	**616w**	G616OTV
601	F601GVO	**605**	F605GVO	**609**	F608GVO	**613w**	G613OTV	**617w**	G617OTV
602	F602GVO	**606**	F606GVO	**610**	F610GVO	**614**	G614OTV	**618w**	G618OTV
603	F603GVO	**607**	F607GVO	**611**	F611GVO	**615**	G615OTV	**621**	G621OTV

The Optare Vecta body is constructed on a MAN 11.190 chassis and gives a more upright appearance when compared to the Delta design that is fitted to the longer DAF SB220. Most of Trent's Vectas are allocated to the Dove Holes depot which has replaced the Buxton site, now an Aldi supermarket. The Trent route between Buxton and Stockport is now extended to Manchester International Airport and was initially branded AirBus, a name now changed to SkyLink as part of branding a network of routes around Ringway and provided by a number of operators aimed to provide staff transport and encourage public transport at the airport. The distinctive Stockport railway viaduct can be seen in the background in this view of 814, M814PRA. *Steve Sanderson*

712-723

				Leyland Olympian ONLXB/1RV		Eastern Coach Works		B45/30F	1985		
712	B712HVO	716	C716LTO	718	C718LTO	720	C720NNN	723	C723NNN		
715	B715HVO	717	C717LTO	719	C719LTO						

801-815

		MAN 11.190			Optare Vecta		B40F	1994			
801	M801PRA	804	M804PRA	807	M807PRA	810	M810PRA	813	M813PRA		
802	M802PRA	805	M805PRA	808	M808PRA	811	M811PRA	814	M814PRA		
803	M803PRA	806	M806PRA	809	M809PRA	812	M812PRA	815	M815PRA		

901-916

		Dennis Dart SLF			Plaxton Pointer		N40F	1996			
901	P901CTO	905	P905CTO	908	P908CTO	911	P911CTO	914	P914CTO		
902	P902CTO	906	P906CTO	909	P909CTO	912	P912CTO	915	P915CTO		
903	P903CTO	907	P907CTO	910	P910CTO	913	P913CTO	916	P916CTO		
904	P904CTO										

917-936

		Dennis Dart SLF			Plaxton Pointer 2		N40F	1997			
917	R917RAU	921	R921RAU	925	R925RAU	929	R929RAU	933	R933RAU		
918	R918RAU	922	R922RAU	926	R926RAU	930	R930RAU	934	R934RAU		
919	R919RAU	923	R923RAU	927	R927RAU	931	R931RAU	935	R935RAU		
920	R920RAU	924	R924RAU	928	R928RAU	932	R932RAU	936	R936RAU		

937-944

		Dennis Dart SLF			Plaxton Pointer 2		N41F	1998			
937	S937UAL	939	S939UAL	941	S941UAL	943	S943UAL	944	S944UAL		
938	S938UAL	940	S940UAL	942	S942UAL						

945-949

945-949		Dennis Dart SLF		Plaxton Pointer 2		N40F	1999		
945	T945BNN	**946**	T946BNN	**947**	T947BNN	**948**	T948BNN	**949**	T949BNN
1641	D641WNU	DAF MB230DKFL600		Plaxton Paramount 3200 III		C49F	1987		

Ancilliary vehicle

| **1592** | PTV592X | Leyland Leopard PSU3F/4R | | Plaxton Supreme IV Express | | TV | 1979 | | |

Previous Registrations:
G600NRC   G910XFC

Livery: Red and cream (Trent & Barton); blue and green (Blue Apple)

Allocations:-

Derby (Meadow Road) - Trent - Barton

Outstations:- Ashbourne; Belper; Matlock.

Mercedes-Benz	47	275	276	277	278	279	280	281
	284	286	287	291				
Volvo B10M	54	55	59	60	61	62	63	
Dart	917	918	919	920	921	922	923	924
	925	926	927	928	929	930	937	938
	939							
Vecta	801	802	803	804	805			
Volvo/Paladin	126	127	128	129	131	132	133	134
	135	136	137	138				
Delta	341	342	343	344	345	346	347	348
	349	350						
Sigma	355	356	357	358	359	360	361	362
	363							

Dove Holes - Trent

Outstation:- Castle Donington, Bradwell

Volvo coach	51	52	53					
National	551	552						
MAN/Vecta	806	807	808	809	810	811	812	813
	814	815						
Volvo/Paladin	130							

Langley Mill (Station Road) - Trent - Barton

Outstation:- Ilkeston

Mercedes-Benz	283	292	293	294	295	296	297	298
	299							
MetroRider	215	217	218	219	220	221	222	223
	224	225	226	237	238	239	240	241
Volvo coach	1	2	3	4	5	6	7	8
	56	57	58					
Dart	931	932	933	934	935	936	945	946
	947	948	949					
National	501	502	504	541	542	543	544	545
	547	548	553					
Volvo/Paladin	117	118	119	120	121	122	123	124
	125							
Delta	318	319	320	321	322	323	324	325
	326	334	335	336	337	338	339	340
Excel	173	174	175	176	177	178	179	180
	181	182	183	184	185	186	900	

Derby (Meadow Road) - Blue Apple

Mercedes-Benz	41	42	43					
National	458	481	496	506	515	516	517	518
	519	520	522	52	524	549		
Sigma	364	365	366	367	368	369	370	
Olympian	712	715	716	717	718	723		

Nottingham (Manvers Street) - Trent - Barton

Outstations: Castle Donington; Grantham; Langar; Leicester; Melton Mowbray; Stamford and Uppingham

Mercedes-Benz	271	272	273	274	282	288	289	290
Dart	901	902	903	904	905	906	907	908
	909	910	911	912	913	914	915	916
	940	941	942	943	944			
Excel	151	152	153	154	155	156	157	158
	159	160	161	162	163	164	165	166
	167	168						
National	480	491	498	554	555	556	557	558
	559	560	561	562	563	564	565	566
	567	568	569	570				
Delta	300	301	302	303	304	305	306	307
	308	309	310	311	312	313	314	316
	317	327	328	329	330	331	332	333
	351	352	353					

Sutton Junction (Midland Road) - Trent

Outstation:- Hucknall (Portland Street)

Mercedes-Benz	39	40	49					
MetroRider	201	202	203	204	205	206	207	208
	209	210	211	212	213	214	227	228
	229	230	231	232	233	234	235	236
National	430	550						
Excel	169	170	171	172				
Volvo/Paladin	101	102	103	104	105	106	107	108
	109	110	111	112	113	114	115	116
Olympian	719	720						
Volvo Citybus B10M	601	602	603	604	605	606	607	608
	609	610	611	612	614	615	621	

Unallocated

MetroRider	216							
Sigma	354							
National	442	450	451	461	464	466	467	468
	479	480	484	491	493	498	500	505
	507	508	509	510	511	512	536	538
	546	554	555					
Volvo Citybus	600	613	616	617	618			
DAF	1641							

Note: Kinch 674/5/8, 816 are currently on long term hire as 674/5/8, 816.
City of Nottingham City 114-6 are currently on long term hire as 14-6.

TRS Coach Services operate the tendered Leicester outer circle serviced (40/1) previously run by ABC. A number of other tendered services are run on market days. In addition, the company runs double-deck Neoplan coaches into other European countries. UTC872 has a Skyliner body with a 77 seat capacity. This coach was new to Trathens and used on National Express Rapide services from the south west of England to London. Now with TRS, it was photographed while on a journey to Legoland near Windsor. *David Heath*

Messrs. Williams and Robinson of Scunthorpe trade as Trent Motors. Just two vehicles remain, the latest arrival being SAE753S. This Leyland National carries a modified version of its former owner's livery and is used on the service run in competition with RoadCar between Scunthorpe and Winterton. *Richard Belton*

T R S

TRS Coach Services, 163 Scudamore Road, Leicester, LE3 1UQ

OTO576M	Leyland Atlantean AN68/1R	East Lancashire	B47/30D	1974	Holloway, Scunthorpe, 1994
HOR307N	Leyland Atlantean AN68/1R	Alexander AL	B45/30D	1975	Shire Coaches, St Albans, 1994
RCU834S	Leyland Fleetline FE30AGR	Alexander AL	B44/30F	1977	Stagecoach Busways, 1998
OEM794S	Leyland Atlantean AN68/1R	MCW	B43/32F	1978	Sheffield Omnibus, 1994
YHT988	Leyland Leopard PSU3C/4R	Plaxton Supreme III	C49F	1977	Stanley Gath, Dewsbury, 1998
TTS885S	Leyland Leopard PSU3E/4R	Plaxton Supreme III	C53F	1978	Fletcher, Offerton, 1998
MGV316V	Bedford YMT	Plaxton Supreme IV	C49F	1979	Smith, Blandford, 1998
KPJ246W	Leyland Atlantean AN68A/1R	Roe	B43/30F	1980	County, 1997
FBV503W	Leyland Atlantean AN68B/1R	Eastern Coach Works	B43/32F	1981	Castle, Clanfield, 1998
LIL6292	Van Hool T818	Van Hool Astron	C49/11FT	1983	Swallow, Bristol, 1998
UTC872	Neoplan N122/3	Neoplan Skyliner	C57/20CT	1983	Caelloi, Pwllheli, 1992
VOI5826	Neoplan N112/3	Neoplan Skyliner	C48/12CT	1984	City Centre, Cardiff, 1997
TRS332	Neoplan N112/3	Neoplan Skyliner	C57/20DT	1984	Park's of Hamilton, 1994
RIB4311	Neoplan N722/3	Plaxton Paramount 4000 II	C53/18CT	1985	Atkinson, Ingleby Arncliffe, 1996
2320DD	Neoplan N722/3	Plaxton Paramount 4000 II	C53/18CT	1986	MC Motors, Tulse Hill, 1997
D936EBP	Iveco Daily 49.10	Robin Hood City Nippy	B19F	1986	Clyde Coast, Ardrossan, 1997
NIL2996	Iveco Daily 49.10	Robin Hood City Nippy	B25F	1987	Stagecoach Transit (KuH), 1996
D741WRC	Ford R1014	Plaxton Paramount 3200 II	C45F	1987	Prirst & Thompson, Baltasound, 1998
JIL8325	Bedford YNV	Duple 320	C55F	1987	Bywater, Rochdale, 1990
TRS835	Hestair Duple 425 SDAK1512	Duple 425	C53FT	1987	Myall, Birmingham, 1989
F162UMD	Leyland Tiger TRCL10/3ARZA	Duple 340	C55F	1987	Evag Canon, 1997
LIL6287	Dennis Javelin 12SDA1907	Plaxton Paramount 3200	C57F	1989	Clarkes Coaches, Pailton, 1994
TRS574	Dennis Javelin 12SDA1907	Duple 320	C53FT	1987	Colchester, 1994
MIL9758	Mercedes-Benz 811D	Optare StarRider	B33F	1990	London Northern, 1999
J241MFP	Dennis Javelin 12SDA1934	Plaxton Paramount 3200 III	C55F	1992	Clarkes Coaches, Pailton, 1994
J242MFP	Dennis Javelin 12SDA1921	Plaxton Paramount 3200 III	C53F	1992	Clarkes Coaches, Pailton, 1994
K522EFL	Iveco TurboDaily 59.12	Marshall C29	B23F	1993	Stagecoach Midland Red, 1999
K528EFL	Iveco TurboDaily 59.12	Marshall C29	B23F	1993	Stagecoach Midland Red, 1999
P473EJF	Mercedes-Benz 709D	Plaxton Beaver	B27F	1997	
P474EJF	Mercedes-Benz 709D	Plaxton Beaver	B27F	1997	
P475EJF	Mercedes-Benz 709D	Plaxton Beaver	B27F	1997	

Previous Registrations:

2320DD	C175KHG	RIB4311	B171REF
JIL8325	E902EAY	TRS332	A350UFE, SKY784, LSK634, A815WSU
LIL6292	2320DD, ATO382Y	TRS574	G105UVX
LIL6287	F627SAY	TRS835	E907EAY
MGV316V	AFC496V, 5516PP	UTC872	BDF875Y
N1TRS	-	VOI5826	A121RTL
NIL2996	D609MKH	YHT988	SNM79R
F162UMD	F162UMD, TRS574	MIL9758	G114KUB

Livery: White, red and blue   **Depots:** Scudamore Road, Leicester; Merrylees Ind Est, Merrylees, Desford.

TRENT MOTORS

B Williams & K Robinson, 43 Station Road, Scunthorpe, North Lincolnshire, DN15 6QE

SAE753S	Leyland National 11351A/1R		B52F	1978	Stagecoach Midland Red, 1999
MFS579X	Leyland Leopard PSU5C/4R	Duple Dominant III	C48FT	1982	Goldgrove, Erith, 1995

Previous Registration:

MFS579X   PWB659X, MSP333

Livery: White and blue

The East Midlands Bus Handbook

UNITY

F & J Marriott, Beck Garage, Clayworth, Retford, Nottinghamshire, DN22 9AG

PRW137M	Leyland Leopard PSU3B/4R	Plaxton Panorama Elite III	C51F	1974	Red House, Coventry, 1979
TUA707R	Bedford YMT	Plaxton Supreme III Express	C53F	1976	Shipley, Baildon, 1982
CAZ6836	Kässbohrer Setra S215HD	Kässbohrer Tornado	C53FT	1982	Walter Martin, Sheffield, 1994
UXI6833	Scania K112CRS	Jonckheere Jubilee P599	C49FT	1984	Lockley, Stafford, 1993
HIL7198	DAF MB200DKFL600	Plaxton Paramount 3500	C49FT	1984	Seaview, Parkstone, 1995
D167LNA	Mercedes-Benz 609D	Made-to-Measure	C27F	1986	
D428JDB	Freight Rover Sherpa	Made-to-Measure	C16F	1986	
E911LVE	Volkswagen LT55	Optare CityPacer	B25F	1987	Cambus, 1996
G110OFE	Bedford Midi	Bedford	M4	1990	private owner, 1994
RJI8861	Scania K113CRB	Irizar Century 12.35	C49FT	1994	Appleby, 1998
L99ABC	Mercedes-Benz 709D	Marshall	B23F	1994	ABC, Ainsdale, 1998
L999ABC	Mercedes-Benz 709D	Marshall	B23F	1994	ABC, Ainsdale, 1998

Previous Registrations:

CAZ6836	GGK724X, 806ECV, JFM541	RJI8861	L502YFE
HIL7198	A106XTX	UXI6833	A58JLW

Livery: Blue, grey and cream

The green foliage of National Trust's Clumber Park surrounds L99ABC, one of a pair of Mercedes-Benz 709D minibuses operated by Unity. A number of services are operated in and around Worksop most of which are assisted by funding provided by the Rural Grant. Route 30, linking Worksop and the park with Tuxford, is one such route serving north Nottinghamshire. *Tony Wilson*

VIKING

VikingTours and Travel Ltd, Ryder Close, Swadlincote, Derbyshire, DE11 9EU

5	XAF759	Volvo B10M-61	Plaxton Paramount 3500	C53F	1984	Stevensons, 1998
6	852YYC	Volvo B10M-61	Plaxton Paramount 3500 II	C53F	1985	Stevensons, 1998
7	430UFM	Volvo B10M-61	Plaxton Paramount 3500	C55F	1988	Plastow, Wheatley, 1999
9	WYR562	Bova FHD12.290	Bova Futura	C36FT	1990	Stevensons, 1998
11	OGL518	Volvo B10M-61	Plaxton Paramount 3200 II	C53F	1985	Stevensons, 1998
14	LUY742	Volvo B10M-61	Plaxton Paramount 3500 III	C49FT	1987	Stevensons, 1998
15	VOI6874	Volvo B10M-61	Plaxton Paramount 3500	C55F	1983	Stevensons, 1998
16	FSU661	Volvo B10M-60	Plaxton Paramount 3500 III	C49F	1991	Stevensons, 1998
17	VLT166	Volvo B10M-60	Plaxton Paramount 3500 III	C49F	1991	Stevensons, 1998
19	468KPX	Volvo B10M-61	Van Hool Alizée H	C44FL	1982	Stevensons, 1998
20	784RBF	Volvo B10M-61	Jonckheere Jubilee P50	C53F	1987	Stevensons, 1998
21	RIL1021	Volvo B10M-61	Jonckheere Deauville P599	C51FT	1990	P & J Ellis, Wembley Park, 1999
23	YXI3054	Volvo B10M-61	Van Hool Alizée H	C53F	1988	Browns of Edinburgh, 1999
24	429UFM	Volvo B10M-61	Van Hool Alizée H	C49F	1992	Warrington, 1999
25	82HBC	Volvo B10M-61	Van Hool Alizée H	C49F	1992	Warrington, 1999
28	PCW946	Volvo B10M-61	Plaxton Paramount 3500	C49FT	1984	Stevensons, 1998
34	PSV323	MCW MetroRider MF154/2	MCW	C28F	1990	Stevensons, 1998

Previous Registrations:

82HBC	J414AWF	FSU661	H908AHS	VLT166	G58RGG
429UFM	J410AWF	LUY742	E562UHS	VOI6874	YNN29Y
430UFM	299UFP	OGL518	B912SPR	WYR562	G417WFP
468KPX	VRR447,UHH575X	PCW946	A703OWY,HIJ3652,A788MEH	XAF759	B555HAL
784RBF	D319VVV	PSV323	G298SKP,HKR11,G918NUP	YXI3054	F733ENE
852YYC	B666XVO	RIL1021	?		

Livery: Blue and red

Viking Tours were last featured in our North & West Midlands Bus Handbook, when Viking formed the coaching unit of Midland Red North. Now independent, the company has moved to an almost all Volvo fleet, one of two exceptions being the Burton Albion coach, WYR562, shown here. *Viking Tours & Travel*

WEST END TRAVEL

J Penniston, 7, Manor Close, Thorpe Park, Melton Mowbray, Leicestershire LE13 1RN

D230UNT	Volvo B10M-60	Plaxton Paramount 3200 III	C53F	1987	Britannia, Telford, 1999
A3ARV	Volvo B10M-61	Van Hool Alizée H	C53F	1987	Laguna, Bournemouth, 1999
WET1K	Toyota Coaster HZB50R	Caetano Optimo III	C21F	1994	Britannia, Telford, 1997
XLC1S	Mercedes-Benz 709D	Alexander AM	B25F	19	?, 1999
VUT1X	LDV Convoy	LDV	M16	1999	

Previous Registrations:

D230UNT	D442CNR, LIL7810	WET1K	L966RUB	XLC1S	?

Livery: Red

Depot: Leicester Road, Melton Mowbray

West End Travel have a contract from Leicestershire County Council to provide service 128 between Leicester and Melton Mowbray which runs through the Wreake Valley villages. A rainy afternoon in Leicester sees XLC1S arriving from Melton Mowbray. This Mercedes 709D minibus was bodied by Alexander and carries West End Travel's all-over red colours. *Steve Sanderson*

WIDE HORIZON

RT, EM & J Clarke, 48 Coventry Road, Burbage, Leicestershire LE10 2HD

457NWL	Leyland Leopard PSU3E/4R	Plaxton Supreme III	C53F	1978	Tappins, Didcot, 1991
SDA764S	Leyland Fleetline FE30AGR	MCW	B43/33F	1978	SerCo, Market Harborough, 1997
SHE545S	Leyland Fleetline FE30AGR	Alexander AL	B45/29D	1978	Midland Fox, 1997
WDA951T	Leyland Fleetline FE30AGR	MCW	B43/33F	1979	Abbey Howe, Waddington, 1998
CWG683V	Leyland Atlantean AN68A/1R	Alexander AL	B45/29D	1979	ABC, Leicester, 1997
MGC338V	Leyland Leopard PSU5C/4R	Plaxton Supreme IV	C52F	1979	Court, Fillongley, 1997
BBB542V	Bedford YMT	Plaxton Supreme IV	C53F	1980	Verulam, St Albans, 1989
GRN898W	Volvo B58-56	Duple Dominant	C53F	1981	Barfordian, Gt Barford, 1997
VAV160X	Volvo B58-56	Plaxton Supreme V	C53F	1982	Country Lion, Northampton, 1996
BGS291X	Bedford YNT	Plaxton Supreme V Express	C53F	1982	Neal, Rainworth, 1998
TJI4027	DAF SB2305DHS585	Van Hool Alizée H	C55F	1987	Sleight, Swinton, 1995
LAT256	DAF SB2300DHS585	Jonckheere Jubilee	C51FT	1987	County, Brentwood, 1995
TJI4028	Scania K93CRB	Plaxton Paramount 3500 III	C51FT	1993	R Bullock, Cheadle, 1996
L643AYS	Volvo B10M-60	Van Hool Alizée HE	C53F	1994	Park's of Hamilton, 1996
N196DYB	Bova FHD 12-340	Bova Futura	C53F	1996	

Previous Registrations:

457NWL	WFH172S		TJI4027	D66CUY
LAT256	D94BNV		TJI4028	K500BUL, K829CNB
L643AYS	HSK654			

Livery: Varies; most vehicles run in former owner's colours; **Depot:** Jacknell Road, Hinckley.

As well as operating a bus service from Hinckley to Sharnford, Sapcote and Stoney Stanton, Wide Horizon are a coaching company. Most vehicles are run in the colours of their former owners but, in the case of N196DYB, the vehicle is white. This Bova Futura, with the distinctive bulbous front - thus known in its home country of Netherlands as the pregnant bus - was purchased new by Wide Horizon in 1996. It was caught by the camera in Skegness in July 1999. *Steve Sanderson*

WINGS

D E Wing, 77 Mareham Lane, Sleaford, Lincolnshire, NG34 7JX

64	HCT990	Volvo B10M-61	Van Hool Alizée	C46FT	1983	Iberian, Kensington, 1984
70	LBH297P	Bedford YRT	Plaxton Supreme III	C53F	1976	Travel Wide, Sparham, 1987
91	C823CBU	Renault-Dodge S56	Northern Counties	B18F	1986	Hayre, Wednesbury, 1995
94	MMJ474V	Bedford YLQ	Duple Dominant II	C45F	1980	Barnard, Kirton-in-Lindsey, 1995
95	JTL37T	Bedford YMT	Plaxton Supreme III Express	C53F	1978	Barnard, Kirton-in-Lindsey, 1995
96	MIW2418	DAF MB230LB615	Van Hool Alizée	C51F	1989	Clarkson, South Elmsall, 1996
97	VTL627	Volvo B10M-60	Plaxton Expressliner	C46FT	1990	SWT, 1996
98	SCT330	Volvo B10M-60	Plaxton Expressliner	C49F	1990	Premier Travel Services, 1996
99	PAY9W	Bedford YNT	Plaxton Supreme IV	C53F	1981	Sun Star, Skegness, 1996
101	D172LTA	Renault-Dodge S56	Reeve Burgess Beaver	B23F	1988	Chambers, Bures, 1996
103	VPW86S	Bristol VRT/SL3/6LXB	Eastern Coach Works	B43/31F	1977	Stagecoach Viscount, 1997
104	BBM47A	Volvo B58-61	Duple Dominant II	C57F	1980	Flintham, Metheringham, 1999

Previous Registrations:

BBM47A	GPA632V		MIW2418	F271RJX		SCT330	G379REG
HCT990	PCG521Y, HCT990, ODO842Y	OIB9392	VTL990K		VTL627	G165LWN
JTL37T	ARB525T					

Livery: Blue

Wings are a long-established coach operator based in the Lincolnshire town of Sleaford. It operates a town service branded as the Sleaford Nipper using an all-over blue livery now replacing the previous two shades of blue and cream. The older scheme was still carried by LBH297P when photographed at the depot. This Bedford YRT has been in the fleet since 1987 and carries a Plaxton Supreme III body. *Steve Sanderson*

WOODS

Woods Coaches Ltd, Bedford Road, Wigston, Leicester, LE8 2XD

6477WF	Bedford YRQ	Duple Dominant	C45F	1976	Cooper, Rothwell, 1983
RJI4240	Volvo B58-56	Duple Dominant II	C53F	1980	
2557NU	Volvo B58-61	Duple Dominant IV	C53F	1981	
JIW9464	Volvo B10M-61	Plaxton Paramount 3500	C49FT	1983	Mandy, Hornsey, 1989
782EUL	Volvo B10M-61	Plaxton Paramount 3500	C49FT	1983	Baker, Biddulph, 1989
564YYB	Volvo B10M-61	Plaxton Paramount 3500	C42FT	1983	Watson, Staindrop, 1995
FIL6617	Volvo B10M-61	Duple Dominant IV	C53FT	1984	
NIB6433	Volvo B10M-61	Plaxton Paramount 3500 II	C50F	1986	Wallace Arnold, 1990
SIB1998	Volvo B9M	Caetano Algarve R-NDH	C39FT	1986	Essex Cs, Bethnal Green, 1992
WDZ3132	Volvo B10M-61	Plaxton Paramount 3	C48FT	1986	Dewhirst, Bradford, 1997
MIL1055	Volvo B10M-61	Plaxton Paramount 3	C50F	1986	Dunn-Line, Nottingham, 1998
XIB3473	Volvo B9M	Plaxton Bustler	BC33F	1986	Lofty, Bridge Trafford, 1996
OIW1321	Volvo B10M-61	Plaxton Paramount 3500 II	C49FT	1986	Appleby, Conisholme, 1993
GIL8879	Volvo B10M-61	Plaxton Paramount 3500 III	C53FT	1987	Wings, Sleaford, 1995
MAZ7015	Volvo B10M-61	Plaxton Paramount	C49FT	1987	Blubell, Hurley, 1997
E120BHS	Mercedes-Benz 709D	Alexander AM	B25F	1988	
6962WF	Mercedes-Benz 811D	Robin Hood	C25F	1988	Smith, High Wycombe, 1994
SIB8312	Mercedes-Benz 609D	Reeve Burgess	B20F	1988	North Western, 1996
JIL4006	Mercedes-Benz 709D	Reeve Burgess Beaver	B25F	1988	Pam's, Enderby, 1999
F137KAO	Mercedes-Benz 609D	Reeve Burgess	B20F	1989	North Western, 1994
J7116USF	Mercedes-Benz 709D	Alexander AM	BC25F	1991	McPherson, Glasgow, 1999
6884WF	Mercedes-Benz 711D	Dormobile Routemaker	BC25F	1992	Nuttall, Penwortham, 1994
K17FTG	Volvo B10M-60	Plaxton Excalibur	C50F	1993	Flight's, Birmingham, 1999
K18FTG	Volvo B10M-60	Plaxton Excalibur	C50F	1993	Flight's, Birmingham, 1999

Many of the Woods coaches carry 'Cherished' pre-1963 marks or non-year registrations obtained from Northern Ireland. GIL8879 is of the latter type, the vehicle carrying it having previously been registered D101VRM. This Volvo B10M carries the MkIII version of the Plaxton Paramount 3500 body which has a rounded front 'bumper'. The passengers conveyed on this coach on the day it was photographed were enjoying a day at Ascot races. *David Heath*

Woods has built up a portfolio of tendered bus services and operate them with Mercedes-Benz minibuses. F137KAO is type 609D and is a van conversion undertaken by Reeve Burgess rather than the fully coachbuilt Beaver model. Originally in the Bootle-based North Western fleet, this vehicle stands in Leicester St Margaret's bus station in between trips. *Steve Sanderson*

4687NU	Mercedes-Benz 709D	Mellor	B25F	1995	Pam's, Enderby, 1999
M570VSF	Mercedes-Benz 709D	Alexander Sprint	B25F	1987	McColl, Balloch, 1998
M671RAJ	Mercedes-Benz 709D	Alexander Sprint	B25F	1987	Go-Ahead (OK), 1999
M679RAJ	Mercedes-Benz 709D	Alexander Sprint	B25F	1987	Go-Ahead (OK), 1999
N957SAY	Mercedes-Benz 709D	Reeve Burgess Beaver	B F	1996	
P37CBC	Mercedes-Benz 811D	Reeve Burgess Beaver	B29F	1996	

Previous Registrations:

2557NU	PBC459W	GIL8879	D101VRM	RJI4240	KBC609V, 5566WF
564VYB	RME973Y	JIL4006	F127TRU	SIB1998	C625KDS
6477WF	LUX524P	JIW9464	A243HMD	SIB8312	F129KAO
6884WF	K660NGB	MAZ7015	E560UHS	TIW2820	-
6962WF	F124TRU, JIL4005	MIL1055	C108DWR, HIL8438, C205HDS, YVS703	WDZ3132	C447CWR
782EUL	8399RU	NIB6433	C124DWR	XIB3473	C853EML
FIL6617	A230GNR	OIW1321	C92RFE, ASV895	4687NU	N11PAM

Livery: Blue, yellow and orange.

Reg	Operator	Reg	Operator	Reg	Operator	Reg	Operator
C113AFX	Paul James	D231OOJ	Fred's	E88HNR	First Leicester	E692UNE	Holloways
C113CAT	Maun Crusader	D282XCX	P C Coaches	E89HNR	First Leicester	E701GCU	City of Nottingham
C136DWT	Carnell Coaches	D308MHS	RoadCar	E90HNR	First Leicester	E701XKR	Arriva Fox County
C181KET	Kettlewell's	D323CLB	Hail and Ride	E90OUH	Fred's	E702XKR	Arriva Fox County
C210VCT	Carnell Coaches	D392TAU	City of Nottingham	E90OUH	Hail and Ride	E721BVO	East Midland
C270CBU	Doyle Mini Coaches	D393TAU	City of Nottingham	E90YWB	East Midland	E725BVO	City of Nottingham
C308NRC	City of Nottingham	D394TAU	City of Nottingham	E91HNR	First Leicester	E726BVO	City of Nottingham
C309NRC	City of Nottingham	D404EFA	Hail and Ride	E91YWB	East Midland	E727BVO	City of Nottingham
C310NRC	City of Nottingham	D428JDB	Unity	E92HNR	First Leicester	E728BVO	City of Nottingham
C311NRC	City of Nottingham	D451CNR	Hulleys	E92YWB	East Midland	E729BVO	City of Nottingham
C312NRC	City of Nottingham	D458BEO	RoadCar	E93HNR	First Leicester	E730BVO	City of Nottingham
C313NRC	City of Nottingham	D459BEO	RoadCar	E93YWB	East Midland	E731BVO	City of Nottingham
C314NRC	City of Nottingham	D481CKV	Doyle Mini Coaches	E94HNR	First Leicester	E732BVO	City of Nottingham
C326HWJ	East Midland	D498NYS	DunnLine	E94YWB	East Midland	E733BVO	City of Nottingham
C327HWJ	East Midland	D500RWF	Isle Coaches	E95HNR	First Leicester	E734BVO	City of Nottingham
C328HWJ	East Midland	D510NDA	Fred's	E95YWB	East Midland	E735BVO	City of Nottingham
C329HWJ	East Midland	D523SKY	RoadCar	E96HNR	First Leicester	E736BVO	City of Nottingham
C330HWJ	East Midland	D527SKY	RoadCar	E96YWB	East Midland	E737BVO	City of Nottingham
C331HWJ	East Midland	D529SKY	RoadCar	E97HNR	First Leicester	E738BVO	City of Nottingham
C332HWJ	East Midland	D530SKY	RoadCar	E97YWB	East Midland	E738VWJ	Avisdors
C333HWJ	East Midland	D531SKY	RoadCar	E98HNR	First Leicester	E739BVO	City of Nottingham
C334HWJ	East Midland	D532SKY	RoadCar	E98YWB	East Midland	E741VWJ	Fred's
C335HWJ	East Midland	D534SKY	RoadCar	E99HNR	First Leicester	E749HJF	Translinc
C336HWJ	East Midland	D536SKY	RoadCar	E100AFW	Delaine Buses	E751JAY	Maun Crusader
C414DML	Translinc	D538VRR	Kettlewell's	E105JPL	Hail and Ride	E752HJF	Skinner
C426MFE	Delaine Buses	D552HNW	Hail and Ride	E106JPL	Hail and Ride	E753HJF	Hulleys
C516KMW	P C Coaches	D627BCK	Hail and Ride	E112YNM	Elseys	E824MDD	Applebys
C530UUT	P C Coaches	D641WNU	Trent	E113FNU	City of Nottingham	E825OMS	City of Nottingham
C538TJF	Fred's	D720PTU	P C Coaches	E120BHS	Woods	E861URH	Kettlewell's
C696DVG	Moxon's	D721PTU	Carnell Coaches	E131PLJ	Skinner	E880DRA	East Midland
C716LTO	Trent	D737JUB	Fred's	E138ATV	City of Nottingham	E899CDS	City of Nottingham
C717LTO	Trent	D741WRC	T R S	E139ATV	City of Nottingham	E902GCU	Fred's
C718LTO	Trent	D748XAU	Reliance	E142ERA	City of Nottingham	E903DRG	Brylaine
C719LTO	Trent	D758WRR	Hail and Ride	E143ERA	City of Nottingham	E907GCU	Fred's
C720MRC	City of Nottingham	D768YCW	Applebys	E149BTO	Arriva Fox County	E910GCU	Fred's
C720NNN	Trent	D769YCW	Applebys	E149KYW	Marshalls	E911EAY	Johnson Bros
C721MRC	City of Nottingham	D776WVO	Glovers	E150BTO	Arriva Fox County	E911LVE	Unity
C721NNN	RoadCar	D811SGB	Carnell Coaches	E151BTO	Arriva Fox County	E924VUG	Doyle Mini Coaches
C722MRC	City of Nottingham	D850PWN	Hulleys	E152BTO	Arriva Fox County	E925CDS	City of Nottingham
C723MRC	City of Nottingham	D854KWR	Haines	E153BTO	Arriva Fox County	E927PBE	East Midland
C723NNN	Trent	D861LWR	Hail and Ride	E186UWF	Bowers	E928PBE	East Midland
C724MRC	City of Nottingham	D906MVU	Arriva Fox County	E200WHS	City of Nottingham	E929PBE	East Midland
C823CBU	Wings	D930ARE	Bowers	E219FLD	P C Coaches	E930PBE	East Midland
C988MWJ	Dent	D932TWE	East Midland	E219GNV	Anstey Busline	E935CDS	City of Nottingham
CAL845T	Travel Wright	D933TWE	East Midland	E220FLD	P C Coaches	E938CDS	City of Nottingham
CAX14V	Hylton Dawson	D935TWE	East Midland	E228FLD	Doyle Mini Coaches	E941CDS	City of Nottingham
CAZ2045	Skills	D936EBP	T R S	E250ADO	Haines	E964SVU	Glovers
CAZ2046	Skills	D956WJH	Johnson's Coaches	E250AKW	East Midland	E977DNK	Go-Bus
CAZ6836	Unity	D959WJH	Bowers	E288KLD	Ringwood	E985GFW	Applebys
CDN711V	P C Coaches	D961WJH	Bowers	E289MMM	Hulleys	EAD122T	Fowler's Travel
CFM347S	Applebys	D965PJA	Scutt	E307BWL	Cavalier	EAH891Y	RoadCar
CFM355S	Applebys	DAR120T	Trent	E307EVW	City of Nottingham	EAT170Y	Applebys
CHH212T	RoadCar	DAZ1400	Kime's	E315BVO	City of Nottingham	EAZ4709	Cropley
CHH215T	RoadCar	DAZ4300	Kime's	E316BVO	City of Nottingham	EAZ5347	Cropley
CIB9152	Hobsons	DAZ4301	Kime's	E317BVO	City of Nottingham	EBW105Y	Applebys
CJN441C	Fowler's Travel	DAZ4302	Kime's	E318BVO	City of Nottingham	EBW110Y	Applebys
CKA951X	Dent	DAZ5455	RoadCar	E318NSX	RoadCar	EDT201V	RoadCar
CKS390X	P C Coaches	DAZ8290	Slack's Coaches	E319BVO	City of Nottingham	EDT204V	RoadCar
CLZ1860	Cropley	DBV198W	RoadCar	E319NSX	RoadCar	EDT214V	RoadCar
CROPLEY		DET472V	RoadCar	E320BVO	City of Nottingham	EDT220V	RoadCar
CSU935	Sweyne	DET477V	RoadCar	E321BVO	City of Nottingham	EFN178L	Kinch Bus
CUL119V	Kinch Bus	DET479V	RoadCar	E322BVO	City of Nottingham	EFU613Y	Emmersons
CWG681V	Holloways	DFW42X	RoadCar	E323BVO	City of Nottingham	EFU935Y	East Midland
CWG683V	Wide Horizon	DHG210W	RoadCar	E324BVO	City of Nottingham	EJC1	Skills
CWG684V	Holloways	DHG211W	RoadCar	E325BVO	City of Nottingham	EJV31Y	East Midland
CWG696V	Isle Coaches	DMS21V	Beaver Bus	E326BVO	City of Nottingham	EJV32Y	East Midland
CWG699V	Holloways	DNG233T	Moxon's	E326LHN	Hail and Ride	EJV33Y	East Midland
CWG746V	Holloways	DOC19V	Applebys	E327BVO	City of Nottingham	EJV34Y	East Midland
CWG756V	Holloways	DSV721	Applebys	E328BVO	City of Nottingham	EKW614V	East Midland
CWG773V	Holloways	DTN958W	Felix	E329BVO	City of Nottingham	EKW615V	East Midland
CWU136T	Dent	DVL940T	Hunt's	E333EVH	Elseys	EKW616V	East Midland
CWX656T	Trent	DWF22V	East Midland	E381ERB	City of Nottingham	EKY21V	East Midland
CWX659T	Trent	DWF23V	East Midland	E381TUB	Doyle Mini Coaches	EKY22V	East Midland
D32SAO	Applebys	DWF24V	East Midland	E393HNR	Butler Bros	EKY23V	East Midland
D36NFU	RoadCar	DWF26V	East Midland	E402WAM	Hail and Ride	EKY24V	East Midland
D41TKA	Avisdors	DXI84	DunnLine	E404EPE	Hunt's	EKY25V	East Midland
D44RWC	Arriva Fox County	DXI92	DunnLine	E405BHK	Avisdors	EKY27V	East Midland
D59TLV	Arriva Fox County	E21ECH	Arriva Fox County	E434YHL	Travel Wright	EKY28V	East Midland
D64OKG	Fred's	E23ECH	Arriva Fox County	E445FNU	DunnLine	EKY29V	East Midland
D77HRU	Fowler's Travel	E24ECH	Arriva Fox County	E450MSE	P C Coaches	ELR109T	Dent
D80UTF	Arriva Fox County	E25ECH	Arriva Fox County	E459WJK	Applebys	ENF514Y	Albert Wilde
D102SPP	P C Coaches	E26ECH	Arriva Fox County	E498HHN	RoadCar	ENF572Y	Carnell Coaches
D114TFT	Fred's	E47HFE	East Midland	E506HHN	RoadCar	ENF574Y	Carnell Coaches
D123OWG	Sweyne	E48HFE	East Midland	E512HHN	RoadCar	EON824V	RoadCar
D131OWG	Graysroft	E48MCK	Applebys	E539VKY	RoadCar	EON831V	Arriva Fox County
D140WCC	Ausden-Clarke	E49HFE	East Midland	E555GFR	Beaver Bus	EPH210V	Arriva Fox County
D163KDN	Avisdors	E50HFE	East Midland	E562MAC	Butler Bros	EPH212V	Arriva Fox County
D167LNA	Unity	E58HFE	East Midland	E582JVN	RoadCar	EPT879S	Trent
D171LTA	DD Travel	E60WDT	East Midland	E590BDB	P C Coaches	EPT881S	RoadCar
D172LTA	Wings	E61WDT	East Midland	E623BVK	Marriott's Travel	ESK965	RoadCar
D223SKD	Arriva Fox County	E62UKL	Arriva Fox County	E626BVK	Marriott's Travel	ETO911V	RoadCar
D224SKD	Arriva Fox County	E70XKW	City of Nottingham	E646KYW	RoadCar	ETT319Y	City of Nottingham
D226SKD	Arriva Fox County	E71MVV	Hulleys	E648CHS	DunnLine	ETU531X	Bowers
D22SAO	Applebys	E75LFR	Applebys	E648KYW	RoadCar	EUA366	Andrews of Tideswell
D230UNT	West End Travel	E87HNR	First Leicester	E650KYW	Bowers	EWE203V	East Midland

Reg	Operator	Reg	Operator	Reg	Operator	Reg	Operator
EWE206V	East Midland	F603VEW	Delaine Buses	FUT240V	First Leicester	G521WJF	Arriva Fox County
EWF474V	P C Coaches	F604GVO	Trent	FUT250V	First Leicester	G522WJF	Arriva Fox County
EWF488V	P C Coaches	F605GVO	Trent	FVR256V	Delaine Buses	G523WJF	Arriva Fox County
EWY26Y	RoadCar	F606GVO	Trent	FW5696	Marshalls	G529MNT	Translinc
EWY27Y	RoadCar	F607GVO	Trent	FWA472V	Isle Coaches	G553RRR	Skills
EWY28Y	RoadCar	F608GVO	Trent	FWA475V	Isle Coaches	G600NRC	Trent
EWY30Y	RoadCar	F608GVO	Trent	FYT335V	Johnson's Coaches	G605JUG	Doyle Mini Coaches
F24HGG	Hulleys	F610GVO	Trent	FYT336V	Johnson's Coaches	G606JUG	Doyle Mini Coaches
F26XVP	Arriva Fox County	F611GET	Ringwood	G53RGG	T M Travel	G608JUG	Doyle Mini Coaches
F27JRC	Arriva Fox County	F611GVO	Trent	G64SNN	Arriva Fox County	G612OTV	Trent
F27XVP	Arriva Fox County	F636BKD	First Leicester	G65SNN	Arriva Fox County	G613OTV	Trent
F28JRC	Arriva Fox County	F637BKD	First Leicester	G79VFW	East Midland	G614OTV	Trent
F29XVP	Arriva Fox County	F640HDB	Doyle Mini Coaches	G80VFW	East Midland	G615OTV	Trent
F43CWY	Cavalier	F642HDB	Doyle Mini Coaches	G81VFW	East Midland	G616OTV	Trent
F46LCH	Skills	F691PAY	Reliance	G83OTU	Arriva Fox County	G617OTV	Trent
F47CWY	DunnLine	F692PAY	Travel Wright	G84OTU	Arriva Fox County	G618OTV	Trent
F53CWY	DunnLine	F697HNU	Felix	G86OTU	Arriva Fox County	G621OTV	Trent
F75TFU	East Midland	F701PAY	Emmersons	G87OTU	Arriva Fox County	G629EKA	First Leicester
F76TFU	East Midland	F702PAY	Emmersons	G110OFE	Unity	G667FKA	First Leicester
F77TFU	East Midland	F703JCN	City of Nottingham	G129NRC	City of Nottingham	G690KNW	Ringwood
F78TFU	East Midland	F704JCN	City of Nottingham	G142GOL	Arriva Fox County	G697NUB	Doyle Mini Coaches
F109YVP	Express Motors	F705JCN	City of Nottingham	G143GOL	Arriva Fox County	G700OCH	Glovers
F114JTO	City of Nottingham	F721SML	Fred's	G154NRC	City of Nottingham	G701AEF	Butler Bros
F115JTO	City of Nottingham	F740HRC	City of Nottingham	G155NRC	City of Nottingham	G704EOX	Haines
F116JTO	City of Nottingham	F741HRC	City of Nottingham	G156NRC	City of Nottingham	G704HPW	Kettlewell's
F118JTO	City of Nottingham	F742HRC	City of Nottingham	G157NRC	City of Nottingham	G745PNN	City of Nottingham
F120YVP	Express Motors	F743HRC	City of Nottingham	G158NRC	City of Nottingham	G746PNN	City of Nottingham
F121YVP	Sweyne	F744HRC	City of Nottingham	G159NRC	City of Nottingham	G747PNN	City of Nottingham
F128KTV	City of Nottingham	F774GNA	Holloways	G160PTO	City of Nottingham	G748PNN	City of Nottingham
F137KAO	Woods	F791JTV	City of Nottingham	G161PVO	City of Nottingham	G749PNN	City of Nottingham
F143MBC	First Leicester	F792JTV	City of Nottingham	G162PVO	City of Nottingham	G751SRB	City of Nottingham
F146MBC	First Leicester	F815CWJ	RoadCar	G163PVO	City of Nottingham	G752SRB	City of Nottingham
F149MBC	First Leicester	F883SMU	Reliance	G164PVO	City of Nottingham	G753SRB	City of Nottingham
F150MBC	First Leicester	F901HAU	Doyle Mini Coaches	G165RRA	City of Nottingham	G754SRB	City of Nottingham
F151GVO	City of Nottingham	F906MPH	Translinc	G166RRA	City of Nottingham	G755SRB	City of Nottingham
F151MBC	First Leicester	F925YWY	T M Travel	G218EOA	Haines	G756SRB	City of Nottingham
F152GVO	City of Nottingham	F92WFA	Holloways	G232EOA	Arriva Fox County	G757SRB	City of Nottingham
F152MBC	First Leicester	F970GJK	Applebys	G232GOJ	Haines	G758SRB	City of Nottingham
F153DET	Arriva Fox County	FAO927V	RoadCar	G236EOA	Arriva Fox County	G820KWF	East Midland
F153GVO	City of Nottingham	FAZ2784	Arriva Fox County	G259LWF	First Leicester	G821KWF	East Midland
F154DET	Arriva Fox County	FBV271W	Express Motors	G274HDW	Fred's	G822KWF	East Midland
F155DET	Arriva Fox County	FBV485W	Applebys	G276VML	Holloways	G823KWF	East Midland
F156DET	Arriva Fox County	FBV492W	Holloways	G281BEL	Translinc	G824KWF	East Midland
F157DET	Arriva Fox County	FBV500W	Holloways	G293MWU	RoadCar	G825KWF	East Midland
F158DET	Arriva Fox County	FBV503W	T R S	G294MWU	RoadCar	G826KWF	East Midland
F162UMD	T R S	FBV510W	Fowler's Travel	G295MWU	RoadCar	G827KWF	East Midland
F165FWY	Cavalier	FBV525S	Trent	G301RJA	Arriva Fox County	G849VAY	Elseys
F172FWY	Cavalier	FDZ4731	Carnell Coaches	G316XEE	Holloways	G865VAY	Travel Wright
F197YDA	Express Motors	FFL138V	T M Travel	G324BHN	Skinner	G870YDU	Maun Crusader
F201HSO	Holloways	FGE438X	Camms	G327MUA	RoadCar	G871WML	RoadCar
F212LTV	Moxon's	FGE440X	Maun Crusader	G331NRC	City of Nottingham	G873WML	RoadCar
F217RMR	Reliance	FIL3451	Arriva Fox County	G332NRC	City of Nottingham	G874WML	RoadCar
F218AKG	Hail and Ride	FIL3452	Arriva Fox County	G333NRC	City of Nottingham	G875WML	RoadCar
F232RNR	Butler Bros	FIL4032	Haines	G334NTV	City of Nottingham	G876WML	RoadCar
F240PAC	Doyle Mini Coaches	FIL6617	Woods	G335PAL	City of Nottingham	G877WML	RoadCar
F256CEW	RoadCar	FIL7622	Hail and Ride	G339KKW	East Midland	G878WML	RoadCar
F257CEW	RoadCar	FIL7997	Moxon's	G340KKW	East Midland	G879TVS	City of Nottingham
F258CEW	RoadCar	FJF193	First Leicester	G341KKW	East Midland	G879WML	RoadCar
F259CEW	Fowler's Travel	FJU973	Paul Winson	G342KKW	East Midland	G880WML	RoadCar
F269UDX	T M Travel	FJV931	Applebys	G343KKW	East Midland	G881WML	RoadCar
F272OPX	Arriva Fox County	FKM304V	Maun Crusader	G362SRB	City of Nottingham	G882WML	RoadCar
F301RUT	Arriva Fox County	FLD634Y	Cropley	G363SRB	City of Nottingham	G883WML	RoadCar
F302RUT	Arriva Fox County	FPR65V	Trent	G364SRB	City of Nottingham	G884WML	RoadCar
F307EKP	Avisdors	FRA515V	Trent	G365FOP	Holloways	G885WML	RoadCar
F312PEV	Fowler's Travel	FRA516V	Trent	G365SRB	City of Nottingham	G886WML	RoadCar
F314RHK	Fowler's Travel	FRA517V	Trent	G366SRB	City of Nottingham	G887WML	RoadCar
F315EJO	Cavalier	FRA518V	Trent	G367SRB	City of Nottingham	G888WML	RoadCar
F364MUT	Fred's	FRA519V	Trent	G368RTO	City of Nottingham	G889WML	RoadCar
F368HTY	Doyle Mini Coaches	FRA520V	Trent	G369RTO	City of Nottingham	G890WML	RoadCar
F379UCP	Arriva Fox County	FRA521L	Fowler's Travel	G370RTO	City of Nottingham	G891WML	RoadCar
F380JTV	City of Nottingham	FRA522V	Trent	G371RTO	City of Nottingham	G893WML	RoadCar
F382GVO	City of Nottingham	FRA523V	Trent	G372RTO	City of Nottingham	G894WML	RoadCar
F383GVO	City of Nottingham	FRA524V	Trent	G373RTO	City of Nottingham	G895WML	RoadCar
F384GVO	City of Nottingham	FRA525V	Kinch Bus	G374NRC	City of Nottingham	G945JPW	Hulleys
F385GVO	City of Nottingham	FRA526V	Trent	G375NRC	City of Nottingham	G959WNR	Fowler's Travel
F386GVO	City of Nottingham	FRA527V	Trent	G376NRC	City of Nottingham	G969KTX	T M Travel
F387GVO	City of Nottingham	FRA528V	Kinch Bus	G377NRC	City of Nottingham	G997KJX	Elseys
F388GVO	City of Nottingham	FRA529V	Kinch Bus	G378NRC	City of Nottingham	G998KJX	Elseys
F389GVO	City of Nottingham,	FRA530V	Kinch Bus	G379NRC	City of Nottingham	GAZ4501	Ausden-Clarke
F390GVO	City of Nottingham	FRA531V	Kinch Bus	G409NAK	Holloways	GAZ4502	Ausden-Clarke
F391GVO	City of Nottingham	FRA533V	Trent	G418RYJ	Johnson's Coaches	GAZ4503	Ausden-Clarke
F406DUG	Arriva Fox County	FRA534V	Trent	G427VAY	Translinc	GCC3	Graysroft
F407DUG	Arriva Fox County	FRA535V	Trent	G429VAY	Translinc	GFO754X	Hail and Ride
F433AYG	Doyle Mini Coaches	FRH615T	Applebys	G430YAY	Travel Wright	GFV155W	Eagre
F433AYG	Doyle Mini Coaches	FRR194J	Moxon's	G440NET	Butler Bros	GHR302W	Camms
F462KKE	Doyle Mini Coaches	FSU681	Viking	G448LKW	RoadCar	GHV67N	Kettlewell's
F510PHN	Fred's	FTL992X	RoadCar	G453PGO	Skinner	GIJ9093	Isle Coaches
F513RTL	T M Travel	FTL993X	RoadCar	G48HDW	Skinner	GIL3122	Ausden-Clarke
F533EWJ	P C Coaches	FTO544V	Applebys	G495VFU	Applebys	GIL4271	Moxon's
F556NGR	Fowler's Travel	FTO550V	East Midland	G497RNE	Bowers	GIL6253	Arriva Fox County
F597HYC	Holloways	FUH32V	RoadCar	G506SFT	Arriva Fox County	GIL6949	Arriva Fox County
F600GVO	Trent	FUH34V	RoadCar	G508SFT	Arriva Fox County	GIL7549	Andrews of Tideswell
F601GVO	Trent	FUJ949V	P C Coaches	G509SFT	Arriva Fox County	GIL8879	Woods
F602GVO	Trent	FUT179V	First Leicester	G512SFT	Arriva Fox County	GJP197	Fowler's Travel
F603GVO	Trent	FUT184V	First Leicester	G513SFT	Arriva Fox County	GLS277W	RoadCar

Reg	Operator	Reg	Operator	Reg	Operator	Reg	Operator
GMS289S	Hunt's	H653GPF	Arriva Fox County	HYD266Y	Translinc	J350XET	East Midland
GNH333T	Ausden-Clarke	H654GPF	Arriva Fox County	IIB847	Silverdale	J351XET	East Midland
GNN218N	Camms	H655GPF	Arriva Fox County	IIL2948	DunnLine	J352XET	East Midland
GNN222N	Camms	H659GPF	Arriva Fox County	IIL6766	Brylaine	J353XET	East Midland
GRF264V	Felix	H663GPF	Arriva Fox County	IIL7074	Skills	J394LJL	RoadCar
GRF703V	P C Coaches	H664GPF	Arriva Fox County	IIL8585	Ausden-Clarke	J395LJL	RoadCar
GRN898W	Wide Horizon	H671GPF	Arriva Fox County	IIL8593	Andrews of Tideswell	J396LJL	RoadCar
GSK664	Paul James	H672GPF	Arriva Fox County	IUI3463	RoadCar	J401FNS	Arriva Fox County
GSO8V	East Midland	H680GPF	Arriva Fox County	IUI5454	RoadCar	J40PSW	Paul Winson
GSO87V	RoadCar	H682GPF	Arriva Fox County	IUI5482	RoadCar	J421WDS	DunnLine
GSU835T	Applebys	H683GPF	Arriva Fox County	IUI9144	Bowers	J430HDS	East Midland
GSU844T	Applebys	H684GPF	Arriva Fox County	J1JBT	Johnson Bros	J439HDS	East Midland
GSU858T	Applebys	H695KKV	Arriva Fox County	J1PCC	P C Coaches	J450HDS	East Midland
GSU860T	Applebys	H697KKV	Arriva Fox County	J6BOB	DunnLine	J473RDU	Arriva Fox County
GTO48V	Arriva Fox County	H706EOD	T M Travel	J8PJC	Paul James	J474RDU	Arriva Fox County
GTO49V	Anstey Busline	H727LOL	City of Nottingham	J8WSB	Maun Crusader	J509LRY	Translinc
GTO301V	Arriva Fox County	H732LOL	City of Nottingham	J23HRH	Applebys	J564URW	Felix
GTO302V	Arriva Fox County	H737THL	RoadCar	J33MCL	MacPherson Coaches	J602KGB	P C Coaches
GTO304V	Arriva Fox County	H742VHS	Cavalier	J46SNY	T M Travel	J626JNP	Butler Bros
GTO305V	Arriva Fox County	H749UTV	Translinc	J48SNY	T M Travel	J627HFW	Translinc
GTO305V	Anstey Busline	H751ENR	First Leicester	J55MCL	MacPherson Coaches	J628HFW	Translinc
GTO306V	Arriva Fox County	H752ENR	First Leicester	J77OLT	Sweyne	J649OWK	Arriva Fox County
GTO307V	Arriva Fox County	H790RWJ	Reliance	J82CRR	Maun Crusader	J650OWK	Arriva Fox County
GTO701V	Applebys	H793HEC	RoadCar	J91DJV	East Midland	J651OWK	Arriva Fox County
GTO703V	RoadCar	H809RWJ	Ausden-Clarke	J92DJV	East Midland	J655OWK	Arriva Fox County
GTO708V	RoadCar	H845UUA	Reliance	J93DJV	East Midland	J656OWK	Arriva Fox County
GTO709V	RoadCar	H912KUD	Arriva Fox County	J94DJV	East Midland	J657OWK	Arriva Fox County
GTO711V	City of Nottingham	H917DFG	Carnell Coaches	J134HME	RoadCar	J658UDU	Arriva Fox County
GTX755W	Carnell Coaches	H946DRJ	DunnLine	J151WEH	Arriva Fox County	J659UDU	Arriva Fox County
GVO717N	Confidence	H976CAY	Doyle Mini Coaches	J168CTO	City of Nottingham	J693AWB	Holloways
GWE617V	East Midland	H998VRR	Nottinghamshire County	J169CTO	City of Nottingham	J693LGA	Skills
GWE618V	East Midland	HAL242V	Travel Wright	J170CNU	City of Nottingham	J7116USF	Woods
GWE619V	East Midland	HAL598V	Kettlewell's	J171CNU	City of Nottingham	J717EUA	T M Travel
GWE620V	East Midland	HAX6W	Johnson's Coaches	J172CNU	City of Nottingham	J718MFE	Holloways
H2PSW	Paul Winson	HCT990	Wings	J173CNU	City of Nottingham	J724CWT	Silverdale
H3PSW	Paul Winson	HD2122	Hylton Dawson	J174CNU	City of Nottingham	J753MFP	First Leicester
H3YRR	Marshalls	HD8755	Hylton Dawson	J175CNU	City of Nottingham	J754MFP	First Leicester
H4JBT	Johnson Bros	HD9923	Hylton Dawson	J175GGG	P C Coaches	J755MFP	First Leicester
H5JBT	Johnson Bros	HDL406N	Hunt's	J176CNU	City of Nottingham	J756MFP	First Leicester
H6GPF	Arriva Fox County	HDX906N	RoadCar	J179CRB	City of Nottingham	J757MFP	First Leicester
H10SUP	Emmersons	HDZ101	Hylton Dawson	J180CRB	City of Nottingham	J758NNR	First Leicester
H24JMJ	T M Travel	HDZ102	Hylton Dawson	J181CRB	City of Nottingham	J759DAU	City of Nottingham
H34DGD	Travel Wright	HDZ205	Hylton Dawson	J182CTO	City of Nottingham	J759NNR	First Leicester
H47NDU	City of Nottingham	HDZ5416	Hunt's	J183CTO	City of Nottingham	J760DAU	City of Nottingham
H126AML	RoadCar	HDZ5440	First Leicester	J184CTO	City of Nottingham	J766SOC	Arriva Fox County
H127AML	RoadCar	HDZ5441	First Leicester	J194NFE	Translinc	J827EWS	Johnson Bros
H128AML	RoadCar	HDZ5457	First Leicester	J201BVO	Trent	J834KTL	Translinc
H129AML	RoadCar	HDZ5459	First Leicester	J201NFE	Translinc	J834KVH	Translinc
H130AML	RoadCar	HDZ5462	First Leicester	J213AET	East Midland	J911VFS	Ausden-Clarke
H131AML	RoadCar	HDZ5463	First Leicester	J213DYL	MacPherson Coaches	J914HGD	Travel Wright
H132AML	RoadCar	HDZ5464	First Leicester	J214AET	East Midland	J917VHP	Arriva Fox County
H133AML	RoadCar	HDZ5465	First Leicester	J215AET	East Midland	J918VHP	Arriva Fox County
H157UUA	T M Travel	HDZ5466	First Leicester	J216AET	East Midland	J961TOF	Arriva Fox County
H160DJU	Travel Wright	HDZ5467	First Leicester	J217AET	East Midland	J963TOF	Arriva Fox County
H163DVM	Graysroft	HDZ5468	Hunt's	J218AET	East Midland	JAF208W	Brylaine
H167ANU	City of Nottingham	HDZ5469	First Leicester	J219AET	East Midland	JAK211W	East Midland
H177EJF	MacPherson Coaches	HDZ5471	First Leicester	J241MFP	T R S	JAU892V	Translinc
H179EJF	Hulleys	HDZ5472	First Leicester	J242MFP	T R S	JAZ6794	Ringwood
H181DHA	Cavalier	HDZ5475	First Leicester	J246MFP	Arriva Fox County	JBR684T	Trent
H182DHA	Cavalier	HDZ5477	First Leicester	J247MFP	Arriva Fox County	JBT3S	Johnson Bros
H183DHA	Cavalier	HDZ5479	First Leicester	J248SHP	Arriva Fox County	JBT16S	Johnson Bros
H184DHA	Cavalier	HDZ5481	First Leicester	J249SHP	Arriva Fox County	JDE972X	Arriva Fox County
H188EJF	Translinc	HDZ5482	First Leicester	J255TJW	Arriva Fox County	JDJ350N	Arriva Fox County
H191YMA	RoadCar	HDZ5484	First Leicester	J261NNC	DunnLine	JDO241W	Fowler's Travel
H220TCP	Holloways	HDZ5485	First Leicester	J264NNC	DunnLine	JEC557T	Dent
H231FFE	Holloways	HDZ5487	First Leicester	J265NNC	DunnLine	JFW915T	RoadCar
H257THL	East Midland	HDZ5488	First Leicester	J267NNC	DunnLine	JGV317V	Applebys
H344SWA	East Midland	HDZ5489	First Leicester	J299NNC	Johnson Bros	JHE177W	P C Coaches
H345SWA	East Midland	HDZ5490	First Leicester	J299KFP	Dent	JHJ139V	Trent
H346SWA	East Midland	HFU531	Eagre	J302BVO	Trent	JHJ146V	Trent
H347SWA	East Midland	HHE348N	Ausden-Clarke	J303BVO	Trent	JHW103P	Trent
H348SWA	East Midland	HHH272N	Eagre	J304BVO	Trent	JIL2156	Arriva Fox County
H362TWJ	RoadCar	HIL2393	DunnLine	J305BVO	Trent	JIL2157	Arriva Fox County
H363TWJ	RoadCar	HIL3075	Moxon's	J306BVO	Trent	JIL2158	Arriva Fox County
H364TWJ	RoadCar	HIL3476	Moxon's	J307BVO	Trent	JIL2159	Arriva Fox County
H365TWJ	RoadCar	HIL4619	Kettlewell's	J308BVO	Trent	JIL2160	Arriva Fox County
H366TWJ	RoadCar	HIL7198	Unity	J309BVO	Trent	JIL2161	Arriva Fox County
H368TWJ	RoadCar	HIL7594	Arriva Fox County	J310BVO	Trent	JIL2162	Arriva Fox County
H380TNG	Elseys	HIL8418	RoadCar	J311BVO	Trent	JIL2163	Arriva Fox County
H393CJF	Translinc	HIL8419	RoadCar	J312BVO	Trent	JIL2164	Arriva Fox County
H397SYG	RoadCar	HIL8420	RoadCar	J313BVO	Trent	JIL2165	Arriva Fox County
H447EVK	Fowler's Travel	HOD76	Paul Winson	J314BVO	Trent	JIL2190	Arriva Fox County
H482BEE	East Midland	HOR305N	Confidence	J315BVO	Trent	JIL2193	Arriva Fox County
H483BEE	East Midland	HOR306N	Confidence	J316BVO	Trent	JIL2196	Arriva Fox County
H484BEE	East Midland	HOR307N	T R S	J317BVO	Trent	JIL2197	Arriva Fox County
H485BEE	East Midland	HRB932V	Glovers	J318BVO	Trent	JIL2198	Arriva Fox County
H611EJF	First Leicester	HSC104T	Sweyne	J319BVO	Trent	JIL2199	Arriva Fox County
H612EJF	First Leicester	HSV781	DunnLine	J320BVO	Trent	JIL3964	Carnell Coaches
H613EJF	First Leicester	HTU155N	Johnson Bros	J321BVO	Trent	JIL3966	T M Travel
H614EJF	First Leicester	HUI4891	Bowers	J322BVO	Trent	JIL4006	Woods
H615EJF	First Leicester	HVL611	Applebys	J323BVO	Trent	JIL5367	Arriva Fox County
H616EJF	First Leicester	HWE826N	Johnson Bros	J324BVO	Trent	JIL7889	Moxon's
H633GHA	Haines	HWJ922W	RoadCar	J325BVO	Trent	JIL7899	Kettlewell's
H650GPF	Arriva Fox County	HWJ923W	RoadCar	J328ONE	Haines	JIL8325	T R S
H652GPF	Arriva Fox County	HWJ925W	RoadCar	J349XET	East Midland	JIL8813	DunnLine

Reg	Operator	Reg	Operator	Reg	Operator	Reg	Operator
JIW3697	Albert Wilde	K390NGG	Arriva Fox County	KWA221W	East Midland	L306VFE	RoadCar
JIW9464	Woods	K393PVL	Translinc	KWA223W	East Midland	L307AUT	Arriva Fox County
JJI1400	Sweyne	K394PVL	Translinc	KWA224W	East Midland	L307VFE	RoadCar
JJI1533	Sweyne	K401STL	MacPherson Coaches	KWA22W	Isle Coaches	L308AUT	Arriva Fox County
JJI1904	Sweyne	K420RFE	Translinc	KWA24W	Isle Coaches	L308VFE	RoadCar
JJL390F	Elseys	K481GNN	City of Nottingham	KYN519X	Kime's	L309AUT	Arriva Fox County
JKV441	Marshalls	K482GNN	City of Nottingham	L3JBT	Johnson Bros	L310AUT	Arriva Fox County
JOV701P	Kettlewell's	K519RJX	Elseys	L4HOD	Hobsons	L311AUT	Arriva Fox County
JOV777P	Kettlewell's	K522EFL	T R S	L4TCC	T M Travel	L312AUT	Arriva Fox County
JOV780P	Kettlewell's	K528EFL	T R S	L5HOD	Hobsons	L313AUT	Arriva Fox County
JOX510P	Bowers	K529EHE	Elseys	L5PSW	Paul Winson	L314AUT	Arriva Fox County
JPM815V	Haines	K550RJX	Butler Bros	L6BOB	DunnLine	L315AUT	Arriva Fox County
JRB416V	Travel Wright	K574EKY	DunnLine	L6PSW	Paul Winson	L316AUT	Arriva Fox County
JRC682V	City of Nottingham	K575DFS	East Midland	L8PCC	P C Coaches	L317AUT	Arriva Fox County
JRR359V	Kettlewell's	K590ABV	Silverdale	L29CAY	Travel Wright	L318AUT	Arriva Fox County
JRR566N	Slack's Coaches	K617SBC	First Leicester	L34PNN	Arriva Fox County	L319AUT	Arriva Fox County
JSV365	Scutt	K618SBC	First Leicester	L35PNN	Arriva Fox County	L320AUT	Arriva Fox County
JTD387P	Applebys	K619SBC	First Leicester	L36PNN	Arriva Fox County	L321AUT	Arriva Fox County
JTL37T	Wings	K620SBC	First Leicester	L37PNN	Arriva Fox County	L322AUT	Arriva Fox County
JTM105V	P C Coaches	K621SBC	First Leicester	L38PNN	Arriva Fox County	L323AUT	Arriva Fox County
JTU131V	Johnson Bros	K622SBC	First Leicester	L50WHF	Fowler's Travel	L324AUT	Arriva Fox County
JTU578T	Applebys	K633FAU	Trent	L66PJC	Paul James	L325AUT	Arriva Fox County
JVY676S	Scutt	K640FAU	Trent	L82YBB	Johnson Bros	L339KCK	East Midland
JWE98W	RoadCar	K645FAU	Trent	L84YBB	Johnson Bros	L340KCK	East Midland
JWL993N	Johnson Bros	K651FAU	Trent	L88PJC	Paul James	L340YAC	Emmersons
JWL997N	Johnson Bros	K701NDO	East Midland	L94HRF	Arriva Fox County	L341KCK	East Midland
JWV255W	T M Travel	K702NDO	East Midland	L95HRF	Arriva Fox County	L342KCK	East Midland
JWW227N	Graysroft	K702RNR	Carnell Coaches	L99ABC	Unity	L343KCK	East Midland
JXI9144	Kettlewell's	K703NDO	East Midland	L101LRA	Trent	L344KCK	East Midland
JYG431V	Applebys	K704NDO	East Midland	L102LRA	Trent	L349MRR	City of Nottingham
K1JBT	Johnson Bros	K741CWK	Arriva Fox County	L103LRA	Trent	L350MRR	City of Nottingham
K2CAV	Cavalier	K742CWK	Arriva Fox County	L104LRA	Trent	L351MRR	City of Nottingham
K3CAV	Cavalier	K745CWK	Arriva Fox County	L105LRA	Trent	L352MRR	City of Nottingham
K17FTG	Woods	K746CWK	Arriva Fox County	L105VFE	Translinc	L353MRR	City of Nottingham
K18FTG	Woods	K746VJU	First Leicester	L106LRA	Trent	L354MKU	Ausden-Clarke
K19FTG	Johnson Bros	K748VJU	First Leicester	L107LRA	Trent	L401CJF	Kinch Bus
K101JWJ	East Midland	K749VJU	First Leicester	L108LHL	East Midland	L402CJF	Kinch Bus
K102JWJ	East Midland	K750VJU	First Leicester	L108LRA	Trent	L403CJF	Kinch Bus
K103JWJ	East Midland	K760SBC	First Leicester	L109LHL	East Midland	L403VGP	Holloways
K104JWJ	East Midland	K761JTV	City of Nottingham	L109LRA	Trent	L404CJF	Kinch Bus
K105JWJ	East Midland	K761SBC	First Leicester	L110LRA	Trent	L406VGP	Moxon's
K106JWJ	East Midland	K770JRA	Skills	L112LRA	Trent	L435LWA	East Midland
K107JWJ	East Midland	K813LMY	Skinner	L113LRA	Trent	L436LWA	East Midland
K112TCP	Slack's Coaches	K813VNF	P C Coaches	L114LRA	Trent	L437LWA	East Midland
K113TCP	Slack's Coaches	K953CJN	Sleafordian	L115LRA	Trent	L438LWA	East Midland
K118KUA	Travel Wright	K983OFW	Translinc	L116LRA	Trent	L439LWA	East Midland
K120OCT	Elseys	KAL578	RoadCar	L117LRA	Trent	L440LWA	East Midland
K131XRE	Arriva Fox County	KAU564V	Confidence	L118LRA	Trent	L441LWA	East Midland
K148BRF	Arriva Fox County	KAX714	Haines	L119LRA	Trent	L442LWA	East Midland
K158BRF	Arriva Fox County	KAZ3253	Eagre	L120LRA	Trent	L443LWA	East Midland
K185HTV	City of Nottingham	KAZ3254	Eagre	L121LRA	Trent	L445LWA	East Midland
K186HTV	City of Nottingham	KAZ4523	Ausden-Clarke	L122LRA	Trent	L446LWA	East Midland
K187HTV	City of Nottingham	KAZ4574	Ausden-Clarke	L123LRA	Trent	L447LWA	East Midland
K188HTV	City of Nottingham	KBC4V	Glovers	L124LRA	Trent	L448LWA	East Midland
K213CBD	Maun Crusader	KBT343S	Reliance	L125LRA	Trent	L449LWA	East Midland
K301NJL	RoadCar	KBV144S	P C Coaches	L125XBD	Skills	L450LWA	East Midland
K302NJL	RoadCar	KBZ8726	Ausden-Clarke	L126LRA	Trent	L451LWA	East Midland
K303NJL	RoadCar	KCK201W	RoadCar	L127LRA	Trent	L452LWA	East Midland
K326FAL	Trent	KCK202W	RoadCar	L128LRA	Trent	L453LHL	East Midland
K327FAL	Trent	KCK203W	RoadCar	L132NHP	Arriva Fox County	L483LNN	City of Nottingham
K328FAL	Trent	KCK204W	RoadCar	L133NHP	Arriva Fox County	L484LNN	City of Nottingham
K329FAL	Trent	KCX304	Haines	L143NHP	Arriva Fox County	L485NTO	City of Nottingham
K330FAL	Trent	KET6	Kettlewell's	L145NHP	Arriva Fox County	L486NTO	City of Nottingham
K331FAL	Trent	KHH375W	RoadCar	L146NHP	Arriva Fox County	L487NTO	City of Nottingham
K332FAL	Trent	KIB6474	RoadCar	L149NHP	Arriva Fox County	L488NTO	City of Nottingham
K334FAL	Trent	KIB6527	RoadCar	L189MAU	City of Nottingham	L489NTO	City of Nottingham
K335FAL	Trent	KIB6620	RoadCar	L190MAU	City of Nottingham	L501OAL	City of Nottingham
K336FAL	Trent	KJW284W	Carnell Coaches	L191MAU	City of Nottingham	L502OAL	City of Nottingham
K337FAL	Trent	KKY833P	Johnson Bros	L192MAU	City of Nottingham	L503OAL	City of Nottingham
K338FAL	Trent	KKY835P	Johnson Bros	L193OVO	City of Nottingham	L504OAL	City of Nottingham
K339FAL	Trent	KMA405T	Applebys	L194OVO	City of Nottingham	L505OAL	City of Nottingham
K341FAL	Trent	KMW176P	Applebys	L195OVO	City of Nottingham	L506OAL	City of Nottingham
K342FAL	Trent	KNN959	Marshalls	L201ONU	City of Nottingham	L507OAL	City of Nottingham
K343FAL	Trent	KON326P	Applebys	L202ONU	City of Nottingham	L508OAL	City of Nottingham
K344FAL	Trent	KPJ246W	T R S	L203ONU	City of Nottingham	L509OAL	City of Nottingham
K346FAL	Trent	KRE276P	T M Travel	L204ONU	City of Nottingham	L510OAL	City of Nottingham
K347FAL	Trent	KRO718	Applebys	L205ONU	City of Nottingham	L591CJW	Holloways
K348FAL	Trent	KSA178P	Fleetline Buses	L206ONU	City of Nottingham	L599YVL	Translinc
K349FAL	Trent	KSA183P	Confidence	L207ONU	City of Nottingham	L601YVL	Translinc
K350FAL	Trent	KSU477	Eagre	L208ONU	City of Nottingham	L623XFP	First Leicester
K352FAL	Trent	KSU479	Eagre	L209ONU	City of Nottingham	L624XFP	First Leicester
K353FAL	Trent	KTL24V	Johnson Bros	L210ONU	City of Nottingham	L625XFP	First Leicester
K354DWJ	East Midland	KTL27V	Johnson Bros	L211ONU	City of Nottingham	L626XFP	First Leicester
K355DWJ	East Midland	KTL27Y	Delaine Buses	L227HRF	Arriva Fox County	L637LDT	East Midland
K356DWJ	East Midland	KTL43Y	RoadCar	L228HRF	Arriva Fox County	L638LDT	East Midland
K357DWJ	East Midland	KTL44Y	RoadCar	L231HRF	Arriva Fox County	L639LDT	East Midland
K358DWJ	East Midland	KTL45Y	RoadCar	L233HRF	Arriva Fox County	L640LDT	East Midland
K359DWJ	East Midland	KTL780	Delaine Buses	L256VSU	City of Nottingham	L641LDT	East Midland
K360DWJ	East Midland	KTL982	Sleafordian	L302YAC	Emmersons	L642LDT	East Midland
K361DWJ	East Midland	KUC179P	Holloways	L303AUT	Arriva Fox County	L643AYS	Wide Horizon
K362DWJ	East Midland	KUC181P	Holloways	L304AUT	Arriva Fox County	L643LDT	East Midland
K363DWJ	East Midland	KVF249V	Dent	L304VFE	RoadCar	L705HFU	East Midland
K378RFE	RoadCar	KVL261	Sleafordian	L305AUT	Arriva Fox County	L706HFU	East Midland
K379RFE	RoadCar	KWA214W	East Midland	L305VFE	RoadCar	L707HFU	East Midland
K380RFE	RoadCar	KWA218W	East Midland	L306AUT	Arriva Fox County	L708HFU	East Midland

Reg	Operator	Reg	Operator	Reg	Operator	Reg	Operator
L709HFU	East Midland	LRB579W	RoadCar	M321VET	DunnLine	M803PRA	Trent
L715VVL	Translinc	LRB580W	RoadCar	M325VET	DunnLine	M804PRA	Trent
L731LWA	East Midland	LRB581W	RoadCar	M331MRW	Arriva Fox County	M805PRA	Trent
L732LWA	East Midland	LRB582W	RoadCar	M332MRW	Arriva Fox County	M806PRA	Trent
L733LWA	East Midland	LRB583W	RoadCar	M351BFE	RoadCar	M807PRA	Trent
L734LWA	East Midland	LRB584W	RoadCar	M352BFE	RoadCar	M808JTY	East Midland
L735LWA	East Midland	LRR689W	City of Nottingham	M353BFE	RoadCar	M808PRA	Trent
L736LWA	East Midland	LRR690W	City of Nottingham	M354BFE	RoadCar	M809PRA	Trent
L737LWA	East Midland	LRR692W	City of Nottingham	M354TMJ	A&S	M810PRA	Trent
L738LWA	East Midland	LSU717	First Leicester	M355BFE	RoadCar	M811PRA	Trent
L739LWA	East Midland	LUG88P	Fowler's Travel	M355PRA	Trent	M812PRA	Trent
L740LWA	East Midland	LUG96P	Camms	M356BFE	RoadCar	M813PRA	Trent
L741LWA	East Midland	LUP894T	Trent	M357BFE	RoadCar	M814PRA	Trent
L742LWA	East Midland	LUX536P	Moxon's	M358BFE	RoadCar	M815KJU	Kinch Bus
L743LWA	East Midland	LUY742	Viking	M405HFP	Kinch Bus	M815PRA	Trent
L744LWA	East Midland	LVL804V	Johnson Bros	M406HFP	Kinch Bus	M821RCP	Reliance
L745LWA	East Midland	LVL807V	RoadCar	M407FTL	Translinc	M879DDS	City of Nottingham
L746LWA	East Midland	LVL809V	Johnson Bros	M410FTL	Translinc	M881UMJ	Ringwood
L748LWA	East Midland	LVS449P	Dent	M411RRN	East Midland	M882DDS	City of Nottingham
L749LWA	East Midland	M1JBT	Johnson Bros	M412RRN	East Midland	M890DHP	Arriva Fox County
L750LWA	East Midland	M1OCT	Delaine Buses	M413RRN	East Midland	M901DHP	Arriva Fox County
L751LHL	East Midland	M2OCT	Delaine Buses	M414RRN	East Midland	M903DHP	Arriva Fox County
L801MRA	Trent	M7PCC	P C Coaches	M417EVL	Translinc	M904DHP	Arriva Fox County
L802MRA	Trent	M8PCC	P C Coaches	M418EVL	Translinc	M905DHP	Arriva Fox County
L803MRA	Trent	M8PJC	Paul James	M424GUS	City of Nottingham	M906DHP	Arriva Fox County
L804MRA	Trent	M18ABU	A&S	M425EVL	Translinc	M907DHP	Arriva Fox County
L804YTL	Holloways	M21UUA	Felix	M426EVL	Translinc	M908DHP	Arriva Fox County
L805MRA	Trent	M22MCL	MacPherson Coaches	M441JJU	Silverdale	M909DHP	Arriva Fox County
L806MRA	Trent	M31TRR	Skills	M453LJF	City of Nottingham	M910DHP	Arriva Fox County
L807MRA	Trent	M32TRR	Skills	M455TCH	Trent	M911DHP	Arriva Fox County
L807YBC	Kinch Bus	M42DLN	City of Nottingham	M471HFE	Translinc	M912DHP	Arriva Fox County
L808MRA	Trent	M44MCL	MacPherson Coaches	M501GRY	First Leicester	M913DHP	Arriva Fox County
L809CJF	Trent	M51PRA	Trent	M502GRY	First Leicester	M914DHP	Arriva Fox County
L810CJF	Trent	M52PRA	Trent	M503GRY	First Leicester	M915DHP	Arriva Fox County
L811CJF	Trent	M53PRA	Trent	M504GRY	First Leicester	M916DHP	Arriva Fox County
L812CJF	Trent	M54PRA	Trent	M506GRY	First Leicester	M917DHP	Arriva Fox County
L813DJU	Trent	M76HOV	DunnLine	M507GRY	First Leicester	M918DHP	Arriva Fox County
L814DJU	Kinch Bus	M83CVL	Translinc	M508GRY	First Leicester	M919DHP	Arriva Fox County
L829HEF	City of Nottingham	M85CVL	Translinc	M509GRY	First Leicester	M919MRW	City of Nottingham
L865BEA	City of Nottingham	M99PCC	P C Coaches	M510GRY	First Leicester	M920DHP	Arriva Fox County
L907RDO	Elseys	M113SLS	City of Nottingham	M511TRA	City of Nottingham	M939JJU	Silverdale
L911LRA	Trent	M129PRA	Trent	M512TRA	City of Nottingham	M942JJU	Silverdale
L911NWW	Silverdale	M130PRA	Trent	M513TRA	City of Nottingham	M942TSX	East Midland
L964VGE	City of Nottingham	M131PRA	Trent	M521UTV	City of Nottingham	M943TSX	East Midland
L965VGE	City of Nottingham	M132PRA	Trent	M522UTV	City of Nottingham	M961FFE	Translinc
L967VGE	City of Nottingham	M133PRA	Trent	M553SSA	Travel Wright	M962FFE	Translinc
L988AEA	City of Nottingham	M133TRR	Skills	M570VSF	Woods	M963FFE	Translinc
L999ABC	Unity	M134PRA	Trent	M594GFE	Applebys	M964FFE	Translinc
LAG188V	East Midland	M135PRA	Trent	M601TTV	City of Nottingham	M983CYS	City of Nottingham
LAG189V	East Midland	M136PRA	Trent	M601VHE	East Midland	M996CYS	City of Nottingham
LAK985W	Travel Wright	M137PRA	Trent	M602TTV	City of Nottingham	MAZ7015	Woods
LAT256	Wide Horizon	M138PRA	Trent	M602VHE	East Midland	MBE613R	East Midland
LAZ2445	Eagre	M150PKM	Skills	M603TTV	City of Nottingham	MBZ7142	RoadCar
LAZ6923	Andrews of Tideswell	M159GRY	Arriva Fox County	M603VHE	East Midland	MCT812	Silverdale
LBH297P	Wings	M160GRY	Arriva Fox County	M604TTV	City of Nottingham	MDG231V	Ausden-Clarke
LBO79X	Applebys	M161GRY	Arriva Fox County	M604VHE	East Midland	MDT337W	RoadCar
LBO81X	Applebys	M162GRY	Arriva Fox County	M605UTV	City of Nottingham	MFE414V	Dent
LBO82X	Applebys	M163GRY	Arriva Fox County	M605VHE	East Midland	MFS579X	Trent Motors
LBO83X	Applebys	M164GRY	Arriva Fox County	M606UTV	City of Nottingham	MGC338V	Wide Horizon
LEO734Y	RoadCar	M165GRY	Arriva Fox County	M606VHE	East Midland	MGE8V	Applebys
LEO735Y	RoadCar	M166GRY	Arriva Fox County	M607VHE	East Midland	MGR915T	Applebys
LGZ6890	Silverdale	M167GRY	Arriva Fox County	M608WET	East Midland	MGV316V	T R S
LGZ6891	Silverdale	M168GRY	Arriva Fox County	M609WET	East Midland	MIB648	Emmersons
LHB50X	Silverdale	M169GRY	Arriva Fox County	M641RCP	Slack's Coaches	MIB9246	P C Coaches
LHE601W	Johnson Bros	M169KAT	Holloways	M642RCP	Slack's Coaches	MIL1055	Woods
LIL2512	P C Coaches	M170GRY	Arriva Fox County	M651ERW	Arriva Fox County	MIL4685	Bowers
LIL2612	Bowers	M171GRY	Arriva Fox County	M652ERW	Arriva Fox County	MIL6214	Maun Crusader
LIL3068	Bowers	M172GRY	Arriva Fox County	M659GVL	Translinc	MIL7621	Beaver Bus
LIL6287	T R S	M173GRY	Arriva Fox County	M664KHP	City of Nottingham	MIL8325	DunnLine
LIL6292	Bowers	M174GRY	Arriva Fox County	M665GVL	Translinc	MIL8326	DunnLine
LIL7568	Bowers	M175GRY	Arriva Fox County	M665JFP	City of Nottingham	MIL8327	DunnLine
LIL7910	Bowers	M176GRY	Arriva Fox County	M667JFP	City of Nottingham	MIL8328	DunnLine
LIL7912	Bowers	M177GRY	Arriva Fox County	M671RAJ	Woods	MIL8329	DunnLine
LIL9842	Travel Wright	M178GRY	Arriva Fox County	M679RAJ	Woods	MIL8330	DunnLine
LJA622P	RoadCar	M196SRR	City of Nottingham	M691MRU	Sleafordian	MIL8332	DunnLine
LJA642P	RoadCar	M197SRR	City of Nottingham	M694BLT	P C Coaches	MIL8334	DunnLine
LJI5632	Arriva Fox County	M198TNU	City of Nottingham	M711FFL	Johnson Bros	MIL8336	DunnLine
LJI8027	Applebys	M201URC	Trent	M732KJU	DunnLine	MIL8337	DunnLine
LJI8156	Anstey Busline	M202URC	Trent	M733KJU	DunnLine	MIL8339	DunnLine
LJI8157	Arriva Fox County	M212STO	City of Nottingham	M734KJU	DunnLine	MIL8340	DunnLine
LJV273	Applebys	M213STO	City of Nottingham	M735KJU	DunnLine	MIL8341	DunnLine
LMS153W	Isle Coaches	M214STO	City of Nottingham	M736RCP	Skills	MIL8342	DunnLine
LMS169W	Fowler's Travel	M215TNU	City of Nottingham	M737RCP	Skills	MIL9758	T R S
LNN353	Marshalls	M216TNU	City of Nottingham	M738RCP	Skills	MIL9765	DunnLine
LNU569W	Confidence	M234EFE	Translinc	M739RCP	Skills	MIW2418	Wings
LPT872T	East Midland	M235EFE	Translinc	M744CVL	Translinc	MIW2422	Johnson Bros
LRB207W	RoadCar	M236EFE	Translinc	M750CVL	Translinc	MIW4890	Ausden-Clarke
LRB208W	RoadCar	M271URC	Trent	M751CVL	Translinc	MMJ474V	Wings
LRB213W	RoadCar	M272URC	Trent	M752CVL	Translinc	MMW49X	Haines
LRB214W	Hulleys	M273URC	Trent	M753CVL	Translinc	MNC513W	Maun Crusader
LRB405W	Camms	M274URC	Trent	M761RCP	Moxon's	MNM31V	Paul Winson
LRB407W	Camms	M290OUR	Elseys	M763SVO	City of Nottingham	MNU623P	Fleetline Buses
LRB409W	Camms	M300ARJ	Paul Winson	M784NBA	Butler Bros	MNU625P	Confidence
LRB577W	RoadCar	M301KRY	Felix	M801PRA	Trent	MNU630P	Fleetline Buses
LRB578W	RoadCar	M306XUA	Translinc	M802PRA	Trent	MNU631P	Confidence

Reg	Operator	Reg	Operator	Reg	Operator	Reg	Operator
MNU632P	Confidence	N166PUT	Arriva Fox County	N381EAK	Glovers	N761CKU	East Midland
MNU693W	City of Nottingham	N166XVO	Arriva Fox County	N382EAK	Glovers	N762EWG	East Midland
MNU694W	City of Nottingham	N167PUT	Arriva Fox County	N400TCC	Skills	N763EWG	East Midland
MNU695W	City of Nottingham	N168PUT	Arriva Fox County	N401ARA	City of Nottingham	N764EWG	East Midland
MNU696W	City of Nottingham	N169PUT	Arriva Fox County	N401LTL	RoadCar	N765EWG	East Midland
MNW131V	Applebys	N170PUT	Arriva Fox County	N402ARA	City of Nottingham	N766EWG	East Midland
MOD816P	Camms	N171PUT	Arriva Fox County	N403ARA	City of Nottingham	N767EWG	East Midland
MRH398V	Applebys	N172PUT	Arriva Fox County	N404ARA	City of Nottingham	N768EWG	East Midland
MRJ270W	East Midland	N173PUT	Arriva Fox County	N429XRC	Arriva Fox County	N768WRC	City of Nottingham
MRT7P	RoadCar	N174PUT	Arriva Fox County	N430XRC	Arriva Fox County	N769EWG	East Midland
MSU433	Arriva Fox County	N175PUT	Arriva Fox County	N431XRC	Arriva Fox County	N769WRC	City of Nottingham
MSV922	RoadCar	N176PUT	Arriva Fox County	N432XRC	Arriva Fox County	N770EWG	East Midland
MSV926	RoadCar	N177PUT	Arriva Fox County	N433XRC	Arriva Fox County	N770WRC	City of Nottingham
MSV927	RoadCar	N178PUT	Arriva Fox County	N448KTL	Translinc	N771EWG	East Midland
MTU117Y	Arriva Fox County	N179PUT	Arriva Fox County	N455KTL	Translinc	N771WRC	City of Nottingham
MTV309W	Arriva Fox County	N196DYB	Wide Horizon	N456KTL	Translinc	N772EWG	East Midland
MTV310W	Arriva Fox County	N203VRC	Trent	N456MFE	Translinc	N773EWG	East Midland
MTV311W	Arriva Fox County	N204VRC	Trent	N457MFE	Translinc	N774EWG	East Midland
MTV312W	Arriva Fox County	N205VRC	Trent	N458KTL	Translinc	N775EWG	East Midland
MTV314W	Arriva Fox County	N206VRC	Trent	N458MFE	Translinc	N776EWG	East Midland
MUT206W	First Leicester	N207VRC	Trent	N459KTL	Translinc	N779DRH	City of Nottingham
MUT257W	First Leicester	N208VRC	Trent	N459MFE	Translinc	N781SJU	DunnLine
MVL750V	Applebys	N209VRC	Trent	N460MFE	Translinc	N795PDS	Travel Wright
MVO414W	Graysroft	N210VRC	Trent	N461KTL	Translinc	N801OFW	Translinc
MVO423W	City of Nottingham	N211TBC	Arriva Fox County	N461MFE	Translinc	N802OFW	Translinc
MVO424W	City of Nottingham	N211VRC	Trent	N462KTL	Translinc	N803OFW	Translinc
MVO425W	City of Nottingham	N212TBC	Arriva Fox County	N463KTL	Translinc	N809NHS	Johnson Bros
MVO426W	City of Nottingham	N212VRC	Trent	N464KTL	Translinc	N816PJU	Kinch Bus
MWG622X	East Midland	N213VRC	Trent	N464MFE	Translinc	N817PJU	Kinch Bus
MWG623X	East Midland	N214VRC	Trent	N465KTL	Translinc	N818RFP	Kinch Bus
MWG624X	East Midland	N215VRC	Trent	N466KTL	Translinc	N819RFP	Kinch Bus
MWG940X	RoadCar	N216VRC	Trent	N466MFE	Translinc	N820RFP	Kinch Bus
N1JBT	Johnson Bros	N217VRC	Trent	N467KTL	Translinc	N821RFP	Kinch Bus
N2JBT	Johnson Bros	N217VVO	City of Nottingham	N467MFE	Translinc	N847YHH	Hulleys
N3OCT	Delaine Buses	N218VRC	Trent	N468MFE	Translinc	N875AKY	Applebys
N3PSW	Paul Winson	N218VVO	City of Nottingham	N469MFE	Translinc	N899JFE	Translinc
N10DME	Eagre	N219VRC	Trent	N470MFE	Translinc	N909JFE	Translinc
N10PCC	P C Coaches	N219VVO	City of Nottingham	N471MFE	Translinc	N910JFE	Translinc
N11PCC	P C Coaches	N220BAL	City of Nottingham	N472MFE	Translinc	N910JFE	Translinc
N12PCC	P C Coaches	N220VRC	Trent	N472XRC	Arriva Fox County	N911JFE	Translinc
N21ARC	Skills	N221BAL	City of Nottingham	N473MFE	Translinc	N912JFE	Translinc
N39ARC	Skills	N221VRC	Trent	N473XRC	Arriva Fox County	N913JFE	Translinc
N40SLK	Skills	N222BAL	City of Nottingham	N474MFE	Translinc	N957SAY	Woods
N43ARC	Skills	N223VRC	Trent	N474XRC	Arriva Fox County	N981FWT	Elseys
N45ARC	Skills	N224BAL	City of Nottingham	N475MFE	Translinc	N983XCT	City of Nottingham
N50SLK	Skills	N224VRC	Trent	N475XRC	Arriva Fox County	N984XCT	City of Nottingham
N60SLK	Skills	N225VRC	Trent	N476XRC	Arriva Fox County	N985XCT	City of Nottingham
N66MCL	MacPherson Coaches	N226VRC	Trent	N477XRC	Arriva Fox County	N991XCT	City of Nottingham
N67NDW	DunnLine	N240NNR	Travel Wright	N478XRC	Arriva Fox County	N992XCT	City of Nottingham
N69MDW	DunnLine	N272DWY	Reliance	N479XRC	Arriva Fox County	N997BWJ	DunnLine
N70SLK	Skills	N290DWY	Reliance	N480DKH	City of Nottingham	N998BWJ	DunnLine
N75FWU	Slack's Coaches	N300TCC	Skills	N480XRC	Arriva Fox County	NAU292W	Travel Wright
N77MCL	MacPherson Coaches	N321JTL	RoadCar	N481XRC	Arriva Fox County	NBF871V	Ausden-Clarke
N80SLK	Skills	N322JTL	RoadCar	N489DJH	Applebys	NBZ1670	Graysroft
N90SLK	Skills	N322WCH	Trent	N523XRR	City of Nottingham	NBZ1671	Graysroft
N97ACH	DunnLine	N323JTL	RoadCar	N524XRR	City of Nottingham	NEE496	Applebys
N101WRC	City of Nottingham	N324JTL	RoadCar	N525XRR	City of Nottingham	NEV675M	T M Travel
N102WRC	City of Nottingham	N325JTL	RoadCar	N539OFE	Applebys	NEV678M	Kettlewell's
N103WRC	City of Nottingham	N326JTL	RoadCar	N607UTV	City of Nottingham	NFB602R	Trent
N104WRC	City of Nottingham	N327JTL	RoadCar	N608UTV	City of Nottingham	NFP205W	First Leicester
N105WRC	City of Nottingham	N328JTL	RoadCar	N609UTV	City of Nottingham	NGM168G	Johnson Bros
N106WRC	City of Nottingham	N331OFP	Arriva Fox County	N610XRC	City of Nottingham	NHL301X	East Midland
N107WRC	City of Nottingham	N344OBC	Arriva Fox County	N611XVO	City of Nottingham	NHL302X	East Midland
N108WRC	City of Nottingham	N345OBC	Arriva Fox County	N612YRA	City of Nottingham	NHL303X	East Midland
N109WRC	City of Nottingham	N346OBC	Arriva Fox County	N613YRA	City of Nottingham	NHL304X	East Midland
N110WRC	City of Nottingham	N347OBC	Arriva Fox County	N614YRA	City of Nottingham	NHL305X	East Midland
N125RJF	Silverdale	N348OBC	Arriva Fox County	N615YRA	City of Nottingham	NIB6064	Andrews of Tideswell
N126RJF	Silverdale	N349OBC	Arriva Fox County	N655EWJ	DunnLine	NIB6433	Woods
N127RJF	Silverdale	N350OBC	Arriva Fox County	N656EWJ	DunnLine	NIB8179	Ausden-Clarke
N130AET	East Midland	N351OBC	Arriva Fox County	N657EWJ	DunnLine	NIB8272	Ausden-Clarke
N131AET	East Midland	N352OBC	Arriva Fox County	N658EWJ	DunnLine	NIL2984	Beaver Bus
N132AET	East Midland	N353OBC	Arriva Fox County	N661OFE	Holloways	NIL2985	Beaver Bus
N133AET	East Midland	N354OBC	Arriva Fox County	N667MEW	Translinc	NIL2996	T R S
N134AET	East Midland	N355OBC	Arriva Fox County	N691AHL	Fowler's Travel	NIL6469	Hobsons
N135AET	East Midland	N356OBC	Arriva Fox County	N692AHL	Fowler's Travel	NIL8163	Bowers
N135OFW	Applebys	N356REE	Applebys	N693AHL	Fowler's Travel	NIL8991	Ausden-Clarke
N136AET	East Midland	N356VRC	Trent	N695AHL	DunnLine	NIL8992	Ausden-Clarke
N137AET	East Midland	N357OBC	Arriva Fox County	N696AHL	DunnLine	NIL8993	Ausden-Clarke
N138AET	East Midland	N357VRC	Trent	N697AHL	DunnLine	NIL9936	Bowers
N139AET	East Midland	N358OBC	Arriva Fox County	N703AAL	Felix	NJI9487	Carnell Coaches
N140AET	East Midland	N358VRC	Trent	N734RBE	Applebys	NKU144X	Isle Coaches
N140ARC	Skills	N359VRC	Trent	N743LUS	City of Nottingham	NLG909T	Johnson's Coaches
N141AET	East Midland	N360VRC	Trent	N744LUS	City of Nottingham	NLO857V	Emmersons
N142AET	East Midland	N361VRC	Trent	N746BAU	Skills	NLS985W	Hulleys
N143AET	East Midland	N362VRC	Trent	N751DAK	DunnLine	NLS988W	RoadCar
N144AET	East Midland	N363VRC	Trent	N752CKU	East Midland	NNN471W	Marshalls
N144ARC	Skills	N364VRC	Trent	N753CKU	East Midland	NNN472W	Paul Winson
N160VVO	Arriva Fox County	N365VRC	Trent	N754CKU	East Midland	NNN473W	Silverdale
N161VVO	Arriva Fox County	N366VRC	Trent	N755CKU	East Midland	NNN474W	Paul Winson
N162VVO	Arriva Fox County	N367VRC	Trent	N756CKU	East Midland	NNN477W	Marshalls
N163VVO	Arriva Fox County	N368VRC	Trent	N757CKU	East Midland	NNN479W	Paul Winson
N164AHP	Silverdale	N369VRC	Trent	N757GWR	Applebys	NNU71W	Glovers
N164VVO	Arriva Fox County	N370VRC	Trent	N758CKU	East Midland	NNU128M	Camms
N165XVO	Arriva Fox County	N378EAK	First Leicester	N759CKU	East Midland	NNW119P	Johnson's Coaches
				N760CKU	East Midland		

Reg	Operator	Reg	Operator	Reg	Operator	Reg	Operator
NOE555R	Trent	P75UJV	Applebys	P306HWG	Holloways	P907CTO	Trent
NOE584R	Trent	P78SVL	Translinc	P306UFW	Translinc	P908CTO	Trent
NOE587R	Bowers	P82WFE	Translinc	P350FRB	Silverdale	P909CTO	Trent
NOE604R	Applebys	P94MOX	Arriva Fox County	P351EAU	DunnLine	P910CTO	Trent
NPA223W	RoadCar	P95HOF	Arriva Fox County	P352EAU	DunnLine	P911CTO	Trent
NPA224W	RoadCar	P95MOX	Arriva Fox County	P353EAU	DunnLine	P912CTO	Trent
NPJ475R	Applebys	P96HOF	Arriva Fox County	P354EAU	DunnLine	P913CTO	Trent
NRP580V	East Midland	P96MOX	Arriva Fox County	P388WVL	Applebys	P914CTO	Trent
NSU180	Emmersons	P101HCH	Arriva Fox County	P394MDT	Silverdale	P915CTO	Trent
NTL939	Sleafordian	P102HCH	Arriva Fox County	P395MDT	Silverdale	P916CTO	Trent
NUB93V	Fowler's Travel	P103HCH	Arriva Fox County	P407BNR	Kinch Bus	P929TFE	Translinc
NUW66Y	Kime's	P104HCH	Arriva Fox County	P408BNR	Kinch Bus	P932TFE	Translinc
NVL165	RoadCar	P105HCH	Arriva Fox County	P409BNR	Kinch Bus	P940TFE	Translinc
NWB163X	RoadCar	P106GHE	Kettlewell's	P410BNR	Kinch Bus	P946TFE	Translinc
NWO457R	Applebys	P106HCH	Arriva Fox County	P411BNR	Kinch Bus	P947TFE	Translinc
NWY433V	RoadCar	P106WJO	City of Nottingham	P415UKH	Applebys	P948TFE	Translinc
OCU819R	East Midland	P107HCH	Arriva Fox County	P418KWF	East Midland	PAD806W	Fowler's Travel
OCU822R	East Midland	P107WJO	City of Nottingham	P419KWF	East Midland	PAK690R	Carnell Coaches
ODL661R	Johnson Bros	P108HCH	Arriva Fox County	P420KWF	East Midland	PAY9W	Wings
ODL662R	Johnson Bros	P108WJO	City of Nottingham	P473EJF	T R S	PAZ2532	Robinson's
ODL663R	Johnson Bros	P109HCH	Arriva Fox County	P474EJF	T R S	PAZ3184	Kime's
ODL664R	Johnson Bros	P110HCH	Arriva Fox County	P475EJF	T R S	PAZ3185	Kime's
OEM785S	RoadCar	P111MML	Arriva Fox County	P482CAL	Arriva Fox County	PAZ7356	Kime's
OEM794S	T R S	P112HCH	Arriva Fox County	P483CAL	Arriva Fox County	PAZ9257	Kime's
OFB968R	Applebys	P113HCH	Arriva Fox County	P484CAL	Arriva Fox County	PAZ9319	Kime's
OGL518	Viking	P114HCH	Arriva Fox County	P485CAL	Arriva Fox County	PAZ9346	Kime's
OGR51T	Camms	P115HCH	Arriva Fox County	P486CAL	Arriva Fox County	PBC458W	Applebys
OHE270X	Carnell Coaches	P116HCH	Arriva Fox County	P487CAL	Arriva Fox County	PCW946	Viking
OHE271X	Applebys	P117HCH	Arriva Fox County	P488CAL	Arriva Fox County	PFE540V	Johnson Bros
OHL912X	Haines	P118HCH	Arriva Fox County	P490CAL	Arriva Fox County	PFE541V	RoadCar
OHW492R	Trent	P119HCH	Arriva Fox County	P490CVO	City of Nottingham	PFE542V	RoadCar
OIL2416	RoadCar	P120HCH	Arriva Fox County	P491CAL	Arriva Fox County	PFE544V	Johnson Bros
OIW1321	Woods	P121HCH	Arriva Fox County	P491CVO	City of Nottingham	PFN787M	Bowers
OIW1608	Graysroft	P122HCH	Arriva Fox County	P492CAL	Arriva Fox County	PFR257X	Sweyne
OJD66R	Express Motors	P123HCH	Arriva Fox County	P492FRR	City of Nottingham	PHW986S	Trent
OJD89R	Express Motors	P124HCH	Arriva Fox County	P493FRR	City of Nottingham	PHW987S	Trent
OJL822Y	East Midland	P125HCH	Arriva Fox County	P493TGA	City of Nottingham	PIL2482	Sweyne
OJL823Y	East Midland	P126HCH	Arriva Fox County	P502RFW	Translinc	PIL2750	Butler Bros
ORA451W	Applebys	P145KWJ	East Midland	P503RFW	Translinc	PIW4456	RoadCar
ORA452W	Slack's Coaches	P146KWJ	East Midland	P505RFW	Translinc	PIW4457	RoadCar
ORA455W	Applebys	P148KWJ	East Midland	P506RFW	Translinc	PJI3042	Travel Wright
ORJ95W	Carnell Coaches	P149KWJ	East Midland	P507RFW	Translinc	PJI3043	Travel Wright
ORJ362W	Delaine Buses	P150KWJ	East Midland	P508RFW	Translinc	PJI3746	Andrews of Tideswell
ORJ365W	Applebys	P151CTV	Trent	P509RFW	Translinc	PJI4314	East Midland
ORJ366W	Applebys	P151KWJ	East Midland	P510RFW	Translinc	PJI4316	East Midland
ORJ380W	Delaine Buses	P152CTV	Trent	P511RFW	Translinc	PJI5529	Andrews of Tideswell
ORJ384W	Delaine Buses	P152KWJ	East Midland	P512RFW	Translinc	PJI5631	DunnLine
ORJ442	Applebys	P153CTV	Trent	P513RFW	Translinc	PJI5924	Hunt's
ORR904W	Travel Wright	P153KWJ	East Midland	P514CVO	City of Nottingham	PJI6075	Ausden-Clarke
OSF305G	Johnson Bros	P154KWJ	East Midland	P514RFW	Translinc	PJI7754	Paul James
OSF307G	Johnson Bros	P156KWJ	East Midland	P540CTO	City of Nottingham	PJI7929	Paul James
OSJ747R	Dent	P157KWJ	East Midland	P541BUT	Kinch Bus	PJI7930	Paul James
OTL3	Delaine Buses	P158KWJ	East Midland	P541CTO	City of Nottingham	PJI7931	Paul James
OTO540M	Confidence	P159KAK	East Midland	P542GAU	City of Nottingham	PJT261R	Go-Bus
OTO551M	Confidence	P160KAK	East Midland	P543GAU	City of Nottingham	PKE810M	Johnson Bros
OTO555M	City of Nottingham	P167BTV	Arriva Fox County	P544GAU	City of Nottingham	PKG741R	Applebys
OTO557M	Confidence	P168BTV	Arriva Fox County	P579DAU	Nottinghamshire County	PNK152R	Bowers
OTO562M	Confidence	P169BTV	Arriva Fox County	P591HMF	Ringwood	PNL163Y	Carnell Coaches
OTO570M	Confidence	P169EUT	A&S	P601CAY	Arriva Fox County	PNW306W	Reliance
OTO576M	T R S	P176NAK	First Leicester	P602CAY	Arriva Fox County	PNW308W	Hunt's
OUH738X	Sweyne	P177NAK	First Leicester	P603CAY	Arriva Fox County	PNW605W	RoadCar
OWB30X	East Midland	P179ANR	Travel Wright	P604CAY	Arriva Fox County	PRD34	Bowers
OWB31X	East Midland	P199ENN	City of Nottingham	P605CAY	Arriva Fox County	PRR442R	Trent
OWB32X	East Midland	P201BNR	Kinch Bus	P606CAY	Arriva Fox County	PRR446R	Glovers
OWB33X	East Midland	P201HRY	Arriva Fox County	P607CAY	Arriva Fox County	PRR450R	Trent
OWB34X	East Midland	P202BNR	Kinch Bus	P608CAY	Arriva Fox County	PRR451R	Trent
OWE854R	Johnson Bros	P202HRY	Arriva Fox County	P609CAY	Arriva Fox County	PRR451R	Trent
OWE857R	Johnson Bros	P203HRY	Arriva Fox County	P610CAY	Arriva Fox County	PRR451R	Trent
OWE858R	Johnson Bros	P204HRY	Arriva Fox County	P611CAY	Arriva Fox County	PRR451R	Trent
P1JBT	Johnson Bros	P205HRY	Arriva Fox County	P612CAY	Arriva Fox County	PRW137M	Unity
P1OTL	Delaine Buses	P206HRY	Arriva Fox County	P613CAY	Arriva Fox County	PS2743	East Midland
P2DFC	DunnLine	P210FRC	Skills	P640ENN	City of Nottingham	PSU443	East Midland
P2OTL	Delaine Buses	P211FRC	Skills	P641ENN	City of Nottingham	PSU764	East Midland
P3HOD	Hobsons	P222MML	Arriva Fox County	P642ENN	City of Nottingham	PSV259	Slack's Coaches
P3JBT	Johnson Bros	P225FRB	City of Nottingham	P681SVL	RoadCar	PSV323	Viking
P6KET	Kettlewell's	P227CTV	Trent	P682SVL	RoadCar	PSV436	Holloways
P10HDC	Hylton Dawson	P228CTV	Trent	P683SVL	RoadCar	PSV503	Slack's Coaches
P14PCC	P C Coaches	P229CTV	Trent	P684SVL	RoadCar	PSV562	Slack's Coaches
P15ABU	A&S	P230CTV	Trent	P685SVL	RoadCar	PTT80R	Bowers
P15PCC	P C Coaches	P231CTV	Trent	P686SVL	RoadCar	PTT98R	Johnson Bros
P25NKW	Slack's Coaches	P232CTV	Trent	P772VVL	Holloways	PTV591X	Confidence
P28LOE	Arriva Fox County	P233CTV	Trent	P822BNR	Kinch Bus	PTV592X	Trent
P29LOE	Arriva Fox County	P234CTV	Trent	P830ADO	Slack's Coaches	PTV601X	Paul James
P36LOE	Arriva Fox County	P235CTV	Trent	P876WFW	Translinc	PWE534R	Arriva Fox County
P37CBC	Woods	P236CTV	Trent	P877WFW	Translinc	PWK2W	T M Travel
P37LOE	Arriva Fox County	P237CTV	Trent	P878WFW	Translinc	PYE841Y	East Midland
P50PSW	Paul Winson	P238CTV	Trent	P880PWW	Moxon's	PYE842Y	East Midland
P50WHF	Fowler's Travel	P239CTV	Trent	P887RHK	Sleafordian	Q364FVT	Hulleys
P56ETO	Trent	P240CTV	Trent	P901CTO	Trent	Q723GHG	Applebys
P57ETO	Trent	P241CTV	Trent	P902CTO	Trent	R1JBT	Johnson Bros
P57LOE	Arriva Fox County	P251AUT	DunnLine	P903CTO	Trent	R1LCB	First Leicester
P58ETO	Trent	P252AUT	DunnLine	P904CTO	Trent	R2JBT	Johnson Bros
P58LOE	Arriva Fox County	P253AUT	DunnLine	P905CTO	Trent	R2LCB	First Leicester
P66KET	Kettlewell's	P298UFW	Translinc	P906CTO	Trent	R3KET	Kettlewell's

Reg	Operator	Reg	Operator	Reg	Operator	Reg	Operator
R3LCB	First Leicester	R337RRA	City of Nottingham	R825MJU	Kinch Bus	RNU430X	Fleetline Buses
R4LCB	First Leicester	R338RRA	City of Nottingham	R826MJU	Kinch Bus	RNU432X	Kinch Bus
R4OCT	Delaine Buses	R339RRA	City of Nottingham	R827WBC	Kinch Bus	RNU433X	Kinch Bus
R5LCB	First Leicester	R340RRA	City of Nottingham	R828WBC	Kinch Bus	RNU434X	Fleetline Buses
R5PSW	Paul Winson	R341RRA	City of Nottingham	R830FWW	Silverdale	RNU442X	Fleetline Buses
R6LCB	First Leicester	R342RRA	City of Nottingham	R839WOH	Holloways	ROI876	Eagre
R6PSW	Paul Winson	R343RRA	City of Nottingham	R841FWW	Silverdale	RRA218X	Hulleys
R7LCB	First Leicester	R344RRA	City of Nottingham	R841WOH	Holloways	RRA220X	Isle Coaches
R8LCB	First Leicester	R344SUT	First Leicester	R862MFE	Applebys	RRA222X	Hulleys
R9LCB	First Leicester	R345RRA	City of Nottingham	R863MFE	Applebys	RRC489R	Silverdale
R10LCB	First Leicester	R345SUT	First Leicester	R865SDT	DunnLine	RTO461R	Trent
R16PCC	P C Coaches	R346SUT	First Leicester	R866SDT	DunnLine	RTO463R	Trent
R42GNW	MacPherson Coaches	R378AWP	Silverdale	R86BUB	Andrews of Tideswell	RTO464R	Trent
R43GNW	MacPherson Coaches	R398NRR	Maun Crusader	R901TCH	DunnLine	RTO466R	Trent
R45VJF	Arriva Fox County	R402RJV	Holloways	R902TCH	DunnLine	RTO467R	Trent
R46VJF	Arriva Fox County	R410YWJ	Slack's Coaches	R903TCH	DunnLine	RTV436X	City of Nottingham
R47LNU	Trent	R411YWJ	Slack's Coaches	R917RAU	Trent	RTV439X	City of Nottingham
R59RAU	Trent	R412DGU	Skills	R918RAU	Trent	RTV443X	City of Nottingham
R61RAU	Trent	R414YWJ	Johnson Bros	R919RAU	Trent	RTV444X	City of Nottingham
R62RAU	Trent	R417LFW	Applebys	R920RAU	Trent	RTV445X	City of Nottingham
R63RAU	Trent	R439FTU	Reliance	R921RAU	Trent	RVE651S	Bowers
R66KET	Kettlewell's	R466RRA	City of Nottingham	R922RAU	Trent	RVL445	Applebys
R109BUB	Andrews of Tideswell	R467RRA	City of Nottingham	R923RAU	Trent	RWA859R	Johnson Bros
R127LNR	Arriva Fox County	R468RRA	City of Nottingham	R924RAU	Trent	RWB801R	Moxon's
R128LNR	Arriva Fox County	R469BUA	Andrews of Tideswell	R925RAU	Trent	RWT544R	Johnson Bros
R129LNR	Arriva Fox County	R469RRA	City of Nottingham	R926RAU	Trent	RWT546R	Johnson Bros
R130LNR	Arriva Fox County	R470RRA	City of Nottingham	R927RAU	Trent	S3YRR	Marshalls
R131LNR	Arriva Fox County	R471RRA	City of Nottingham	R928RAU	Trent	S4YRR	Marshalls
R132LNR	Arriva Fox County	R472RRA	City of Nottingham	R929RAU	Trent	S5OCT	Delaine Buses
R133LNR	Arriva Fox County	R473RRA	City of Nottingham	R930RAU	Trent	S8KET	Kettlewell's
R134LNR	Arriva Fox County	R474RRA	City of Nottingham	R931RAU	Trent	S10HOD	Hobsons
R135LNR	Arriva Fox County	R475RRA	City of Nottingham	R932RAU	Trent	S17PCC	P C Coaches
R136LNR	Arriva Fox County	R476RRA	City of Nottingham	R933RAU	Trent	S20PJC	Paul James
R137LNR	Arriva Fox County	R477GFM	Express Motors	R934RAU	Trent	S32FFW	Translinc
R138LNR	Arriva Fox County	R477RRA	City of Nottingham	R935RAU	Trent	S34FFW	Translinc
R139LNR	Arriva Fox County	R478RRA	City of Nottingham	R936RAU	Trent	S35FFW	Translinc
R140LNR	Arriva Fox County	R479RRA	City of Nottingham	R951ETL	Translinc	S36FFW	Translinc
R140XWF	Hulleys	R480RRA	City of Nottingham	R952ETL	Translinc	S37FFW	Translinc
R141LNR	Arriva Fox County	R498UFP	Silverdale	R954ETL	Translinc	S38FFW	Translinc
R142LNR	Arriva Fox County	R499UFP	Silverdale	R960RAU	Trent	S39FFW	Translinc
R143LNR	Arriva Fox County	R49SCH	Trent	R961LFE	Translinc	S41FFW	Translinc
R144LNR	Arriva Fox County	R501BUA	Skills	R962ETL	Translinc	S130NRB	City of Nottingham
R145LNR	Arriva Fox County	R501JFE	RoadCar	R963ETL	Translinc	S131NRB	City of Nottingham
R146LNR	Arriva Fox County	R502JFE	RoadCar	R964RCH	Silverdale	S150WOLI	Applebys
R147UAL	Arriva Fox County	R503JFE	RoadCar	R965RCH	Silverdale	S154UAL	Trent
R148UAL	Arriva Fox County	R504JFE	RoadCar	R987LFE	Translinc	S156UAL	Trent
R149UAL	Arriva Fox County	R505MFE	RoadCar	R987VAU	City of Nottingham	S157UAL	Trent
R150UAL	Arriva Fox County	R506MFE	RoadCar	R988LFE	Translinc	S158UAL	Trent
R151UAL	Arriva Fox County	R612AAU	Skills	R988VAU	City of Nottingham	S159UAL	Trent
R152UAL	Arriva Fox County	R614AAU	Skills	R989VAU	City of Nottingham	S160UAL	Trent
R153UAL	Arriva Fox County	R614MNU	Arriva Fox County	R990VAU	City of Nottingham	S161RET	East Midland
R154UAL	Arriva Fox County	R615AAU	Skills	RAL795	Marshalls	S161UAL	Trent
R155UAL	Arriva Fox County	R615MNU	Arriva Fox County	RAU624R	Marshalls	S162RET	East Midland
R156UAL	Arriva Fox County	R616AAU	Skills	RAU804M	Hulleys	S162UAL	Trent
R157UAL	Arriva Fox County	R616MNU	Arriva Fox County	RAZ8973	Eagre	S163RET	East Midland
R158UAL	Arriva Fox County	R617MNU	Arriva Fox County	RAZ8974	Eagre	S163UAL	Trent
R159UAL	Arriva Fox County	R618MNU	Arriva Fox County	RBA480	Andrews of Tideswell	S164RET	East Midland
R160UAL	Arriva Fox County	R619MNU	Arriva Fox County	RBC500W	Arriva Fox County	S164UAL	Trent
R161UAL	Arriva Fox County	R620MNU	Arriva Fox County	RBO504Y	Applebys	S165RET	East Midland
R162UAL	Arriva Fox County	R621MNU	Arriva Fox County	RBO505Y	Applebys	S165UAL	Trent
R163UAL	Arriva Fox County	R622MNU	Arriva Fox County	RBO510Y	Confidence	S166RET	East Midland
R164UAL	Arriva Fox County	R623MNU	Arriva Fox County	RCT3	Delaine Buses	S166UAL	Trent
R165UAL	Arriva Fox County	R624MNU	Arriva Fox County	RCU834S	T R S	S167RET	East Midland
R166UAL	Arriva Fox County	R625MNU	Arriva Fox County	RDT89R	Moxon's	S167UAL	Trent
R167UAL	Arriva Fox County	R626MNU	Arriva Fox County	RDX11R	RoadCar	S168RET	East Midland
R168UAL	Arriva Fox County	R627MNU	Arriva Fox County	RDX12R	RoadCar	S168UAL	Trent
R169UAL	Arriva Fox County	R628MNU	Arriva Fox County	RDX13R	RoadCar	S169RET	East Midland
R170UUT	Arriva Fox County	R629MNU	Arriva Fox County	RDX14R	RoadCar	S169UAL	Trent
R189NFE	Holloways	R630MNU	Arriva Fox County	RDX15R	RoadCar	S170UAL	Trent
R226SCH	City of Nottingham	R631MNU	Arriva Fox County	RDX16R	RoadCar	S171UAL	Trent
R227SCH	City of Nottingham	R632MNU	Arriva Fox County	RDX17R	RoadCar	S172UAL	Trent
R228SCH	City of Nottingham	R633MNU	Arriva Fox County	RDZ4275	Carnell Coaches	S193MRH	Applebys
R229SCH	City of Nottingham	R634MNU	Arriva Fox County	RFS582V	Eagre	S207DTO	Arriva Fox County
R230SCH	City of Nottingham	R635MNU	Arriva Fox County	RFS590V	RoadCar	S208DTO	Arriva Fox County
R231SCH	City of Nottingham	R636MNU	Arriva Fox County	RGS820V	Kinch Bus	S259AVL	Translinc
R232SCH	City of Nottingham	R637MNU	Arriva Fox County	RIB4311	T R S	S260AVL	Translinc
R233SCH	City of Nottingham	R638MNU	Arriva Fox County	RIB5092	Bowers	S261AVL	Translinc
R253EJV	Applebys	R639MNU	Arriva Fox County	RIL1018	P C Coaches	S262AVL	Translinc
R275RAU	Trent	R640MNU	Arriva Fox County	RIL1019	P C Coaches	S263AVL	Translinc
R276RAU	Trent	R641MNU	Arriva Fox County	RIL1021	Viking	S264AVL	Translinc
R277RAU	Trent	R642MNU	Arriva Fox County	RIW8127	Andrews of Tideswell	S266AVL	Translinc
R278RAU	Trent	R643MNU	Arriva Fox County	RJI1653	Graysroft	S267AVL	Translinc
R278RRH	Applebys	R663TKU	East Midland	RJI1655	Graysroft	S276LGA	Ringwood
R278VOK	Arriva Fox County	R664TKU	East Midland	RJI1656	Camms	S282NRB	City of Nottingham
R279RAU	Trent	R667KFE	Holloways	RJI1657	Camms	S283NRB	City of Nottingham
R279VOK	Arriva Fox County	R687MFE	RoadCar	RJI1658	Camms	S284NRB	City of Nottingham
R280RAU	Trent	R688MFE	RoadCar	RJI4240	Woods	S285NRB	City of Nottingham
R281RAU	Trent	R704RNN	Felix	RJI8583	Holloways	S285UAL	Kinch Bus
R282RAU	Trent	R705MNU	Felix	RJI8608	Holloways	S286NRB	City of Nottingham
R283RAU	Trent	R706MNU	Felix	RJI8861	Unity	S286UAL	Trent
R284RAU	Trent	R726EGD	Travel Wright	RKA886T	Camms	S287NRB	City of Nottingham
R288VOK	Arriva Fox County	R762NFW	Hobsons	RKH766T	Johnson Bros	S287UAL	Trent
R289VOK	Arriva Fox County	R823MJU	Kinch Bus	RKW606R	RoadCar	S288NRB	City of Nottingham
R336RRA	City of Nottingham	R824MJU	Kinch Bus	RNU426X	Kinch Bus	S288UAL	Trent

The East Midlands Bus Handbook

Nottingham's 408, T408BNN is one of a batch of Dennis Trident buses that carry East Lancashire Lolyne bodywork. This low-floor double-deck bus continues the classic livery while many other operators would have been tempted to apply gimmicky lettering. The vehicle is seen on Park and Ride duties. *D J Stanier*

Reg	Operator	Reg	Operator	Reg	Operator	Reg	Operator
S289NRB	City of Nottingham	S508BTL	RoadCar	S940UAL	Trent	SND501X	Silverdale
S289UAL	Trent	S509BTL	RoadCar	S941UAL	Trent	SND518X	Silverdale
S290NRB	City of Nottingham	S510BTL	RoadCar	S942UAL	Trent	SNN747R	Travel Wright
S290UAL	Trent	S511BTL	RoadCar	S943UAL	Trent	SNS826W	Reliance
S291NRB	City of Nottingham	S512BTL	RoadCar	S944UAL	Trent	SNU456X	Fleetline Buses
S291UAL	Trent	S533BTL	Translinc	S949RBE	Robinson's	SNU457X	Applebys
S292UAL	Trent	S535BTL	Translinc	S951RBE	Hobsons	SNU458X	Applebys
S293UAL	Trent	S536BTL	Translinc	S955PRA	Trent	SNU460X	Applebys
S294UAL	Trent	S537BTL	Translinc	SAE751S	Trent Motors	SNU461X	Travel Wright
S295UAL	Trent	S538BTL	Translinc	SAE753S	Trent Motors	SNU465X	Applebys
S296UAL	Trent	S562AVE	Translinc	SAE755S	Trent	SPC270R	RoadCar
S333HEB	Fowler's Travel	S564AVE	Translinc	SCH117X	Hulleys	SRC114X	Arriva Fox County
S347MFP	First Leicester	S565AVE	Translinc	SCN250S	RoadCar	SSU837	First Leicester
S348MFP	First Leicester	S577FFE	Travel Wright	SCT330	Wings	STA381R	Carnell Coaches
S350MFP	First Leicester	S590KJF	Felix	SDA764S	Wide Horizon	STK132T	Kinch Bus
S351MFP	First Leicester	S595CJF	DunnLine	SDA768S	Brylaine	SUA141R	Holloways
S353MFP	First Leicester	S596CJF	DunnLine	SDA784S	Brylaine	SVL177W	Johnson Bros
S354MFP	First Leicester	S597CJF	DunnLine	SDX21R	RoadCar	SVL178W	Johnson Bros
S355MFP	First Leicester	S598CJF	DunnLine	SDX26R	RoadCar	SVL179W	Johnson Bros
S356MFP	First Leicester	S599CJF	DunnLine	SDX28R	RoadCar	SVL180W	Johnson Bros
S357MFP	First Leicester	S602ACT	Slack's Coaches	SFH477W	Translinc	SVL830R	Arriva Fox County
S358MFP	First Leicester	S644KJU	Arriva Fox County	SHE306Y	East Midland	SVM378W	Hail and Ride
S374SET	DunnLine	S645KJU	Arriva Fox County	SHE307Y	East Midland	SVV586W	East Midland
S376TMB	Express Motors	S646KJU	Arriva Fox County	SHE308Y	East Midland	SWE439S	RoadCar
S382FVL	Translinc	S647KJU	Arriva Fox County	SHE309Y	East Midland	SWS769S	Applebys
S401SDT	East Midland	S648KJU	Arriva Fox County	SHE310Y	East Midland	SXF319	Maun Crusader
S402SDT	East Midland	S649KJU	Arriva Fox County	SHE311Y	East Midland	T3JBT	Johnson Bros
S403SDT	East Midland	S650KJU	Arriva Fox County	SHE545S	Wide Horizon	T4JBT	Johnson Bros
S450ATV	City of Nottingham	S651KJU	Arriva Fox County	SHE557S	Isle Coaches	T6OCT	Delaine Buses
S451ATV	City of Nottingham	S652KJU	Arriva Fox County	SIB1278	Arriva Fox County	T7HOD	Hobsons
S452ATV	City of Nottingham	S653KJU	Arriva Fox County	SIB1998	Woods	T7PCC	P C Coaches
S453ATV	City of Nottingham	S665SDT	East Midland	SIB8312	Woods	T7PSW	Paul Winson
S454ATV	City of Nottingham	S670SDT	East Midland	SJI5569	Arriva Fox County	T8PSW	Paul Winson
S455ATV	City of Nottingham	S671SDT	East Midland	SJI5570	Arriva Fox County	T9PSW	Paul Winson
S456ATV	City of Nottingham	S672SDT	East Midland	SJI6568	Kime's	T20ACL	Ausden-Clarke
S457ATV	City of Nottingham	S673SDT	East Midland	SJI6569	Kime's	T32CNN	DunnLine
S458ATV	City of Nottingham	S743RNE	Ringwood	SJI6570	Kime's	T32JBA	Travel Wright
S459ATV	City of Nottingham	S782FFW	Reliance	SJI6571	Kime's	T34CNN	DunnLine
S460ATV	City of Nottingham	S801SJV	RoadCar	SKY31Y	East Midland	T35CNN	DunnLine
S461ATV	City of Nottingham	S802SJV	RoadCar	SKY32Y	East Midland	T36CNN	DunnLine
S462ATV	City of Nottingham	S803SJV	RoadCar	SMY631X	Carnell Coaches	T37CNN	DunnLine
S463ATV	City of Nottingham	S930ATO	Skills	SMY632X	Carnell Coaches	T38CNN	DunnLine
S464ATV	City of Nottingham	S937UAL	Trent	SMY637X	Carnell Coaches	T39CNN	DunnLine
S465ATV	City of Nottingham	S938UAL	Trent	SND422X	Applebys	T41CNN	DunnLine
S507BTL	RoadCar	S939UAL	Trent	SND488X	Applebys	T42CNN	DunnLine

The East Midlands Bus Handbook

Unibus livery is applied to this Optare Vecta-bodied MAN service bus. Part of the Trent fleet, 1370, N370VRC is seen in St Chad's Road, Derby. *D J Stanier*

T43CNN	DunnLine	T365AJF	Silverdale	T799XVO	Trent	TJI4698	Camms
T45CNN	DunnLine	T366AJF	Silverdale	T814RTL	Applebys	TJI4699	Camms
T46CNN	DunnLine	T366JWA	Slack's Coaches	T859JBC	Slack's Coaches	TNN696X	Travel Wright
T47CNN	DunnLine	T381RFW	Translinc	T945BNN	Trent	TOF708S	Applebys
T48CNN	DunnLine	T383RFW	Translinc	T946BNN	Trent	TPC105X	Applebys
T49CNN	DunnLine	T384RFW	Translinc	T947BNN	Trent	TPD109Y	Silverdale
T51CNN	DunnLine	T399OWA	DunnLine	T948BNN	Trent	TPD127X	Arriva Fox County
T52CNN	DunnLine	T405BGB	Cavalier	T949BNN	Trent	TPD128X	Arriva Fox County
T100ANN	Eagre	T405BNN	City of Nottingham	T975LCH	Trent	TRN467V	RoadCar
T110JBC	Fowler's Travel	T406BNN	City of Nottingham	T976LCH	Trent	TRN468V	RoadCar
T111JBC	Fowler's Travel	T407BNN	City of Nottingham	T977LCH	Trent	TRN469V	RoadCar
T142KBC	Holloways	T408BNN	City of Nottingham	TAE638S	Trent	TRN471V	RoadCar
T156AUA	MacPherson Coaches	T409BNN	City of Nottingham	TAE643S	Trent	TRN472V	RoadCar
T173LCH	Trent	T410BNN	City of Nottingham	TAZ4061	Kime's	TRN473V	RoadCar
T174LCH	Trent	T411BNN	City of Nottingham	TAZ4062	Kime's	TRN479V	RoadCar
T178LCH	Trent	T412BNN	City of Nottingham	TAZ4063	Kime's	TRN484V	RoadCar
T179LCH	Trent	T413BNN	City of Nottingham	TAZ4064	Kime's	TRN485V	RoadCar
T180AUA	Silverdale	T414BNN	City of Nottingham	TBC42X	First Leicester	TRN803V	RoadCar
T180LCH	Trent	T415BNN	City of Nottingham	TBC43X	First Leicester	TRS332	T R S
T181LCH	Trent	T416BNN	City of Nottingham	TBC45X	First Leicester	TRS574	T R S
T182LCH	Trent	T417LCU	City of Nottingham	TBC46X	First Leicester	TRS835	T R S
T183LCH	Trent	T418LCU	City of Nottingham	TBC49X	First Leicester	TSJ46S	RoadCar
T183SFW	Translinc	T419LCU	City of Nottingham	TBC50X	First Leicester	TSJ58S	RoadCar
T184LCH	Trent	T420LCU	City of Nottingham	TBC52X	First Leicester	TSJ73S	RoadCar
T184SFW	Translinc	T421LCU	City of Nottingham	TCH118X	Arriva Fox County	TSN585S	Ausden-Clarke
T185LCH	Trent	T422LCU	City of Nottingham	TCH120X	Arriva Fox County	TSO18X	RoadCar
T185SFW	Translinc	T513SVL	RoadCar	TCH121X	Arriva Fox County	TSO22X	RoadCar
T186LCH	Trent	T514SVL	RoadCar	TDC856X	Applebys	TSO25X	RoadCar
T187SFW	Translinc	T654LAT	Applebys	TDT864S	Johnson Bros	TSO26X	RoadCar
T208KJV	Holloways	T707SUT	Travel Wright	TET745S	Isle Coaches	TSO27X	RoadCar
T293BNN	City of Nottingham	T744JHE	Fowler's Travel	TFE1R	Eagre	TSO28X	RoadCar
T293BNN	City of Nottingham	T781LCH	City of Nottingham	TFJ61X	Camms	TTC532T	Trent
T294BNN	City of Nottingham	T782LCH	City of Nottingham	THX120S	Kettlewell's	TTS885S	T R S
T295BNN	City of Nottingham	T783LCH	City of Nottingham	THX173S	Holloways	TUA707R	Unity
T296BNN	City of Nottingham	T787XVO	Trent	THX196S	Kettlewell's	TVC402W	Arriva Fox County
T297BNN	City of Nottingham	T788XVO	Trent	THX212S	RoadCar	TWF201Y	East Midland
T297LCH	Trent	T789XVO	Trent	THX542S	Holloways	TWF202Y	East Midland
T298BNN	City of Nottingham	T790XVO	Trent	TIB2875	Sweyne	TWJ340Y	Hunt's
T298LCH	Trent	T791XVO	Trent	TIW2654	Andrews of Tideswell	TWJ341Y	Hunt's
T299BNN	City of Nottingham	T792XVO	Trent	TIW5645	Travel Wright	TWJ342Y	Hunt's
T299LCH	Trent	T793XVO	Trent	TJI1676	Graysroft	TWO84	RoadCar
T322KNN	Skills	T794XVO	Trent	TJI1677	Graysroft	UBV84L	RoadCar
T361AJF	Silverdale	T795XVO	Trent	TJI1678	Graysroft	UBV85L	RoadCar
T362AJF	Silverdale	T796XVO	Trent	TJI1679	Graysroft	UBV87L	RoadCar
T363AJF	Silverdale	T797XVO	Trent	TJI4027	Wide Horizon	UDL668S	Johnson Bros
T364AJF	Silverdale	T798XVO	Trent	TJI4028	Wide Horizon	UDT312Y	East Midland

ISBN 1 897990 66 9

Reg	Operator	Reg	Operator	Reg	Operator	Reg	Operator
UDT313Y	East Midland	VFW721	Applebys	XAL491S	Trent	XRM623Y	Dent
UET1S	RoadCar	VFX985S	Trent	XAL493S	Trent	XRR616M	Confidence
UFG53S	RoadCar	VIB7471	T M Travel	XAL494S	Marshalls	XRR831S	Slack's Coaches
UFP233S	First Leicester	VIW3785	Sweyne	XAL495S	Trent	XSG71R	RoadCar
UFX849S	Trent	VKE565S	Trent	XAL496S	Trent	XSG72R	RoadCar
UFX852S	Trent	VLT166	Viking	XAL498S	Trent	XSU978	Haines
UHG146V	RoadCar	VNH155W	Dent	XAL500S	Trent	XSV839	Cropley
UHG752R	RoadCar	VOI5826	T R S	XAM130A	Moxon's	XTV667S	Fleetline Buses
UHG756R	RoadCar	VOI6874	Viking	XAT586	Applebys	XWC339	Applebys
UHW101T	Trent	VPT586R	Bowers	XAZ1293	Brylaine	XXI2489	Johnson's Coaches
UIW2285	Skills	VPW86S	Wings	XAZ1294	Brylaine	YAE518V	Applebys
UIW9748	Skills	VRC480S	Marshalls	XAZ1297	Brylaine	YAU126Y	Arriva Fox County
UJI2439	RoadCar	VRC611Y	Confidence	XAZ1301	Brylaine	YAU127Y	Arriva Fox County
UJV489	Applebys	VSK207	Cropley	XAZ1310	Brylaine	YAU128Y	Arriva Fox County
UKY608Y	Applebys	VTL358	Hobsons	XAZ1311	Brylaine	YAZ4142	Kime's
ULS321T	RoadCar	VTL627	Wings	XAZ1312	Brylaine	YAZ4143	Kime's
ULS335T	RoadCar	VUA473X	Applebys	XAZ1314	Brylaine	YBJ159X	RoadCar
ULS615X	P C Coaches	VUT1X	West End Travel	XAZ1315	Brylaine	YBO67T	Applebys
UNA787S	Marshalls	VWA34Y	East Midland	XAZ1316	Brylaine	YBO68T	Applebys
UNA864S	Eagre	VWA35Y	East Midland	XAZ1320	Brylaine	YCT463	Sleafordian
UPB311S	Express Motors	VWA36Y	East Midland	XAZ1321	Brylaine	YDX100Y	First Leicester
URA481X	Glovers	VWM83L	Confidence	XAZ1321	Brylaine	YDZ3458	RoadCar
URB468S	Trent	VWM89L	Confidence	XAZ1346	Brylaine	YFB970V	Go-Bus
URB471S	Trent	VWO995S	Ausden-Clarke	XAZ1398	Brylaine	YHT988	T R S
URN207V	RoadCar	VXI4453	Fowler's Travel	XAZ1399	Brylaine	YIA9006	Reliance
URN208V	RoadCar	WAC828	Applebys	XAZ1403	Brylaine	YJK932V	RoadCar
URN209V	RoadCar	WAE193T	Applebys	XAZ1408	Brylaine	YJK934V	RoadCar
UTC872	T R S	WAZ8278	Kime's	XAZ1409	Brylaine	YJK935V	RoadCar
UTL798	Applebys	WBR5V	Camms	XAZ1410	Brylaine	YJV178	Applebys
UTV218S	Fleetline Buses	WCK215Y	Eagre	XAZ1411	Brylaine	YNA887	Applebys
UTV219S	Fleetline Buses	WDA948T	Applebys	XAZ1412	Brylaine	YNL228V	Applebys
UVE288	Applebys	WDA951T	Wide Horizon	XAZ1413	Brylaine	YNN396Y	Glovers
UVL653W	Applebys	WDA994T	Brylaine	XAZ1427	Brylaine	YOT545V	Beaver Bus
UVL89W	Applebys	WDS112V	T M Travel	XBF54S	Camms	YPD112Y	Hulleys
UWA150S	East Midland	WDZ3132	Woods	XEF11Y	Fowler's Travel	YPD121Y	Carnell Coaches
UWA151S	East Midland	WEE584	Applebys	XEU858T	Go-Bus	YPF763T	Go-Bus
UWA154S	T M Travel	WET1K	West End Travel	XFC486	Emmersons	YPL407T	Go-Bus
UWA159S	T M Travel	WFS139W	Hunt's	XFK173	Emmersons	YPL428T	Go-Bus
UWY65X	RoadCar	WFS149W	RoadCar	XFP1Y	Kettlewell's	YPL80T	Camms
UWY70X	RoadCar	WFU561V	Emmersons	XFP2Y	Kettlewell's	YRH808S	Applebys
UWY73X	RoadCar	WGY578S	Trent	XFP502S	Hunt's	YRR3	Marshalls
UWY76X	RoadCar	WIW6172	Graysroft	XFW951S	Hunt's	YRR501T	Trent
UXI6833	Unity	WJI5167	Sweyne	XFW983S	Holloways	YRR502T	Trent
UXI8651	Dent	WJI9361	DunnLine	XGS736S	East Midland	YSF73S	RoadCar
V515XTL	RoadCar	WJI9362	DunnLine	XIB3473	Woods	YSF74S	RoadCar
V516XTL	RoadCar	WJI9363	DunnLine	XJF61Y	First Leicester	YSF80S	RoadCar
V517XTL	RoadCar	WJY760	Applebys	XJF62Y	First Leicester	YSF81S	RoadCar
V518XTL	RoadCar	WLT655	Confidence	XJF63Y	First Leicester	YSF82S	RoadCar
V519XTL	RoadCar	WLT702	DunnLine	XJF64Y	First Leicester	YSF89S	RoadCar
V520XTL	RoadCar	WOI3001	RoadCar	XJF65Y	First Leicester	YSX929W	RoadCar
V521XTL	RoadCar	WOI3002	RoadCar	XJF66Y	First Leicester	YSX930W	RoadCar
V581XTL	RoadCar	WPR150S	Trent	XJF67Y	First Leicester	YTO861Y	Travel Wright
V582XTL	RoadCar	WRC826S	Felix	XJF68Y	First Leicester	YTO996T	Reliance
V583XTL	RoadCar	WSV317	Applebys	XJF69Y	First Leicester	YVL599X	East Midland
V584XTL	RoadCar	WSV418	Elseys	XJF888S	Skinner	YWG466T	RoadCar
V585XTL	RoadCar	WSV535	DunnLine	XJV146	Applebys	YWG470T	RoadCar
VAT176S	Applebys	WUK155	Holloways	XKA883T	RoadCar	YWH978	Bowers
VAV160X	Wide Horizon	WUM100S	Dent	XLC1S	West End Travel	YXI3054	Viking
VAY58X	First Leicester	WUY713	Cropley	XLK673	Applebys	YXI4381	Johnson Bros
VBH50W	Emmersons	WVL515	RoadCar	XNK199X	Brylaine	YXI5503	Skills
VBT191	Fowler's Travel	WXH612	Kettlewell's	XOV754T	Applebys	YXI5860	Skills
VCH479S	Trent	WYR562	Viking	XPA110	Arriva Fox County	YXI7380	Skills
VCX340X	RoadCar	WYV53T	Kinch Bus	XPD233N	Go-Bus	YXI7906	Skills
VEU228T	Trent	WYV62T	Kinch Bus	XPG171T	Applebys	YXI8421	Skills
VEU229T	Trent	XAF759	Viking	XPK52T	Camms	YXI9243	Skills
VEU230T	Trent	XAL481S	Trent	XPM41	RoadCar	YXI9256	Skills
VEU232T	Trent	XAL484S	Trent	XPM42	RoadCar	YXI9258	Skills
VFA70X	Paul James			XRF26S	RoadCar		

Published by *British Bus Publishing* Ltd
The Vyne, 16 St Margaret's Drive, Wellington, Telford, TF1 3PH